INTELLIGENT KNOWLEDGE-BASED SYSTEMS

BUSINESS AND TECHNOLOGY IN THE NEW MILLENNIUM

VOLUME 5
NEURAL NETWORKS, FUZZY THEORY AND GENETIC ALGORITHMS

INTELLIGENT KNOWLEDGE-BASED SYSTEMS

BUSINESS AND TECHNOLOGY IN THE NEW MILLENNIUM

VOLUME 5
NEURAL NETWORKS, FUZZY THEORY AND GENETIC
ALGORITHMS

Edited by

CORNELIUS T. LEONDES
University of California, Los Angeles, USA

KLUWER ACADEMIC PUBLISHERS
BOSTON/DORDRECHT/LONDON

Distributors for North, Central and South America:
Kluwer Academic Publishers
101 Philip Drive
Assinippi Park
Norwell, Massachusetts 02061 USA
Telephone (781) 871-6600
Fax (781) 871-6528
E-Mail <kluwer@wkap.com>

Distributors for all other countries:
Kluwer Academic Publishers Group
Post Office Box 322
3300 AH Dordrecht, THE NETHERLANDS
Telephone 31 78 6576 000
Fax 31 78 6576 474
E-Mail <orderdept@wkap.nl>

Electronic Services <http://www.wkap.nl>

Library of Congress Cataloging-in-Publication Data

Intelligent knowledge-based systems : business and technology in the new millennium. /
edited by Cornelius T. Leondes.

    Includes bibliographical references and index.
    Contents: v. 1. Knowledge-based systems—v. 2. Information technology—
    v. 3. Expert and agent systems—v. 4. Intelligent systems—
    v. 5. Neural networks, fuzzy theory and genetic algorithms.
    ISBN 1-40207-746-7 (set)—ISBN 1-40207-824-2 (v.1)—ISBN 1-40207-825-0 (v.2)—
    ISBN 1-40207-826-9 (v.3)—ISBN 1-40207-827-7 (v.4)—ISBN 1-40207-828-5 (v.5)
    ISBN 1-40207-829-3 (electronic book set)

(LOC information to follow.)

CONTENTS

FOREWORD

Almost unknown to the academic world, and to the general public, the application of intelligent knowledge-based systems is rapidly and effectively changing the future of the human species. Today, human well-being is, as it has been for all of history, fundamentally limited by the size of the world economic product. Thus, if human economic well-being (which I personally define as the bottom centile annual per capita income) is ever soon to reach an acceptable level (e.g., the equivalent of $20,000 per capita per annum in 2004), then intelligent knowledge-based systems must be employed in vast quantities. This is primarily because of the reality that few humans live in efficient societies (such as the United States, Canada, Japan, the UK, France, and Germany, for example) and that inefficient societies, many of which are already large, and growing larger, may require many decades to become efficient. In the meantime, billions of people will continue to suffer economic impoverishment—an impoverishment that inefficient human labor cannot remedy. To create the extra economic output so urgently needed, we have only one choice: to employ intelligent knowledge-based systems in great numbers, which will produce economic output prodigiously, but will consume hardly at all.

This multi-volume major reference work, architected by its editor, Cornelius T. Leondes, provides a wealth of 'case studies' illustrating the state of the art in intelligent knowledge-based systems. In contrast to ordinary academic pedagogy, where 'ivory tower' abstraction and elegance are the guiding principles, practical applications require detailed relevant examples that can be used by practitioners to successfully innovate new operational capabilities. The economic progress of the species depends upon the flow of these innovations, which requires multi-volume major reference works with carefully selected, well-written, and well-edited 'case studies.' Professor Leondes knows these realities well, and the five volumes in this work resoundingly reflect his success in achieving their requirements.

Volume 1 addresses Knowledge-Based Systems. These eleven chapters consider the basic question of how accumulated data and staff expertise from business operations can be abstracted into valuable knowledge, and how such knowledge can then be applied to ongoing operations. Wide and representative situations are considered, ranging from product innovation and design, to intelligent database exploitation, to business model analysis.

Volume 2, Information Technology, addresses in ten chapters the important question of how data should be stored and used to maximize its overall value. Case studies consider a wide variety of application arenas: product development, manufacturing, product management, and even product pricing.

Volume 3 addresses Expert and Agent Systems in ten chapters. Application arenas considered include image databases, business process monitoring, e-commerce, and production planning and scheduling. Again, the coverage is designed to provide a wide range of perspectives and business-function concentrations to help stimulate innovation by the reader.

Volume 4, Intelligent Systems, provides nine chapters considering such topics as mission-critical functions, business forecasting, medical patient care, and product design and development.

Volume 5 addresses Neural Networks, Fuzzy Theory, and Genetic Algorithm Techniques. Its ten chapters cover examples in areas including bioinformatics, product life-cycle cost estimating, product development, computer-aided design, product assembly, and facility location.

The examples assembled by Professor Leondes in this work provide a wealth of practical ideas designed to trigger the development of innovation. The contributors to this grand project are to be congratulated for the major efforts they have expended in creating their chapters. Humans everywhere will soon benefit from the case studies provided herein. Intelligent Knowledge-Based Systems: Business and Technology in the New Millennium, is a reference work that belongs on the desk of every innovative technologist.

It has taken many decades of experience and unflagging hard work for Professor Leondes to accumulate the wisdom and judgment reflected in his editorial stewardship of this reference work. Wisdom and judgment are rare—but indispensable—commodities that cannot be obtained in any other way. The world of innovative technology, and the world at large, stand in his debt.

Robert Hecht-Nielsen
Computational Neurobiology
Institute for Neural Computation
Department of Electrical and Computer Engineering
University of California, San Diego

PREFACE

At the start of the 20th century, national economies on the international scene were, to a large extent, agriculturally based. This was, perhaps, the dominant reason for the protraction, on the international scene, of the Great Depression, which began with the Wall Street stock market crash of October, 1929. After World War II the trend away from agriculturally based economies and toward industrially based economies continued and strengthened. Indeed, today, in the United States, approximately only 1% of the population is involved in the agriculture requirements of the US and, in addition, provides significant agriculture exports. This, of course, is made possible by the greatly improved techniques and technologies utilized in the agriculture industry.

The trend toward industrially based economies after World War II was, in turn, followed by a trend toward service-based economies. In the United States today, roughly over 70% of the employment is involved with service industries—and this percentage continues to increase. Separately, the electronic computer industry began to take hold in the early 1960s, and thereafter always seemed to exceed expectations. For example, the first large-scale sales of an electronic computer were of the IBM 650. At that time, projections were that the total sales for the United States would be twenty-five IBM 650 computers. Before the first one came off the projection line, IBM had initial orders for over 30,000. That was thought to be huge by the standards of that day, and today it is a very miniscule number, to say nothing of the fact that its computing power was also very miniscule by today's standards. Computer mainframes continued to grow in power and complexity. At the same time, Gordon Moore, of "Moore's Law" fame, and his colleagues founded INTEL. Then around 1980 MICROSOFT was founded, but it was not until the early 1990s, not that long ago, that WINDOWS were created—incidentally, after the APPLE computer family started. The first browser was the NETSCAPE browser, which appeared in 1995, also not that long ago. Of course, computer networking equipment, most notably CISCO's, also appeared about that time. Toward the end of the last century the "DOT COM bubble" occurred and "burst" around 2000.

Coming to the new millennium, for most of our history the wealth of a nation was limited by the size and stamina of the work force. Today, national wealth is measured in intellectual capital. Nations possessing skillful people in such diverse areas as science, medicine, business, and engineering produce innovations that drive the nation to a higher quality of life. To better utilize these valuable resources, intelligent, knowledge-based systems technology has evolved at a rapid and significantly expanding rate, and can be utilized by nations to improve their medical care, advance their engineering technology, and increase their manufacturing productivity, as well as play a significant role in a very wide variety of other areas of activity of substantive significance.

The breadth of the major application areas of intelligent, knowledge-based systems technology is very impressive. These include the following, among other areas.

Agriculture	Electronics
Business	Engineering
Chemistry	Environment
Communications	Geology
Computer Systems	Image Processing
Education	Information
Management	Military
Law	Mining
Manufacturing	Power Systems
Mathematics	Science
Medicine	Space Technology
Meteorology	Transportation

It is difficult now to imagine an area that will not be touched by intelligent, knowledge-based systems technology.

The great breadth and expanding significance of such a broad field on the international scene requires a multi-volume, major reference work to provide an adequately substantive treatment of the subject, "Intelligent Knowledge-Based Systems: Business and Technology of The New Millennium." This work consists of the following distinctly titled and well integrated volumes.

Volume I.	Knowledge-Based Systems
Volume II.	Information Technology
Volume III.	Expert and Agent Systems
Volume IV.	Intelligent Systems
Volume V.	Neural Networks

This five-volume set on intelligent knowledge-based systems clearly manifests the great significance of these key technologies for the new economies of the new millennium. The authors are all to be highly commended for their splendid contributions, which together will provide a significant and uniquely comprehensive reference source for research workers, practitioners, computer scientists, students, and others on the international scene for years to come.

Cornelius T. Leondes
University of California, Los Angeles
January 5, 2004

CONTRIBUTORS

VOLUME 1: KNOWLEDGE-BASED SYSTEMS

N. Bassiliades
Department of Informatics
Aristotle University of Thessaloniki
Thessaloniki
GREECE
Chapter 6. Aggregator: A Knowledge-Based Comparison Chart Builder for eShopping

Peter Bernus
Griffith University
School of CIT
Nathan
Queensland
AUSTRALIA
Chapter 10. Business Process Modeling and Its Applications in the Business Environment

Mariano Corso
Department of Management Engineering
Polytechnic University of Mailand
Milano
ITALY
Chapter 2. Knowledge Management Systems in Continuous Product Innnovation

Eugenio di Sciascio
Dipartimento Elettrotecnica ed Elettronica
Politecnico di Bari
Bari
ITALY
Chapter 11. Knowledge-Based Systems Technology and Applications in Image Retrieval

Francesco M. Donini
Università della Tuscia
Viterbo
ITALY
Chapter 11. Knowledge-Based Systems Technology and Applications in Image Retrieval

Janis Grundspenkis
Faculty of Computer Science and Information Technology
Riga Technical University
Riga
LATVIA
Chapter 7. Impact of the Intelligent Agent Paradigm on Knowledge Management

P. Humphreys
Faculty of Business and Management
University of Ulster
Northern Ireland
UNITED KINGDOM
Chapter 4. Knowledge-Based Systems Technology in the Make-or-Buy Decision in Manufacturing Strategy

Brane Kalpic
ETI Elektroelement Jt. St. Comp.
Izlake
SLOVENIA
Chapter 10. Business Process Modeling and Its Applications in the Business Environment

Marite Kirikova
Faculty of Computer Science and Information Technology
Riga Technical University
Riga
LATVIA
Chapter 7. Impact of the Intelligent Agent Paradigm on Knowledge Management

F. Kokkoras
Department of Informatics
Aristotle University of Thessaloniki

Thessaloniki
GREECE
Chapter 6. Aggregator: A Knowledge-Based Comparison Chart Builder for eShopping

Shian-Hua Lin
Department of Computer Science and Information Engineering
National Chi Nan University
Taiwan
REPUBLIC OF CHINA
Chapter 5. Intelligent Internet Information Systems in Knowledge Acquisition: Techniques and Applications

Antonella Martini
Faculty of Engineering
University of Pisa
Pisa
ITALY
Chapter 2. Knowledge Management Systems in Continuous Product Innovation

R. McIvor
Faculty of Business and Management
University of Ulster
UNITED KINGDOM
Chapter 4. Knowledge-Based Systems Technology in the Make-or-Buy Decision in Manufacturing Strategy

István Mezgár
CIM Research Laboratory
Computer and Automations Research Institute
Hungarian Academy of Sciences
Budapest
HUNGARY
Chapter 9. Security Technologies to Guarantee Safe Business Processes in Smart Organizations

Marina Mongiello
Dipartimento di Elettrotecnica ed Elettronica
Politecnico di Bari
Bari
ITALY
Chapter 11. Knowledge-Based Systems Technology and Applications in Image Retrieval

Ralf Muhlberger
University of Queensland
Information Technology & Electrical Engineering

Queensland
AUSTRALIA
Chapter 10. Business Process Modeling and Its Applications in the Business Environment

Cezary Orlowski
Gdansk University of Technology
Gdansk
POLAND
Chapter 8. Methods of Building Knowledge-Based Systems Applied in Software Project Management

Emilio Paolucci
Department of Operation and Business Management
Polytechnic University of Turin
Torino
ITALY
Chapter 2. Knowledge Management Systems in Continuous Product Innovation

Luisa Pellegrini
Faculty of Engineering
University of Pisa
Pisa
ITALY
Chapter 2. Knowledge Management Systems in Continuous Product Innovation

Ram D. Sriram
Design and Process Group
Manufacturing Systems Integration Division
National Institute of Standards and Technology
Gaithersburg, Maryland
USA
Chapter 1. Platform-Based Product Design and Development: Knowledge Support Strategy and Implementation

Nikos C. Tsourveloudis
Department of Production Engineering and Management
Technical University of Crete
Chania, Crete
GREECE
Chapter 3. Knowledge-Based Measurement of Enterprise Agility

I. Vlahavas
Department of Informatics
Aristotle University of Thessaloniki

Thessaloniki
GREECE
Chapter 6. Aggregator: A Knowledge-Based Comparison Chart Builder for eShopping

Xuan F. Zha
Design and Process Group
Manufacturing Systems Integration Division
National Institute of Standards and Technology
Gaithersburg, Maryland
USA
Chapter 1. Platform-Based Product Design and Development: Knowledge Support Strategy and Implementation

VOLUME 2: INFORMATION TECHNOLOGY

Aleš Brezovar
Faculty of Mechanical Engineering
University of Ljubljana
Ljubljana
SLOVENIA
Chapter 4. Techniques and Analysis of Sequential and Concurrent Product Development Processes

Chris R. Chatwin
School of Engineering and Information Technology
University of Sussex
Brighton
UNITED KINGDOM
Chapter 3. Modeling Techniques in Integrated Operations and Information Systems in Manufacturing

Ke-Zhang Chen
Department of Mechanical Engineering
The University of Hong Kong
HONG KONG
Chapter 5. Design and Modeling Methods for Components Made of Multi-Heterogeneous Materials in High-Tech Applications

Adrian E. Coronado
Management School
The University of Liverpool
Liverpool
UNITED KINGDOM
Chapter 2. Information Systems Frameworks and Their Applications in Manufacturing Systems

Xin-An Feng
School of Mechanical Engineering
Dalian University of Technology
Dalian
CHINA
Chapter 5. Design and Modeling Methods for Components Made of Multi-Heterogeneous Materials in High-Tech Applications

Janez Grum
Faculty of Mechanical Engineering
University of Ljubljana
Ljubljana
SLOVENIA
Chapter 4. Techniques and Analysis of Sequential and Concurrent Product Development Processes

George Hadjinicola
Department of Public and Business Administration
School of Economics and Management
University of Cyprus
Nicosia
CYPRUS
Chapter 9. Product Design and Pricing in Response to Competitor Entry: A Marketing-Production Perspective

Jared Jackson
IBM Almaden Research Center
San Jose, California
USA
Chapter 7. Web Data Extraction Techniques and Applications Using the Extensible Markup Language (XML)

D. F. Kehoe
Management School
The University of Liverpool
Liverpool
UNITED KINGDOM
Chapter 2. Information Systems Frameworks and Their Applications in Manufacturing Systems

Andreas Koeller
Department of Computer Science
Montclair State University
Upper Montclair, New Jersey
USA
Chapter 6. Quality and Cost of Data Warehouse Views

K. Ravi Kumar
Department of Information and Operations Management
Marshall School of Business
University of Southern California
Los Angeles, California
USA
Chapter 9. Product Redesign and Pricing in Response to Competitor Entry: A Marketing-Production Perspective

Janez Kušar
Faculty of Mechanical Engineering
University of Ljubljana
Ljubljana
SLOVENIA
Chapter 4. Techniques and Analyses of Sequential and Concurrent Product Development Processes

Henry C. W. Lau
Department of Industrial and Systems Engineering
The Hong Kong Polytechnic University
Hunghom
HONG KONG
Chapter 10. Knowledge Discovery by Means of Intelligent Information Infrastructure Methods and Their Applications

Amy Lee
The Ohio State University
Columbus, Ohio
USA
Chapter 6. Quality and Cost of Data Warehouse Views

Choon Seong Leem
School of Computer and Industrial Engineering
Yonsei University
Seoul
KOREA
Chapter 1. Techniques in Integrated Development and Implementation of Enterprise Information Systems

A. C. Lyons
Management School
The University of Liverpool
Liverpool
UNITED KINGDOM
Chapter 2. Information Systems Frameworks and Their Applications in Manufacturing Systems

Jussi Myllymaki
IBM Almaden Research Center
San Jose, California
USA
Chapter 7. Web Data Extraction Techniques and Applications Using the Extensible Markup Language (XML)

Anisoara Nica
Sybase Incorporated
Waterloo, Ontario
Canada
Chapter 6. Quality and Cost of Data Warehouse Views

Jörg Niemann
IFF University of Stuttgart
Fraunhofer IPA
Stuttgart
GERMANY
Chapter 8. Product Life Cycle Management in the Digital Age

Andrew Ning
Department of Industrial and Systems Engineering
The Hong Kong Polytechnic University
Hunghom
HONG KONG
Chapter 10. Knowledge Discovery by Means of Intelligent Information Infrastructure Methods and Their Applications

Elke A. Rundensteiner
Department of Computer Science
Worcester Polytechnic Institute
Worcester Massachusetts
USA
Chapter 6. Quality and Cost of Data Warehouse Views

Marko Starbek
Faculty of Mechanical Engineering
University of Ljubljana
Ljubljana
SLOVENIA
Chapter 4. Techniques and Analyses of Sequential and Concurrent Product Development Processes

Jong Wook Suh
School of Computer and Industrial Engineering
Yonsei University

Seoul
KOREA
Chapter 1. Techniques in Integrated Development and Implementation of Enterprise Information Systems

Qian Wang
School of Engineering and Information Technology
University of Sussex
Brighton
and
Department of Mechanical Engineering
University of Bath
Bath
UNITED KINGDOM
Chapter 3. Modeling Techniques in Integrated Operations and Information Systems in Manufacturing Systems

Engelbert Westkämper
IFF University of Stuttgart
Fraunhofer IPA
Stuttgart
GERMANY
Chapter 8. Product Life Cycle Management in the Digital Age

Christina W. Y. Wong
Department of Industrial and Systems Engineering
The Hong Kong Polytechnic University
Hunghom
HONG KONG
Chapter 10. Knowledge Discovery by Means of Intelligent Information Infrastructure Methods and Their Applications

R. C. D. Young
School of Engineering and Information Technology
University of Sussex
Brighton
UNITED KINGDOM
Chapter 3. Modeling Techniques in Integrated Operations and Information Systems in Manufacturing Systems

VOLUME 3: EXPERT AND AGENT SYSTEMS

Dimitris Askounis
Institute of Communications & Computer Systems
National Technical University of Athems

Athens
GREECE
Chapter 2. Expert Systems Technology in Production Planning and Scheduling

G. A. Britton
Design Research Center
School Of Mechanical and Production Engineering
Nanyang Technological University
SINGAPORE
Chapter 1. Techniques in Knowledge-Based Expert Systems for the Design of Engineering Systems

Jing Dai
School of Computing
National University of Singapore
SINGAPORE
Chapter 9. Finding Patterns in Image Databases

Robert Gay
Institute of Communication and Information Systems
School of Electrical and Electronic Engineering
Nanyang Technological University
SINGAPORE
Chapter 6. Agent-Based eLearning Systems: A Goal-Based Approach

Angela Goh
School of Computer Engineering
Nanyang Technological University
SINGAPORE
Chapter 4. The Knowledge Base of a B2B eCommerce Multi-Agent System

Ivan Romero Hernandez
Technological University of Grenoble
LCIS Research Laboratory
Valence
FRANCE
Chapter 5. From Roles to Agents: Considerations on Formal Agent Modeling and Implementation

Tu Bao Ho
Japan Advanced Institute of Science and Technology
Ishikawa
JAPAN
Chapter 7. Combining Temporal Abstraction and Data-Mining Methods in Medical Data Analysis

Wynne Hsu
School of Computing
National University of Singapore
SINGAPORE
Chapter 9. Finding Patterns in Image Databases

Chun-Che Huang
Department of Information Management
National Chi Nan University
Taiwan
REPUBLIC OF CHINA
Chapter 3. Applying Intelligent Agent-Based Support Systems in Agile Business Processes

K. Karibasappa
Department of Electronics and Telecommunication Engineering
University College of Engineering, Burla
Sambalpur, Orissa
INDIA
Chapter 10. Cognition Techniques and Their Applications

Nelly Kasim
Singapore-MIT Alliance
National University of Singapore
SINGAPORE
Chapter 4. The Knowledge Base of a B2B eCommerce Multi-Agent System

Saori Kawasaki
Japan Advanced Institute of Science and Technology
Ishikawa
JAPAN
Chapter 7. Combining Temporal Abstraction and Data-Mining Methods in Medical Data Analysis

Jean-Luc Koning
Technological University of Grenoble
LCIS Research Laboratory
Valence
FRANCE
Chapter 5. From Roles to Agents: Considerations on Formal Agent Modeling and Implementation

Si Quang Le
Japan Advanced Institute of Science and Technology
Ishikawa

JAPAN
Chapter 7. Combining Temporal Abstraction and Data-Mining Methods in Medical Data Analysis

Mong Li Lee
School of Computing
National University of Singapore
SINGAPORE
Chapter 9. Finding Patterns in Image Databases

Antonio Liotta
Center for Communication Systems Research
University of Surrey
Guildford, Surrey
UNITED KINGDOM
Chapter 8. Distributed Monitoring: Methods, Means, and Technologies

Kostas Metaxiotis
Institute of Communications & Computer Systems
National Technical University of Athens
Athens
GREECE
Chapter 2. Expert Systems Technology in Production Planning and Scheduling

Chunyan Miao
School of Computer Engineering
Nanyang Technological University
SINGAPORE
Chapter 4. The Knowledge Base of a B2B eCommerce Multi-Agent System

Yuan Miao
Institute of Communication and Information Systems
Nanyang Technological University
SINGAPORE
Chapter 6. Agent-Based eLearning Systems: A Goal-Based Approach

Trong Dung Nguyen
Japan Advanced Institute of Science and Technology
Ishikawa
JAPAN
Chapter 7. Combining Temporal Abstraction and Data-Mining Methods in Medical Data Analysis

Srikanta Patnaik
Department of Electronics and Telecommunication Engineering
University College of Engineering, Burla

Sambalpur, Orissa
INDIA
Chapter 10. Cognition Techniques and Their Applications

John Psarras
Institute of Communications & Computer Systems
National Technical University of Athens
Athens
GREECE
Chapter 2. Expert Systems Technology in Production Planning and Scheduling

Zhiqi Shen
Institute of Communication and Information Systems
School of Electrical and Electronic Engineering
Nanyang Technological University
SINGAPORE
Chapter 6. Agent-Based eLearning Systems: A Goal-Based Approach

S. B. Tor
Singapore–MIT Alliance
Nanyang Technological University
SINGAPORE
Chapter 1. Techniques in Knowledge-Based Expert Systems for the Design of Engineering Systems

W. Y. Zhang
Design Research Center
School of Mechanical and Production Engineering
Nanyang Technological University
SINGAPORE
Chapter 1. Techniques in Knowledge-Based Expert Systems for the Design of Engineering Systems

VOLUME 4: INTELLIGENT SYSTEMS

Cheng-Leong Ang
Singapore Institute of Manufacturing Technology
SINGAPORE
Chapter 4. An Intelligent Hybrid System for Business Forecasting

Sistine A. Barretto
Advanced Computing Research Centre
The University of South Australia
Adelaide

AUSTRALIA
Chapter 6. Techniques in the Utilization of the Internet and Intranets in Facilitating the Development of Clinical Decision Support Systems in the Process of Patient Care

Billy Fenton
International Test Technologies
and
University of Ulster
Letterkenny, Donegal
IRELAND
Chapter 5. Intelligent Systems Technology in the Fault Diagnosis of Electronic Systems

Robert Gay
Institute of Communication and Information Systems
School of Electrical and Electronic Engineering
Nanyang Technological University
SINGAPORE
Chapter 4. An Intelligent Hybrid System for Business Forecasting

Victor Giurgiutiu
Mechanical Engineering Department
University of South Carolina
Columbia, South Carolina
USA
Chapter 8. Mechatronics and Smart Structures Design Techniques for Intelligent Products, Processes and Systems

Marc-Philippe Huget
Leibnitz Laboratory
Grenoble
France
Chapter 9. Engineering Interaction Protocols for Multiagent Systems

Richard W. Jones
School of Engineering
University of Northumbria
Newcastle upon Tyne
England
UNITED KINGDOM
Chapter 2. Intelligent Patient Monitoring in the Intensive Care Unit and the Operating Room

Jean-Luc Koning
Technological University of Grenoble
LCIS Research Laboratory

Valence
FRANCE
Chapter 9. Engineering Interaction Protocols for Multiagent Systems

Xiang Li
Singapore Institute of Manufacturing Technology
SINGAPORE
Chapter 4. An Intelligent Hybrid System for Business Forecasting

Liam Maguire
Department of Informatics
University of Ulster
Derry
NORTHERN IRELAND
Chapter 5. Intelligent Systems Technology in the Fault Diagnosis of Electronic Systems

T. M. McGinnity
Department of Informatics
University of Ulster
Derry
NORTHERN IRELAND
Chapter 5. Intelligent Systems Technology in the Fault Diagnosis of Electronic Systems

Tolety Siva Perraju
Verizon Communications
Waltham, Massachusetts
USA
Chapter 3. Mission Critical Intelligent Systems

Mauricio Sanchez–Silva
Department of Civil and Environmental Engineering
Universidad de los Andes
Bogotá
COLOMBIA
Chapter 7. Risk Analysis and the Decision-Making Process in Engineering

Garimella Uma
South Asia International Institute
Hyderabad
INDIA
Chapter 3. Mission Critical Intelligent Systems

James R. Warren
Advanced Computing Research Centre
The University of South Australia

Mawson Lakes
AUSTRALIA
Chapter 6. Techniques in the Utilization of the Internet and Intranets in Facilitating the Development of Clinical Decision Support Systems in the Process of Patient Care

Xuan F. Zha
Design and Process Group
Manufacturing Systems Integration Division
National Institute of Standards and Technology
Gaithersburg, Maryland
USA
Chapter 1. Artificial Intelligence and Integrated Intelligent Systems: Applications in Product Design and Development

VOLUME 5: NEURAL NETWORKS, FUZZY THEORY AND GENETIC ALGORITHM TECHNIQUES

Kazem Abhary
School of Advanced Manufacturing and Mechanical Engineering
University of South Australia
Mawson Lakes
AUSTRALIA
Chapter 8. Assembly Sequence Optimization Using Genetic Algorithms

F. Admiraal-Behloul
Division of Image Processing
Leiden University Medical Center
Leiden
THE NETHERLANDS
Chapter 4. Fuzzy Rule Extraction Using Radial Basis Function Neural Networks in High-Dimensional Data

Kemal Ahmet
Faculty of Creative Arts and Technologies
University of Luton
Luton
UNITED KINGDOM
Chapter 1. Neural Network Systems Technology and Applications in CAD/CAM Integration

Carl K. Chang
Department of Computer Science
Iowa State University
Ames, Iowa
USA
Chapter 7. Genetic Algorithm Techniques and Applications in Management Systems

Lian Ding
Faculty of Creative Arts and Technologies
University of Luton
Luton
UNITED KINGDOM
Chapter 1. Neural Network Systems Technology and Applications in CAD/CAM Integration

Shing-Hwang Doong
Department of Information Management
Shu-Te University
Yen Chau
TAIWAN
Chapter 10. Computational Intelligence for Facility Location Allocation Problems

Yujia Ge
Department of Computer Science
Iowa State University
Ames, Iowa
USA
Chapter 7. Genetic Algorithm Techniques and Applications in Management Systems

Andrew Kusiak
Department of Mechanical and Industrial Engineering
University of Iowa
Iowa City, Iowa
USA
Chapter 5. Fuzzy Decision Modeling of Product Development Processes

Chih-Chin Lai
Department of Information Management
Shu-Te University
Yen-Chau
TAIWAN
Chapter 10. Computational Intelligence for Facility Location Allocation Problems

Wen F. Lu
Product Design and Development Group
Singapore Institute of Manufacturing Technology
SINGAPORE
Chapter 6. Evaluation and Selection in Product Design for Mass Customization

Lee H. S. Luong
School of Advanced Manufacturing and Mechanical Engineering
University of South Australia

Mawson Lakes
AUSTRALIA
Chapter 8. Assembly Sequence Optimization Using Genetic Algorithms

Romeo Marin Marian
CSIRO Manufacturing & Infrastructure Technology
Woodville North, SA
AUSTRALIA
Chapter 8. Assembly Sequence Optimization Using Genetic Algorithms

Stergios Papadimitriou
Department of Information Management
Technological Education Institute of Kavala
Kavala
GREECE
Chapter 9. Kernel-Based Self-Organized Maps Trained with Supervised Bias for Gene Expression Data Mining

Johan H. C. Reiber
Division of Image Processing
Department of Radiology
Leiden University Medical Center
Leiden
THE NETHERLANDS
Chapter 4. Fuzzy-Rule Extraction Using Radial Basis Function Neural Networks in High-Dimensional Data

Kwang-Kyu Seo
Division of Computer, Information and Telecommunication Engineering
Sangmyung University
Chungnam
KOREA
Chapter 2. Neural Network Systems Technology and Applications in Product Life–Cycle Cost Estimates

Joaquin Sitte
Faculty of Information Technology
Queensland University of Technology
Brisbane
AUSTRALIA
Chapter 3. Neural Network Systems Technology in the Analysis of Financial Time Series

Renate Sitte
Faculty of Engineering and Information and Technology
Griffith University
Queensland
AUSTRALIA
Chapter 3. Neural Network Systems Technology in the Analysis of Financial Time Series

Ram D. Sriram
Design and Process Group
Manufacturing Systems Integration Divison
National Institute of Standards and Technology
Gaithersburg, Maryland
USA
Chapter 6. Evaluation and Selection in Product Design for Mass Customization

Fu J. Wang
Design and Process Group
Manufacturing Systems Integration Division
National Institute of Standards and Technology
Gaithersburg, Maryland
USA
Chapter 6. Evaluation and Selection in Product Design for Mass Customization

Juite Wang
Department of Industrial Engineering
Feng Chia University
Taichung, Taiwan
REPUBLIC OF CHINA
Chapter 5. Fuzzy Decision Modeling of Product Development Processes

Chih-Hung Wu
Department of Information Management
Shu-Te University
Yen Chau
TAIWAN
Chapter 10. Computational Intelligence for Facility Location Allocation Problems

Yong Yue
Faculty of Creative Arts and Technologies
University of Luton
Luton
UNITED KINGDOM
Chapter 1. Neural Network Systems Technology and Applications in CAD/CAM Integration

Xuan F. Zha
Design and Process Group
Manufacturing Systems Integration Divison
National Institute of Standards and Technology
Gaithersburg, Maryland
USA
Chapter 6. Evaluation and Selection in Product Design for Mass Customization

VOLUME V. NEURAL NETWORKS, FUZZY THEORY AND GENETIC ALGORITHMS

NEURAL NETWORK SYSTEMS TECHNOLOGY AND APPLICATIONS IN CAD/CAM INTEGRATION

YONG YUE, LIAN DING AND KEMAL AHMET

1. INTRODUCTION

With the growing trend towards global market, industry is facing fierce competition. Traditional design and manufacturing practice is no longer suitable for the new requirements. It has been widely recognised that genuine integration of design and manufacturing is needed to make products of higher quality with lower cost and shorter lead times. Although CAD and CAM have been extensively used in industry, effective CAD/CAM integration has not been implemented and human intervention is often required to interpret design data and intents to downstream applications.

One of the major obstacles of CAD/CAM integration is the representation of design and process knowledge. Geometrical models only provide the geometric and topological information of a component, which is not sufficient for the manufacturing applications, e.g. process planning. Thus, features encapsulating the engineering significance are considered as a key element in the integration of design and manufacturing and feature-based models have been widely used. Computer-aided process planning (CAPP) is considered as another key element for CAD/CAM integration, which automates to some extent, the decision making in process selection, sequencing and parameter calculations.

Much of research has been seen in CAD/CAM integration using various approaches and techniques, such as design by features, feature recognition, artificial neural networks (ANNs), fuzzy logics and genetic algorithms (GAs). Considerable progress has been made towards a genuine integration in practical applications, especially in tackling interacting features and inability of self-learning for certain tasks.

3

This Chapter provides a comprehensive review of the current developments in feature recognition and CAPP for CAD/CAM integration. It covers neural network-based applications that may incorporate other contemporary techniques such as fuzzy logics and GAs.

2. ARTIFICIAL NEURAL NETWORKS

An ANN is an interconnected assembly of simple processing elements, units or nodes, whose functionality is loosely based on the animal neuron [1]. The function of an ANN-based system is determined by four parameters: the net topology, training or learning rules, input node characteristics and output node characteristics [2]. Neural network-based methods can eliminate some drawbacks of the conventional approaches, and therefore have attracted research attention particularly in recent years:

- it can tolerate slight errors from input during learning or problem solving;
- it is faster because the process is limited to simple mathematical computations and does not use either a search or logical rules to parse information; and
- it has the ability to derive rules or knowledge through training with examples and can allow exceptions and irregularities in the knowledge/rule base.

This chapter gives a brief introduction to ANN techniques and its applications in feature recognition and CAPP.

3. ANN TECHNIQUES FOR FEATURE RECOGNITION

Feature recognition extracts features from a model of an object for a specific application. As one of major feature technology, feature recognition has been regarded as a key tool to integrate design and manufacturing processes. Various methods have been proposed such as graph matching, rule-based reasoning, volume decomposition, multiple feature modelling and hybrid approaches. However, none of them have the learning capability of artificial neural networks (ANNs). This section discusses the following aspects of ANN applications to feature recognition: the network topology, input representation, output format, training or learning method, and a summary of the results.

3.1. The topology

There are three main ANN architectures: feed-forward, recurrent and competitive networks [1].

3.1.1. Feedforward networks

Feedforward network is the network whose neurons are strictly fed forward to activate the neurons in the next higher layer. As shown in Figure 1, for a typical single-layer feedforward network, its input neurons are fully connected to output neurons, but not vice versa. On the other hand, the input neurons are not connected to other input neurons and the output neurons are not connected to other output neurons. Different from the single-layer feedforward network, a multi-layer feedforward network has one or more hidden layers. Although there is no theoretical limit on the number of hidden

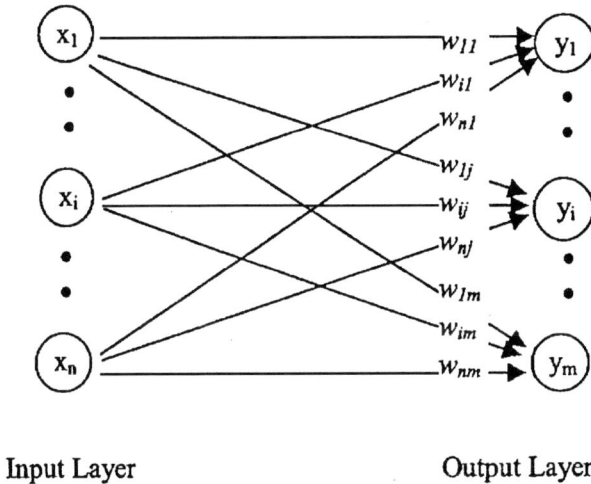

Figure 1. Single-layer feedforward neural network.

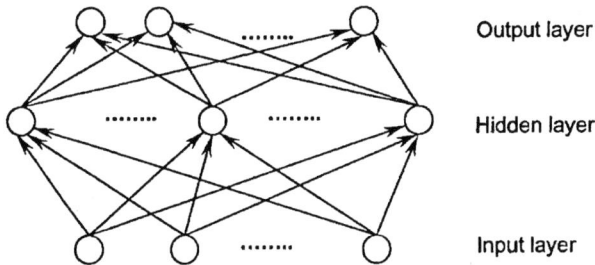

Figure 2. Three-layer feed-forward neural network model.

layers, in general, only one or two hidden layers are used in practice. It has been shown theoretically that it is sufficient to use a maximum of three layers (two hidden layers and one output layer) to solve an arbitrarily complex pattern classification problem [3]. By adding one or more hidden layers, multi-layer feedforward networks can solve more complicated mapping problems than single-layer feedforward networks. Figure 2 illustrates an example of multi-layer feedforward network structure with one hidden layers.

3.1.2. Competitive networks

In a competitive network, a group of neurons compete for the opportunity to become active. Generally, in order to activate only the winner neuron, an algorithm is used to assign the winner neuron or inhibit other neurons. Typically, it includes two layers: the input layer which receives input information, and the competitive layer which outputs the winner. Figure 3 gives an example of competitive network structure.

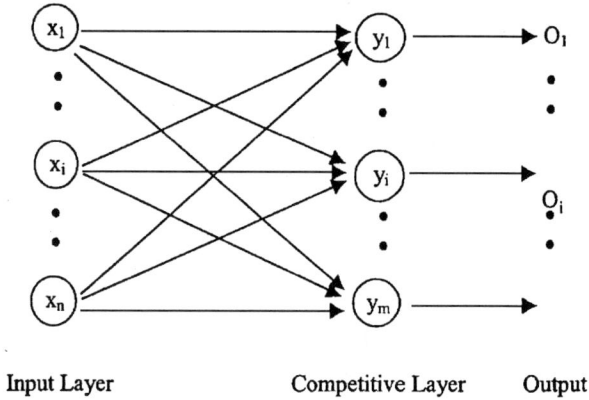

Figure 3. Competitive neural network.

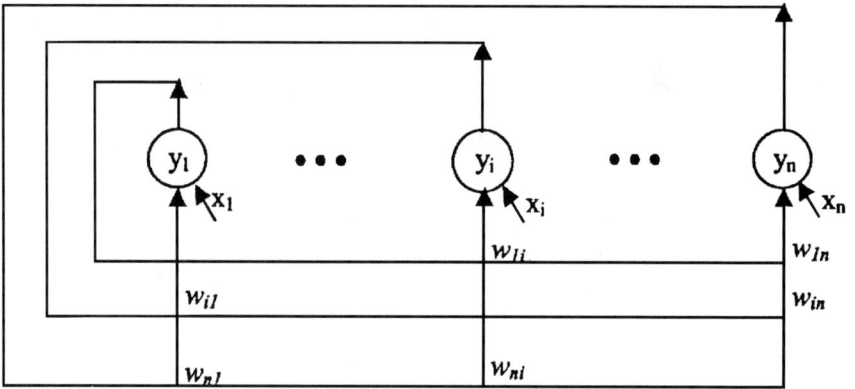

Figure 4. Hopfield network.

3.1.3. Recurrent networks

A recurrent network distinguishes itself from a feedforward neural network in that it has at least one feedback loop [4]. Typically recurrent networks include Hopfield net, Boltzmann machine and recurrent backpropagation net. In the structure depicted in Figure 4, the output of each neuron feed into the input of other neurons in the same layer so that the network is "recursive".

Comparing to competitive network and recurrent network, feedforward network is more suitable for feature recognition. The reasons are

• Manufacturing feature recognition is not the kind of recognition based on the input probability, but it is possible to collect enough samples including inputs and targets.

• Manufacturing feature recognition is a complicated process, for which entire information including both geometric and topologic information needs to be inputted.

The typical topology used by most feature recognition system can be defined by an input layer of neurons that receive binary or continuously valued input signals, an output layer with a corresponding number of neurons, and a number of hidden layers that are highly interconnected [5]. Hence, the design of network topology can be reduced to three problems: the number of hidden layers, the optional number of neurons in the hidden layer, and the use of networks with incompletely connected layers. At present, three main feed-forward architectures have been developed for feature recognition as described below.

3.1.4. The three-layer feed-forward neural network

This model has an input, a hidden and an output layer (shown in Figure 2). Neurons on the hidden and output layers are defined from the neurons on the previous layer, the weights and a processing algorithm. That is, the lth neuron on the current layer, N_l, can be calculated as:

$$N_l = \sum_{k=1}^{n} u_k w_{kl},$$

where

$\quad$ u_k is the kth neuron on the previous layer, and
$\quad$ w_{kl} is the weight representing the strength of the relationship between the kth neuron on the previous layer and the lth neuron on the current layer.

In order to constrain the value of each neuron on the current layer, an appropriate transfer function is used. For example, in order to restrict the output value from 0 to 1, a sigmoid transfer function can be applied, such as Chuang's system [6]:

$$F(N_l) = \frac{1}{1 + e^{-N_l}}$$

The Bipolar sigmoid function is a commonly used activation function to make the output fall in a continuous range from -1 to 1. It is closely related to the hyperbolic tangent function, which can be described approximately by the following equation

$$f(x) = \tanh \sigma x = \frac{1 - e^{-2\sigma x}}{1 + e^{-2\sigma x}}$$

There have been several instances of using three-layer feed-forward neural networks, such as [6, 7, 8, 9].

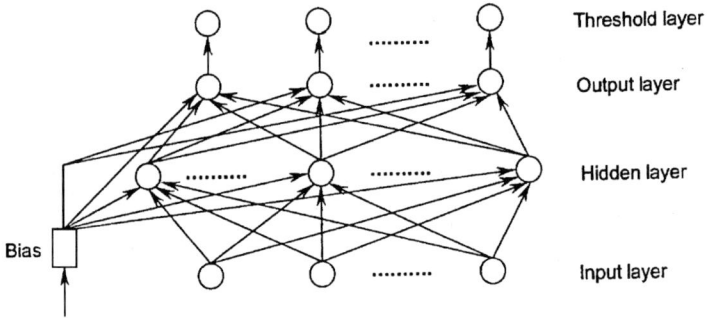

Figure 5. Four-layer feed-forward neural network model.

3.1.5. The four-layer feed-forward neural network

This approach uses four layers: an input, a hidden, an output, and a threshold layer, which is added to the network as the training is completed. The threshold layer performs the function of activating the neurons of the output layer by a threshold, e.g. 0.5. Nezis and Vosniakos [5] provided an example of this kind of topology. As shown in Figure 5, there are 20 neurons in the input layer, 10 neurons in the hidden layer and eight output neurons. All elements of the hidden and output layers are connected with a bias element that can be considered as an activation threshold. Although four-layer feed-forward networks are more versatile than three-layer feed-forward networks, they train more slowly due to the attenuation of errors through the non-linearities [10].

3.1.6. The five-layer, perceptrons quasi-neural network

Prabhakar and Henderson [2] developed a five-layer, perceptrons quasi-neural network system called PRENET. The system has five layers which respectively, consist of N nodes, N groups of M nodes, N nodes with a threshold non-linearity, M nodes corresponding to the M conditions for a feature, and one node, where N is the number of faces in the test part and M the number of conditions required for the feature.

3.2. Input representation

Neural nets typically, although not necessarily, receive a set of integer values. The problem then is how to convert a solid model to a format suitable for neural net input in a convenient and efficient way. There are three basic characteristics for a satisfactory input representation:

- Complete information (e.g. faces, edges and vertices) for feature recognition. It is extremely important that this representation describes features correctly and does not distort any information.
- An identifiable format by the input layer of the neural network.
- A unique input representation without overlaps. In other words, features belonging to different feature classes must have different input representation.

Input representation is a key task for ANN-based feature recognition, and several studies have been carried out. However, some problems are still to be solved, such as limited range of recognised features, large size and ambiguity. Generally, the proposed input representations can be broadly classified into the following types.

3.2.1. 2D feature representation

In engineering drawings, the wire-frame profiles of shapes can be subdivided into connected loops of edges. Peters [8] proposed an ordered triplet (C_i, A_i, L_i) to represent each edge of a connected loop, where C_i, A_i and L_i are the curvature, interior angle and arc length of the ith element respectively. An encoded feature vector of the triplet (C_i, A_i, L_i) for a given profile is used as the input.

Chen and Lee [11] developed an improved encoded feature vector, in which the representation of each edge is expanded from an ordered 3-tuple to an ordered 7-tuple in the form: $(L_i, A_i, C_i, J_i, OL_i, OA_i, OC_i)$ where J_i is the intersection type between the line segment and its subsequent line segment, and OL_i, OA_i and OC_i are the ordinal values assigned to L_i, A_i and C_i respectively. The ordinal values are assigned to the parameter in order to capture the magnitudes. The input layer has thirty-five neurons corresponding to five edges, seven neurons representing each edge. Although this method can recognise three and four-sided features, more neurons are needed in the input, output and hidden layers when the number of edges of a feature is increased.

3.2.2. Face adjacency matrix code

A face adjacency matrix is a 2D array of integer vectors converted from a solid model. Each integer vector represents a face and its relationship to another face, i.e. adjacency or common edge. The length of an integer vector depends on the number of parameters considered for the recognition of a feature. In Prabhakar and Henderson's work [2], the vector has eight integers indicating characteristics such as edge type, face type, face angle type, number of loops, etc. This method is limited to features defined by a primary face and a set of secondary faces. It cannot differentiate between features with the same topology but different dimensions of compound faces.

3.2.3. Face score vector

This represents the relationship between the main face of a feature and its neighbouring faces [7]. The eight-element face score vector is formed in three steps.

a) A face score is defined as $F_s = f(F_g, E_g, V_g, A_t)$, where F_s is the face score, F_g, E_g and V_g are the information about the face, edge and vertex geometry, and A_t is the adjacency among the faces, edges and vertices. A high face score indicates a likely feature face, which in turn indicates the addition or removal of material.

b) A face score graph representing the relationship of face scores between a face and its neighbouring faces is drawn based on the face scores for all faces of the given object. A non-zero difference between a face score and its neighbouring face score indicates a geometric or topological change between these faces, which form a region. The region may be defined as a feature.

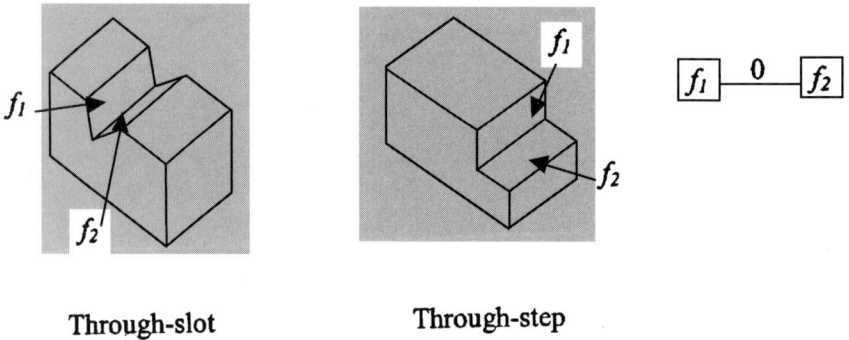

Through-slot   **Through-step**

Figure 6. Features with the same face-edge graph.

c) An eight–element face score vector is formed and input to the net. Chan's work [12] is another example of a face score vector while Srinath [13] tackled partial features. This representation can recognise a very limited number of compound features, and there is no one-to-one correspondence between feature patterns and features.

3.2.4. Attributed adjacency matrix

An attributed adjacency matrix [5,14] describing the geometry and topology of a feature pattern is converted from the attributed adjacency graph (AAG) [15]. In Nezis and Vosniakos' research [5], the adjacency matrix (AM) is a 2D, square, binary matrix with two triangular areas: an upper and a lower which are the convex and concave spaces respectively. $AM[i, j]$ and $AM[j, i]$ indicate the connection between the ith and jth faces of the object. One of them belongs to the concave space and the other to the convex space. The representation vector is formed as follows:

a) the AAG is broken into sub-graphs which are converted into AM using a heuristic method;
b) each matrix is convert into a representation vector (RV) by interrogating a set of 12 questions about the AM layout and the number of faces in the sub-graph; and
c) a binary vector is formed combining the 12 positive answers and the other 8 elements corresponding to the number of external faces linked to the sub-graph.

This method can recognise planar and simple curved faces, but it still has several problems, such as ambiguity (e.g. Figure 6), non-unique (e.g. Figure 7), limited features recognised, etc.

3.2.5. F-adjacency matrix and V-adjacency matrix

Aiming to solve the problems of AAG, an input representation with two matrices is proposed [9]. The input scheme describes the topological and geometrical information of a feature as a spatial virtual entity (SVE), which is an equivalent to the volume

	f_1	f_2	f_3	f_4
f_1		1	0	1
f_2	1		1	1
f_3	0	1		1
f_4	1	1	1	

Matrix A

	f_1	f_2	f_3	f_4
f_1		0	1	1
f_2	0		1	1
f_3	1	1		1
f_4	1	1	1	

Matrix B

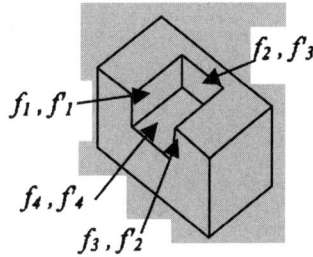

Figure 7. A feature with two matrices.

removed from the initial material stock in order to obtain the final boundary of the feature. The input representation works in three stages.

a) Employing a depth-first method to search for all faces in the feature SVE, building its UndiGraph and determining the Node Sequence. The UndiGraph is defined as a face graph describing a feature pattern:

UndiGraph $= (F, R)$,

where

　　F is the finite non-NULL set of faces consisting of the feature, and
　　R is a set of relationships between faces: $R = \{FR\}$.
　　FR is a relationship with no specific direction between two faces.

A Node Sequence corresponding to each face is defined as the following:

$$NS_{facei} = N_f^* 10 + (6 - N_v) + T_{ftype}^* 0.1,$$

where

　　NS_{facei} is the Node Sequence of face i;
　　N_f is the number of adjacent faces of face i;
　　N_v is the number of adjacent virtual faces of face i; and
　　T_{ftype} is the value of the type of face i (the value allocated is shown in Table 1).

Table 1 Value of face type

Face type	Value
Cylindrical face	1
Part–cylindrical face	2
Conical face	3
Part–conical face	4
Semi–spherical face	5
Planar face	6
Linear–group	7
Circular–group	8

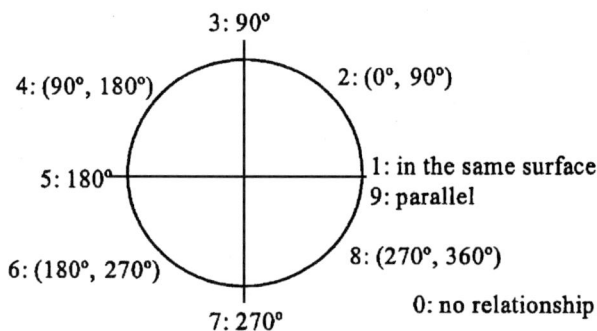

Figure 8. Values of relationship between two features.

b) Defining the F-adjacency matrix

F-adjacency matrix is defined as $I_F = [a_{ij}]_{i \times j}$, where $1 <= i <= 5$ and $1 <= j <= 5$.

$$I_F = \begin{bmatrix} a_{11} & a_{12} & a_{13} & a_{14} & a_{15} \\ a_{21} & a_{22} & a_{23} & a_{24} & a_{25} \\ a_{31} & a_{32} & a_{33} & a_{34} & a_{35} \\ a_{41} & a_{42} & a_{43} & a_{44} & a_{45} \\ a_{51} & a_{52} & a_{53} & a_{54} & a_{55} \end{bmatrix}$$

The layout of I_F is ergonomically designed to have a one-to-one correspondence between the feature pattern and the input matrix. The middle elements of I_F, i.e. a_{ii}, show the type of the ith face, $face_i$ (e.g. 6 for a planar face). Table 1 denotes the values for various face types. Other elements of I_F (a_{ij}, where $i \neq j$) indicate the connection between the ith and jth faces of the object. A numerical value between 0 and 9 is allocated according to the relationship between the two faces. The values are given in Figure 8.

The layout presentation of I_F is symmetrical so that the input format consists of 15 nodes, $a_{11}, a_{12}, \ldots, a_{15}, a_{22}, a_{23}, \ldots, a_{25}, \ldots, a_{55}$.

c) Constructing the V-adjacency matrix

The V-adjacency matrix I_V can be determined in the following steps.

Step 1: Determine three pairs of boundary planes in the x, y and z directions, which can be represented as $+x, -x, +y, -y, +z$ and $-z$.

Step 2: Define the SVE for the given feature, which is completely enclosed based on the above six directions.

Step 3: Attach the attributes of FF/VF, which are face types used to define the feature [9], to all faces in the SVE.

Step 4: Define a 6*6 matrix, I_V showing the relationships between VF faces in the SVE. The middle element, b_{ii}, show whether there is a VF in the corresponding direction. If in the ith direction (e.g. $+x$), the given SVE exists a VF face, and $b_{ii} = 1$; if not, $b_{ii} = 0$. Other elements, b_{ij} ($i \neq j$), describe whether the two VFs, corresponding to direction i and direction j, are connected or not (i.e. 1 or 0).

$$I_V = \begin{bmatrix} b_{11} & b_{12} & b_{13} & b_{14} & b_{15} & b_{16} \\ b_{21} & b_{22} & b_{23} & b_{24} & b_{25} & b_{26} \\ b_{31} & b_{32} & b_{33} & b_{34} & b_{35} & b_{36} \\ b_{41} & b_{42} & b_{43} & b_{44} & b_{45} & b_{46} \\ b_{51} & b_{52} & b_{53} & b_{54} & b_{55} & b_{56} \\ b_{61} & b_{62} & b_{63} & b_{64} & b_{65} & b_{66} \end{bmatrix}$$

Similarly, the symmetric characteristic of V-adjacency matrix is used to simplify the input. A vector consisting of 21 codes is input to the neural network, That is, $b_{11}, b_{12}, \ldots, b_{16}, b_{22}, b_{23}, \ldots, b_{26}, \ldots, b_{66}$.

With the number of faces increased, the size of matrix will become quite large. For example, the pocket shown in Figure 9a consists of seven faces and the size of the adjacency matrix will be 7*7. In practice, the size of the matrices can be reasonably decreased. As shown in Figure 9a, the topological information is similar to the pocket in Figure 9b and can be described as the graph shown in Figure 9c. If the number of faces in the ordered adjacency list (OAL) is larger than 5, the OAL should be simplified. The rules for simplification are described below.

Rule 1: A series of faces, $face_i, face_{i+1}, \ldots, face_{i+n}$, are regarded as a Linear Group if they satisfy the following conditions:

• $int(NS_{i+j}) = 35$, where $j = 1, \ldots, n-1$;
• $int(NS_{i+j}) = 24$, where $j = 0, n$;
• They are consecutively connected;
• $face_i$ and $face_{i+n}$ are not connected with each other.

Rule 2: A serial of faces, $face_i, face_{i+1}, \ldots, face_{i+n}$, are regarded as a Circular Group if they satisfy the following conditions:

• $int(NS_{i+j}) = 35$, where $j = 0, 1, \ldots, n$;
• They are consecutively connected;
• $face_i$ and $face_{i+n}$ are connected with each other.

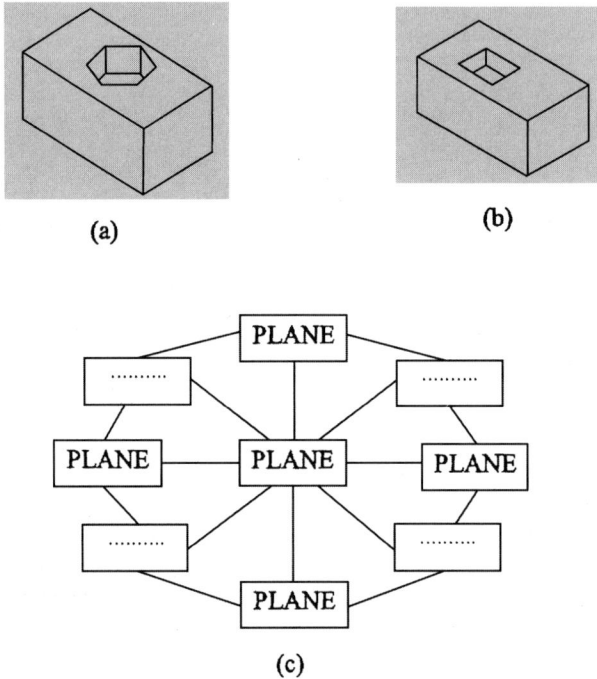

Figure 9. Simplification of topology.

3.2.6. 2D input patterns of 3D feature volume

Zulkifli and Meeran [16] presented an input matrix based on a cross-sectional method. The B-rep solid model is searched through cross-sectional layers and converted into 2D feature patterns, which are then translated into a matrix appropriate to the network. Four input matrices correspond to four feature classes: simple primitive, circular, slanting, and non-orthogonal primitive features. There are several disadvantages, e.g. simple primitive features are limited to four rectangular vertices, and features with non-orthogonal faces in the z direction cannot be dealt with.

3.2.7. A vector based on the partitioned view-contours of a given object

The given object is represented by nine partitioned view-contours from $+x$, $-x$, $+y$, $-y$, $+z$, $-z$, x, y and z respectively. The vector is built in three steps.

a) A graph with a representative ring code is defined from a partitioned view-contour in which the nodes represent the regions and the arcs the adjacency relations among the regions; the representative ring code is a cyclic string of digits formed for each region based on both the graph and a two-layer octal coding system.

b) Based on the weighting value computed with the representative ring code, the graphs are converted to a reference tree in which each node is associated with $6 + m$ values using heuristics from several experiments, assuming each graph node has at most $m + 1$ adjacent nodes.

c) The vector is then generated with the first $6 + m$ elements for the tree root and the next $6 + m$ elements for the second tree node ranked, and so on.

This method is only suitable for block-shaped objects with rectangular view-contour boundaries. The work by Chuang et al [6] provides an example.

3.2.8. Simplified skeleton

A simplified skeleton is a tree structure with line segments [17] represented by an input vector that is formed in the following process:

a) A standard tree structure in which each parent branch has the same number of descendants is predefined;

b) A simplified skeleton with several standard trees is represented;

c) Six attributes of a branch in the standard tree to describe each real link (non-null assignment branch) and the spatial relationships among them are defined; and

d) The standard tree is converted into a vector in which each element corresponds to a branch; there can be several standard trees for a simplified skeleton.

This representation can be used to classify 3D prismatic parts, but only the contour information of the part is considered.

3.3. The output format

The output of an ANN is the result of many operations with the inputs and weights. Commonly, a good output format should have the following characteristics:

• Representation scheme: It is essential that the output describes the results clearly and correctly as expected.

• Appropriate format: Similar to the input format, the output is designed as a nodal value in the format of a vector.

• Activation principle: For feature recognition, it is not practicable to activate two classes at the same time. If one or more output neurons are activated, the pattern presented to the network does not belong to a known class.

Based on the information in the output vector, there are three types of output format.

3.3.1. Each neuron corresponding to a feature class

If the number of feature classes to be recognised is not large, it is possible that each output neuron represents a certain feature class. At this situation, only one of the output neurons will be activated (e.g. its value will be the greatest one and greater than the threshold value, 0.5). Many systems adopt this output format. In Chen and Lee's work

[11], for example, the six neurons on the output layer represent six feature classes: rectangle, slot, trapezoid, parallelogram, v-slot and triangle. Nezis and Vosniakos' system [5] provides eight output neurons corresponding to eight feature classes. In the first level of recognised system developed by Ding and Yue [9], five output neurons are designed for five basic feature classes: Hole, General Hole, Conical Hole, Slot/Step and Pocket.

3.3.2. Neurons representing the information of the recognised feature

Hwang [7] uses six neurons for the output, representing the class, name, confidence factor, the main-face name, the list of associated faces of the feature found, and the total execution time. A file storing the information of different features is constructed. In the file, each vector corresponding to a feature has thirteen elements as follows: the feature name, the number of elements in the weight vector, eight elements representing the weights, a threshold factor, a gain factor, and the number of iterations before converging to an acceptable value.

3.3.3. A matrix file containing the code for each recognised feature and its machining directions

The output has the information on tool access direction, which in turn reflects the feature orientation. Zulkifli and Meeran's system [16] is a typical example: the output is a binary matrix $O = [b_{ij}]$, $1 \leq i \leq 2$, $1 \leq j \leq 5$, with b_{1j} representing the code for the feature recognised, and b_{2j} showing the tool accessibility to machine the feature, namely $+x$, $-x$, $+y$, $-y$ and $-z$ directions.

3.4. The training method

The training or learning method determines how the network will react when an unknown input is presented [2]. Before the process of recognition, the neurons in the network have to be trained with some set of training features. The training process is generally classified as supervised learning or unsupervised learning. During supervised training, the correct class corresponding to the training pattern is given. The net produces an output based on its current weights, and compares it with the correct output. If there is a difference, the weights are adjusted according to a learning algorithm based on the output difference.

3.4.1. Back propagation algorithms

Most ANN-based feature recognition work employs supervised training with a back propagation algorithm [5, 11, 16]. During back propagation a given input, called the training input, is mapped to a specified target output. The training process comprises four stages:

a) the weights are initialised;
b) training vectors/matrices are presented to the network;
c) the actual and desired outputs are compared, and the network's error is calculated as the difference between its output and target—the mean squared error is commonly

used as the test norm. In the system developed by Chen and Lee [11], the root-mean-square (RMS) error is defined by the equation:

$$RMS = \sqrt{\frac{\sum_p \sum_j (t_{jp} - a_{jp})^2}{n_p n_o}},$$

where

    t_{jp} is the target value for output neuron j after presentation of pattern p,

    a_{jp} is the output value produced by output neuron j after presentation of pattern p,

    n_p is the number of patterns in the training set, and

    n_o is the number of neurons in the output layer.

d) information about this error is propagated backwards to the hidden neurons and the weights adjusted accordingly.

After a number of iterations, the output will converge towards the target. The delta rule, also known as the Widrow-Hoff learning rule is used to modify the weights [5, 11].

3.4.2. Conjugate gradient algorithm by the authors

The basic back propagation algorithm adjusts the weights in the steepest descent direction (negative of the gradient) [18]. Although this direction makes the performance function (error function E) decrease most rapidly, it does not necessarily produce the fastest convergence. Alternative approaches, known as conjugate gradient algorithms, make a search along conjugate directions, which produces generally faster convergence than in the steepest directions. A set of mutually conjugate directions can be achieved through the following steps:

a) An initial weight vector (w_0) is chosen randomly;

b) The steepest descent direction (d_0) is selected on the first iteration, which is the negative of the gradient (g_0), $d_0 = -g_0$;

c) The weights are updated by an optimal distance (called learning rate, α_k) along the current search direction, $w_{k+1} = w_k + \alpha_k d_k$
where α_k is determined using a line search method proposed by Charalambous [19], which minimises the error function along the current search direction;

d) The stopping criterion (performance goal to satisfy the error set) is examined. If it is satisfied, the training stops; otherwise, proceeds to the next step;

e) The new gradient vector of performance (g_{k+1}) is evaluated, which is orthogonal to the previous search direction, $d_k^T g_{k+1} = 0$, where d_k^T denotes the transpose of d_k^T;

f) Each successive direction (d_{k+1}) is chosen as a linear function of the current gradient and the previous search direction (d_k), $d_{k+1} = -g_{k+1} + \beta_k d_k$;

g) Set $k = k + 1$, go to step c).

3.4.3. Training method by Prabhakar and Henderson

Prabhakar and Henderson [2] developed a system that allows the feature class to be stored in the net as it is defined. Although in a sense it used a supervised training method, it is not receptive to traditional neural net training. During a training session, the trained feature is presented only once, and the weights and other parameters are set at the same time. Thus there is a lack of fundamental quality to the learning.

3.5. Summary of ANN-based feature recognition

At present, the results of neural network-based methodologies are limited to a range of particular features which are outlined in Table 2. From the previous discussions, it can be seen that neural networks have the potential in devising general methods of feature recognition that are effective and robust. Most of the neural network-based systems have shown a higher recognition speed, and any features that are moderately similar to the training examples can be recognised.

4. ANN TECHNIQUES FOR CAPP

Process planning is a function that establishes a set of manufacturing operations and their sequence, and specifies the appropriate tools (machine tools, cutting tools, jigs and fixtures, etc.) and process parameters in order to convert a part from its initial raw

Table 2 Capabilities of ANN-based feature recognition

Work by	Features recognised
Hwang [7]	a. Simple and partial features whose main face must be directly connected to all its associated faces, e.g. pocket, slot, through-hole, blind hole and step b. Compound features formed by two or more non-intersecting simple features
Prabhakar and Henderson [2]	3-D features that can be defined by one primary face and a set of secondary faces, e.g. flat bottom hole, through-slot, through-hole
Peters [8]	2-D features: square, rectangle, parallelogram, slot
Dagli [20]	2-D features: bracket, circle
Chan [12]	3-D features: block, hole, slot, pocket, groove, cylinder and boss
Gu et al. [14]	Depression features: step, slot, blind step, blind slot, pocket, inverted dove tail slot, blind hole
Wu and Jen [17]	Some 3-D prismatic components
Nezis and Vosniakos [5]	a. Features such as slot, blind slot, step, pocket and hole which only have planar faces b. Simple curved faces
Chen and Lee [11]	2-D features: rectangle, slot, trapezoid, parallelogram, V-slot and triangle
Zulkifli and Meeran [16]	a. Simple primitive features defined by four rectangular vertices, such as step, slot, blind slot and pocket b. Circular features c. Z-slanting features d. Non-orthogonal faces in the x and y directions
Chuang [6]	3-D block-shaped components
Ding and Yue [9]	3-D prismatic components

state to a final form predetermined from an engineering drawing [21]. The use of computer techniques to automate the tasks of process planning has been the subject of extensive research. A variety of CAPP systems have been developed, using both retrieval and generative methods, with varying degrees of success. ANN techniques, which have been prevalent in recent years, offer promising potentials in solving CAPP tasks, such as selection of technical parameters for a cutting tool, adaptation of cutting conditions, operation selection and operation sequence.

4.1. The topology

Four main ANN architectures have been used in CAPP are introduced: Feedforward network, Hopfield network, Brain-State-in-a-Box (BSB) and MAXNET.

4.1.1. Feedforward network

Most neural network-based CAPP systems use the feedforward architecture, e.g. Li et al [22], especially three-layer feedforward network because it is suitable for a mapping in a continuous decision region [23]. Examples include a network by Osakada and Yang [24] consisting of a *256*-unit input layer, an *8*-unit hidden layer and a *4*-unit output layer to relate forming methods for rotationally symmetric products; a network with a *5*-neuron hidden layer for manufacturing evaluation by Gu et al [25]; and a network for selecting technological parameters for a cutting tool using the hyperholic tangent sigmoid function [26].

Park et al. [27] developed a four-layer feedforward network with two hidden layers to modify cutting condition based on several tests. Le Tumelin et al. [28] proposed a five-layer feedforward network to determine appropriate sequence of operations for machining holes.

4.1.2. Hopfield network

The Hopfield network is a single layer recurrent network that uses threshold process elements and an interconnect symmetric matrix as shown in Figure 4 [10]. A minimum point or attractor has been demonstrated to be existence in this network, which corresponds to one of the stored patterns. It can be described as the following [10]:

$$y(n + 1) = \text{sgn} \left(\sum_{j=1}^{N} w_{ij} y_j(n) - b_i + x_i(n) \right),$$

where

$i = 1, \ldots N,$
sgn represents the threshold nonlinearity $(-1, 1)$, and
b is a bias.

The dynamics of the Hopfield network can be described by the state of an energy function which eventually gets to a minimum point. Therefore, optimal operation sequencing can be expected with the continuous download trend of a global energy function. Shan et al [29] adapted the Hopfield network to the operation sequencing problem. Supposing the number of operations is n, the network is then composed of n^2 neurons, each identified by double subscripts: the operation and the sequence to be executed. The global energy function of the network is given by the following equations:

$$E = E_1 + E_2 + E_3,$$

$$E_1 = \frac{1}{2}A\sum_i\sum_j\sum_{i\neq j}v_{ij}v_{il} + \frac{1}{2}B\sum_j\sum_i\sum_{k\neq i}v_{ij}v_{kj} + \frac{1}{2}C\left[\left(\sum_i\sum_j v_{ij}\right) - n\right]^2$$

$$E_2 = D\sum_i\sum_j\sum_{k\neq i}\sum_{i>j}p_{ki}v_{ij}v_{ki}$$

$$E_3 = F\sum_j^{n-1}\sum_i\sum_{k\neq i}t_{ki}v_{ij}v_{k,j+1},$$

where

A, B, C, D and F are constants,
v_{ij} is the output of neuron in position (i, j) of the matrix, and
t_{ki} is tool travelling time form the position i to k.

The change in energy ΔE_{ij} due to a change in the state of neuron is:

$$\Delta E_{ij} = \left[\sum_l\sum_k w_{kl,ij}v_{kl} + I_{ij}\right]\Delta v_{ij}, \quad \text{where } I_{ij} \text{ is a bias weight.}$$

The weight connecting neurons kl and ij can be found as the following:

$$w_{ij,kl} = -A\delta_{ki}(1 - \delta_{lj}) - B\delta_{lj}(1 - \delta_{ki}) - C - Dp_{ki}\phi_{lj}(1 - \delta_{ki}) - Ft_{ki}\delta_{lj+1},$$

where

$$\delta_{xy} = \begin{cases} 0 & \text{if } x \neq y \\ 1 & \text{if } x = y \end{cases}$$

$$\phi_{xy} = \begin{cases} 0 & \text{if } x \leq y \\ 1 & \text{if } x > y \end{cases}$$

The Hopfield network provides one of the strongest links between information processing and dynamics. However, spurious memories limit its capacity to store patterns.

4.1.3. Brain-State-in-a-Box (BSB)

As a discrete-time recurrent network with a continuous state, the output values of a BSB, consisting of interconnected neurons, depend on the learnt patterns, the initial values of given patterns and the recall coefficients. The motion of a BSB network can be described by the following equation [10]:

$$y_i(n+1) = f\left(x_i(n) + \alpha \sum_{j=1}^{N} w_{ij}x_j(n)\right)$$

$$f(u) = \begin{cases} 1 & \text{if } u \geq 1 \\ u & \text{if } -1 \leq u \leq 1 \\ -1 & \text{if } u \leq -1 \end{cases}$$

A BSB can be used as a subnet for decision feedback applications because it amplifies the present input until all neurons saturate, and eventually converges to one of the corners of the hypercube $[-1, 1]^n$.

Sakakura and Inasaki [30] adapted a BSB network in a CAPP system. The number of neurons assigned for the dressing depth of cut, dressing feed and surface roughness are 5, 5 and 9 respectively. The initial values are given by a feedforward network run at the same time. The BSB repeats, performing a calculation using the following equation until the output value of each neuron converges to a certain value:

$$o_m = LIMIT(a_m),$$

$$a_m = c_1 \sum_{n \neq m} w_{mn}o_n + c_2 o_m + c_3 o_m(0),$$

where

> $LIMIT(\ )$ is the function which limits the value in the parentheses between -1.0 to $+1.0$;
> c_1, c_2, c_3 are recall coefficients; and
> $o_m(0)$ is initial value of neuron m.

The limitation of the BSB network is that the location of the attractors must be predefined as the vertices of the hypercube.

4.1.4. MAXNET

MAXNET is a competitive network in which only one neuron will have a non-zero output when the competition is completed. The network consists of interconnected neurons and symmetric weights. There is no training algorithm for MAXNET and the weights are fixed as depicted in Figure 10 [31]. Its application procedure includes two steps: activation and initialisation of weights, and updating the activation of each unit until only one unit responds.

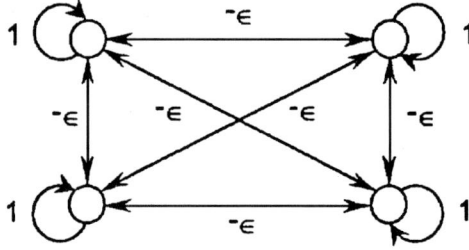

Figure 10. Example of MAXNET.

MAXNET is suitable for situations where more information is needed than can be incorporated. Knapp and Wang [32] used a MAXNET to force a decision between the competing operation alternatives. In their work, a sequence of operations for machining each feature of the part is generated independently by the MAXNET.

However, few systems use only BSB or MAXNET independently. BSB and MAXNET are typically used in multi-type architectures, e.g. Sakakura and Inasaki [30] used a BSB with a three-layer feed-forward network while Knapp and Wang [32] utilised a co-operating architecture combining a three-layer feed-forward network and a MAXNET.

4.2. Input representation

The input representation for neural network-based CAPP involves the conversion of design data into a proper input format. Three aspects must be resolved.

a) Input information. Process planning deals with a number of detailed activities, such as selecting manufacturing operations, determining setups, specifying appropriate tools and so on. Each activity requires a different set of information. For example, setup generation requires information about tolerance, material and operations.
b) The need for unique input. Each piece of the input information for a neural network must be uniquely represented in a proper format.
c) The need for unique input. Each piece of the input information for a neural network must be uniquely represented in a proper format.

Standard input image data and input vector are the two main types of input representation in CAPP.

4.2.1. Standardised image data

Standardised image data converted the cross-sectional shape data of the product into standardised image data for the input [24]. They use 12 "colours" to represent 12 outer or inner geometric primitives, such as cylinder and cone. Half of the product shapes are converted into a 16*16 "colour" data image. These 256 units are regarded as the input to the neural network. This representation can only be used for rotationally symmetric products.

4.2.2. Input vector with value ranging from 0 to 1

It is one of n-unit vector input formats, whose units are coded with numerical values ranging between 0 and 1. Certain special transformations have to be performed, which different formulae need to be established for different units. For instance, a unit related to the workpiece material is calculated from the cutting force per unit area, k_c using the following formula [26]:

$$i_6 = \frac{k_c - 1900}{2600}$$

Park et al [33] defined the input values from 0 to 1 according to its real values, e.g. 0.5000 for a hardness unit for a real value of 225 BHN, and 0.4366 for a cutting speed unit for a real value of 80 m/min.

4.2.3. Input vector with integer value

Each input unit is given a particular integer instead of the original value. A common method is to classify the value for each parameter and assign a discrete integer to the corresponding unit. Park et al [27] used 15 input parameters concerning seven factors, such as the feature type, ratio of feature width to depth, tool length, and tool material. A class number is given for each parameter based on its real value, e.g. the class number is 6 if the ratio of selected tool length over standard length is 2. Similarly, in the system by Sakakura and Inasaki [30], the unit of dressing depth of cut is assigned a value of 4 for a real value of 11.0 μm. Mei et al [23] developed a scheme for rotational parts in which the surface orientations (i.e. right, left or both) are represented by values -1, 1 and 0.

4.2.4. Input vector in binary form

The value of each unit uses only two characters (i.e. 0 and 1) representing whether the corresponding parameter is needed or not. In order to determine feature clusters, Chen and LeClair [34] represented a feature with a $(6 + n)$-unit vector in binary form, which defines the *six* approach directions and n tool types.

4.2.5. Input vector in mixed form

A typical example is the work of Devireddy and Ghosh [21]. An *eight*-unit input vector is used specifying the feature type (e.g. hole, step, taper, thread), and its attributes, e.g. diameter, length, tolerance, surface finish, etc. The value of feature type is in binary form while the values for attributes are in the range of 0 to 1.

4.3. Output format

Several output formats have been proposed which are summarised below.

4.3.1. Output vector in ordered binary form

The output vector is usually applied for the operation selection, machine tool or cutting tool selection. Commonly, it consists of a number of neurons, each with a value (i.e. 0 or 1) showing whether the corresponding item (e.g. machining operation, machine tool or cutting tool) belongs to the process plan or not. For instance, an output vector consists of eight neurons representing respectively drilling, reaming, boring, turning, taper turning, grooving, grinding and precision. If the value of a neuron is '1', the corresponding operation is needed for the feature; otherwise, the value is '0', e.g. a hole requires the drilling operation, so the first neuron is assigned the value '1'. Li et al [22] used a 4-neuron vector corresponding to the abrasive type, grade, grit size and bond. Le Tumelin et al [28] designed a 23-neuron vector.

4.3.2. Output vector with special values

This type of output is specified for determining some technological parameters, such as parameters of a cutting tool and cutting conditions. Each neuron in the output vector has a possible value that the corresponding parameter may assume. Santochi and Dini [26] developed a system for selecting the eight technological parameters of a cutting tool. For example, to select a normal clearance angle α_n, the number of output neurons is 5 which represents $4°, 5°, 6°, 7°, 8°$ respectively. The neuron with the value '1' represents the optimal value and '0.5' a second choice.

4.3.3. One-unit output in binary form

This output format has only one unit whose value is either 0 or 1 [23]. The output shows which surfaces should be used as manufacturing datums. For instance, '1' means that the surface will be used for the part setups and '0' means that it has nothing to do with part setups.

4.3.4. One-unit output in integer form

Each discrete integer is concerned with a special class [34]. The output integer represents a cluster of features according to the approach directions and the tool types.

4.3.5. Output matrix

Shan et al [29] devised a binary incidence matrix V (n*n) in which the rows denote operations and the columns correspond to sequences. The value '1' indicates that a specified operation is performed. Because each operation is performed only once and only one operation is carried out at a time, one and only one of the entries in each row and column should take the value of 1 whereas the rest should be set to 0.

4.4. Training method

In CAPP applications, the training method usually employs either an unsupervised learning algorithm or back-propagation.

4.4.1. Unsupervised learning algorithm

With an unsupervised learning algorithm, the training set only contains input samples; no desired or sample outputs are available. The neural network must construct an internal model that captures regularities in input training patterns instead of measuring its predictive performance for a given input. Hence this method is also called self-organisation. In CAPP applications, a logical AND/OR operation-based unsupervised learning approach is used. Chen and LeClair [34] clustered features based on the approach direction and tool type and then generated a process plan using an Episodal Associative Memory (EAM) approach. The AND operation was applied to solve multiple approach directions for some features. If the digit is 1 for the corresponding approach direction, the update weight for the cluster j is

$$^{a}b_{ij}(s+1) = {}^{a}x_i^{(p)} \quad AND \quad {}^{a}b_{ij}(s) = {}^{a}x_i^{(p)\,a}b_{ij}(s),$$

where $^{a}x_i^{(p)}$ is the approach direction sub-pattern, $< +x, +y, +z, -x, -y, -z >$, of pattern p.

In the meantime, the OR rule is used to update the weight so that the probability of common tools can be increased. If the digit is 1 for the corresponding tool, then $b_{ij}\,(s+1)$ is modified according the following equation [34]:

$$^{t}b_{ij}(s+1) = {}^{t}x_i^{(p)} \quad OR \quad {}^{t}b_{ij}(s) = f\left({}^{t}x_i^{(p)} + {}^{t}b_{ij}(s)\right),$$

where

$^{t}x_i^{(p)}$ is the tool sub-pattern, and
$f(\eta) = 1$ if $\eta/1$, else $f(\eta) = 0$.

4.4.2. Back-propagation

A back-propagation algorithm is a form of unsupervised training. Back-propagation methods have proven highly successful in CAPP applications [23, 24]; they can be classified into three groups.

The Delta Rule: One of the back-propagation learning algorithms is the delta rule based on the cumulative error. It is also known as the least mean squares (LMS) or Windrow-Hoff rule. The learning rule changes the connection weights so as to minimise the mean squared error between the network output and the target over all training patterns.

Sakakura and Inasaki [30] chose the delta rule for both a feedforward network and a BSB network. In the three-layer feedforward network, the weight connecting neuron

j in the hidden layer to neuron k in the output layer is updated as follows:

$$\Delta w_{kj} = \eta_f \sum_p \delta_{pk} o_{pj}$$

$$\delta_{pk} = (t_{pk} - o_{pk}) f'(a_{pk}),$$

where

> $f()$ is the output function of neuron,
> η_f is the learning coefficient of the FF network,
> p is the learning pattern number,
> t_{pi} is the learning value of neuron i for learning pattern p,
> a_{pi} is the status value of neuron i for learning pattern p, and
> o_{pi} is the output value of neuron i for learning pattern p.

For the BSB network, the modified value of the weight which interconnects neuron m and neuron n is calculated as the following:

$$\Delta w_{mn} = \eta_b \sum_p (t_{pm} - w_{nm} t_{pn}) t_{pn},$$

where

> η_b is the learning coefficient of BSB netowrk, and
> t_{ji} is the learning value of neuron i for learning pattern j.

Levemberg-Marquardt Approximation: A back–propagation algorithm using the approximation of Levemberg-Marquardt is also used in some applications [26]. This algorithm allows a better performance in terms of training time in comparison with other training methods. However, it may require a very large storage space for some complex situations.

The matrix of the connection weights is updated through the following equation:

$$w = (J^T J + \mu U)^{-1} J^T e,$$

where

> J is the Jacobian matrix of derivatives of the errors to each weight w_{ij},
> μ is a scalar,
> U is the unit matrix, and
> e is the error vector of the network.

Batch Training: Either the delta rule of the Levemberg-Marquardt approximation is used as the on-line learning rule. The batch training is an off-line training process. Rather than adjust the weights after each pattern presentation, batch training accumulates the errors over the whole training set and adjusts each weight according to the accumulated errors. It can generally be expressed as follows [10]:

$$\Delta w_{ji} = \eta \sum_p \delta_{out} H_{in}$$

where the subscripts *in* and *out* refer to the net input and output signals associated with a given unit, and *i* and *j* refer to the connection from unit *i* to unit *j*.

The form of δ will vary depending on the type of layer to which the formula applies. In some cases it is advantageous because of its smoothing effect on the correction terms and increasing of convergence to a local minimum [31]. Devireddy and Ghosh [21] trained a system with a batch training back-propagation algorithm.

4.5. Summary of ANN-based CAPP

The achievements of neural network-based CAPP systems are summarised in Table 3. Although the capabilities are limited at present, there is great potential for further applications of neural networks to CAPP. It has been shown that ANN techniques can significantly improve the performance of CAPP systems. The self-learning functions allow empirical rules to be learnt through typical examples. Faster processing makes systems more effective, especially in parallel environments. There has been effort in incorporating neural networks with other techniques, which will be discussed in the next section.

5. ANN-BASED HYBRID APPROACHES TO CAPP

There has been research on neural networks incorporating other techniques. This section presents ANN-based hybrid approaches to CAPP with expert systems, genetic algorithms and fuzzy logics.

5.1. CAPP using expert system and ANN techniques

Expert systems employ explicit rules, such as manufacturing and production rules. However, CAPP is not only concerned with explicit judgements but also implicit judgements, for example, how does a system run when it cannot guarantee all manufacturing rules are satisfied at the same time. On the contrary, neural networks are an implicit reference method, which is formed through a training process with a set of examples. Therefore, it can be seen that the incorporation of expert system and neural network techniques in a CAPP system can benefit from the advantages of both and make the system more flexible and adaptive.

Such a hybrid system generally consists of two control modules as depicted in Figure 11, the expert system control module and neural network control module.

5.1.1. Expert system control module

This module is mainly applied to the activities with explicit rules, such as machine tool selection, cutting tool selection and process sequencing. In addition, it is also used when the input design data is new to the system.

Table 3 Achievements of ANN-based CAPP

Work by	Functions	Type of ANN	Manufacturing processes/components
Osakada and Yang [24]	Generation of process plan	Three-layer Feed-Forward network	Cold forging for axis-symmetric components
Roy et al. [35]	Generation of process plan	Feed-Forward network	Cold forging
Knapp and Wang [32]	Operation selection and operation sequencing	Three-layer Feedforward network and MAXNET	Machining operations
Devireddy and Ghosh [21]	Operation selection and operation sequencing	Three-Layer Feed-Forward network	Machining operations for rotational components
Shan et al. [29]	Operation sequencing	Hopfield	Cutting operations for components machined on single spindle Swiss-type automatics
Le Tumelin et al. [28]	Operation sequencing	Five-layer Feed-Forward network	Machining operations for holes
Dong et al. [36]	Operation sequencing	Feedforward network and Hopfield	Machining operations
Gu et al. [25]	Operation sequencing	Three-layer Feedforward network	Machining operations for prismatic components with regular machining features
Giusti et al. [37]	Tool selection	Unknown	Rotational components
Chen and LeClair [34]	Generation of setups	Unknown	Machining operations
Santochi and Dini [26]	Selection of optimal values of a tool parameter	Three-layer Feedforward network	Turning operations
Mei et al. [23]	Selection of manufacturing datums	Three-layer Feedforward network	Rotational components
Li et al. [22]	Selection of grinding wheels	Feedforward network	Grinding operations for ground components
Sakakura and Inasaki [30]	Selection of dressing conditions	BSB/Three-layer Feedforward network	Grinding operations for ground components
Park et al. [27]	Generation of modified cutting conditions	Four-layer Feedforward network	Milling and turning for sheet metal
Park et al. [33]	Generation of cutting conditions	Fuzzy ARTMAP network	Milling operations

5.1.2. Neural network control module

This module is trained by a set of examples before it is used. When the input data is familiar to the system and can be recognised by the neural network, the module will be adopted. Neural network is particularly suitable for the activities, which have no explicit rules but enough examples, such as setup planning, cutting condition selection, technological parameters selection for cutting tool and process sequencing. The neural network control module usually has the ability to learn and is trained to learn with newly generated CAPP results.

Shan et al. [29] developed an integrated system for machining operation sequencing using expert system and neural network techniques. In their system, an expert system is designed to produce partial orders according to expert rules that satisfy the specific

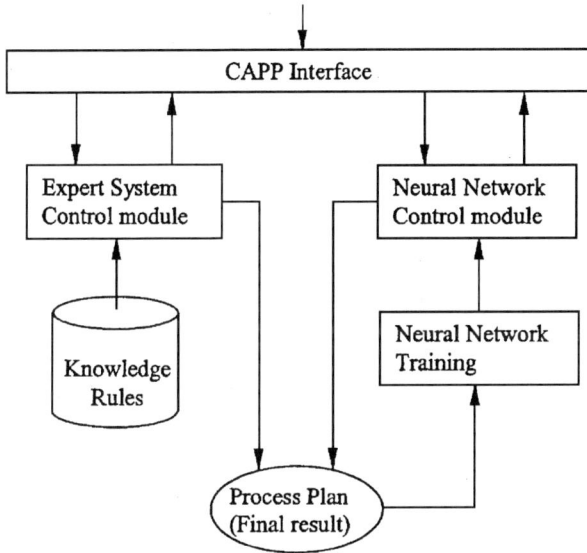

Figure 11. Architecture of CAPP with expert system and neural network.

operation constraints, including operation constraints, geometric constraints, rigidity constraints, accuracy constraints and setup constraints. Then, a Hopfield network is presented to determine the final sequence based on the partial operation sequence produced by the expert system. Finally, a binary incidence matrix is determined where the rows denote operations and the columns correspond to sequence.

Ming et al [38] proposed a hybrid intelligent inference model combining an expert system and a neural network for CAPP consisting of inference functions, global inference control strategy, hybrid control manager, cooperative communication processor, hybrid process knowledge base, and CAPP inference methods. The hybrid control manager is first executed to judge the initial condition and select the appropriate control strategy (by the expert system or neural network) or other functions (through the calculation function or optimisation function). The corresponding module is then called.

Other examples of this kind of hybrid approach include the systems proposed by Kandel and Langholz [39] and Medsker and Liebowitz [40].

5.2. CAPP using ANN, fuzzy logic and expert system techniques

There are often uncertainty or intangible factors in CAPP, especially during manufacturing evaluation, such as geometrical complexity and manufacturability. Fuzzy set theory may be employed as a solution to uncertainty. On the other hand, new manufacturing methods and technological development which may lead to easier manufacture and influence process planning, should be adapted in the manufacturing environment

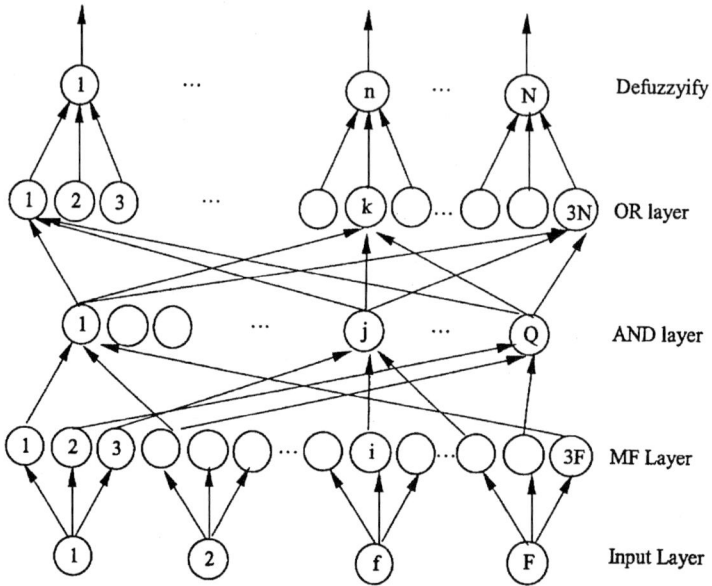

Figure 12. FL–BP neural network.

(e.g. new machine tools purchased). Thus, adaptability is needed for CAPP. Based on the above requirements, it is useful to incorporate fuzzy logic techniques to perform certain CAPP tasks.

Chang and Chang [42] developed an artificial intelligent CAPP system integrating neural network, fuzzy logic and expert system techniques. Their system consists of the following parts:

- A back-propagation neural network for evaluating the manufacturability of important features of the component.
- A fuzzy logical back-propagation neural network (FL-BPN) for evaluating the suitability of the existing plans stored in the database. The FL-BPN has five layers as shown in Figure 12 [41]: the input layer, membership function layer which fuzzifies the crisp input values, AND layer where each neuron represents the premise part of a rule and is connected with an 'AND' operator, OR layer where each neuron represents the conclusion part of a rule and is connected with an 'OR' operator, and defuzzification layer which defuzzifies the final evaluating result.
- Functional modules for process planning using an expert system, such as manufacturing process selection, machine selection, cell selection, fixture selection, part setup determination, cutting tool selection, machining parameters calculation, and final operations sequencing.

5.3. CAPP using GA, ANN and Fuzzy logic techniques

Operation sequencing is task responsible for arranging the selected operations in a suitable order to fabricate the part [29]. An optimal process sequence can largely increase the efficiency and reduce the cost of production. However, what is the most optimal process sequence? It is influenced by various constraints and factors, such as geometric constraints of the component, manufacturing rules, manufacturing cost and time.

Genetic algorithms (GAs) as one of the most popular combinatorial algorithms, are a search technique for solving optimisation problems based on the mechanics of the survival of the fittest [42]. Generally, a GA starts with some valid solutions generated randomly, then makes a random change to them and accepts the ones whose fitness functions reduced, and the process is repeated until no changes for fitness function reduction can be made.

The authors have applied ANN, GA and fuzzy logic techniques to feature-based process sequencing. In order to generate a process sequence that satisfies both the geometric constraints of the component and the restrictions due to manufacturing rules while minimising the machining cost and time at the same time, a complete fitness function can be defined for a GA, that is,

$$F = w_m f_m + w_c f_c + w_t f_t,$$

where

F is the fitness;
f_m is the degree of the satisfactory with manufacturing sequence rules;
f_c is the relative evaluating value for manufacturing cost;
f_t is the relative evaluating value for manufacturing time; and
w_m, w_c, w_c, are the weights for the above evaluations, respectively.

However, it is difficult to find explicit rules to determine the values of weights for the evaluation. Moreover, the values of weights vary according to the complexity of the component (e.g. feature relationships, tolerance and roughness), production requirements (e.g. batch size and urgency), and manufacturing environment (e.g. machine tools and cutting tools available). Based on the above characteristics, the neural network may be used as a suitable tool to solve this problem.

5.3.1. Input representation

Three main factors are considered as input to the neural network.
Complexity of component. It may be difficult to evaluate the complexity of a component because many factors need to be considered. The main factors include the number of features, the complexity of features, the relationships between features, the design and technical requirements (such as tolerance, surface roughness and material) for the component. Aiming to simplify such complicated evaluation, 20 input neurons are designed and divided into five groups. Each four-neuron group denotes a binary number to represent the number of features in the component, with an increase in

Table 4 Example of input neurons 1 to 20

Input neurons 1 → 20																			
0	1	0	1	0	0	0	1	0	0	1	1	0	0	0	1	0	0	0	0
Type I 5				Type II 1				Type III 3				Type IV 1				Type V 0			

manufacturing difficulty. Thus, neurons 1–4 in the first group represent the number of features which are very easy to manufacture (Type I) while neurons 17–20 in the first group represent the number of features which are very difficult to manufacture (Type V).

For example, if a component has 10 features and 5, 1, 3 and 1 features belong to Type I, Type II, Type III and Type IV, respectively, then the values for the 20 input neurons are shown in Table 4.

Due to the uncertainty and complexity in feature evaluation, a fuzzy synthesis evaluation model is established, which is described below.

Assume that the domain of the evaluation factors is A,

$$A = \{a_1, a_2, \ldots, a_i, \ldots, a_n\},$$

where a_i represents the factor of evaluation, and $i = 1, 2, 3, \ldots, n$.

Seven factors are considered; they are feature class, nominal dimensions, accuracy, surface roughness, material, shape and position tolerance, and feature relationship.

The domain of the evaluation grades is V,

$$V = \{v_1, v_2, \ldots, v_j, \ldots, v_m\},$$

where v_j expresses the evaluation results of complexity obtained from each factor considered, and $j = 1, 2, 3, \ldots, m$.

Five grades are adopted, i.e.

$$V = \{\text{very simple, simple, general, complex, very complex}\}.$$

Accordingly, a vector with five values is defined as

$$\bar{V} = \begin{bmatrix} \bar{v}_1 \\ \bar{v}_2 \\ \bar{v}_3 \\ \bar{v}_4 \\ \bar{v}_5 \end{bmatrix} = \begin{bmatrix} 0 \\ 0.25 \\ 0.5 \\ 0.75 \\ 1 \end{bmatrix}$$

Supposing that a fuzzy evaluation matrix U can be established as

$$
U = \begin{bmatrix}
u_{11} & \cdots & u_{1j} & \cdots & u_{15} \\
\vdots & & \vdots & & \vdots \\
u_{i1} & \cdots & u_{ij} & \cdots & u_{i5} \\
\vdots & & \vdots & & \vdots \\
u_{n1} & \cdots & u_{nj} & \cdots & u_{n5}
\end{bmatrix}
$$

where u_{ij} indicates the evaluation value of the ith evaluation factor a_i as the membership of the jth evaluation grade v_j.

Then, a fuzzy vector $\bar{U}$ can be calculated as

$$
\bar{U} = \begin{bmatrix}
\bar{u}_1 \\
\vdots \\
\bar{u}_i \\
\vdots \\
\bar{u}_n
\end{bmatrix} = U\bar{V} = \begin{bmatrix}
\sum_{j=1}^{5}(u_{1j} \times \bar{v}_j) \\
\vdots \\
\sum_{j=1}^{5}(u_{ij} \times \bar{v}_j) \\
\vdots \\
\sum_{j=1}^{5}(u_{nj} \times \bar{v}_j)
\end{bmatrix}
$$

In order to consider the influence of interactions among the evaluation factors, a weight is introduced for the synthesis evaluation of each factor. The fuzzy set of weight factors is W, which is normalised as

$$
W = \{w_1, w_2, \ldots, w_i, \ldots, w_n\},
$$

where w_i denotes the corresponding weight of the ith factor a_i, and $\sum_{i=1}^{n} w_i = 1$.

Finally, the fuzzy synthesis evaluation can be carried out using the fuzzy operation

$$
Y = W \bullet \bar{U} = \max(w_1 \times \bar{u}_1, w_2 \times \bar{u}_2, \ldots, w_5 \times \bar{u}_5).
$$

Production batch size. In practice, the process plan of a component for mass production, medium production, small production or single production may be different significantly. Therefore production batch size must be taken into account. The value allocated to the production batch size is shown in Table 5.

Production urgency. An indicator is designed to consider how urgent the component is needed. The value is allocated in Table 6.

Table 5 Values for production batch size

Production batch size	Quantity	Value
Single production	<20	1
Small production	20 − 200	0.6
Medium production	201 − 5000	0.3
Mass production	>5000	0

Table 6 Values for production urgency

Production urgency	Time (day)	Indicator value
Very urgent	<7	1
Urgent	7–14	0.6
Normal time	15–30	0.3
No time requirement	>30	0

5.3.2. Output format

Based on the problem to be solved, the output consists of three neurons, representing w_m, w_c and w_t, respectively. They are assigned a value of a real number between 0 and 1, i.e. [0, 1]. As relative weights, w_m, w_c and w_t are usually normalised before they are input into the final fitness calculation, that is $w_m + w_c + w_t = 1$.

5.3.3. Topology and the training method of the proposed neural network

The proposed neural network uses a typical three-layer back-propagation architecture, consisting of an input layer, a hidden layer and an output layer. There are 22 neurons and 3 neurons in the input layer and the output layer, respectively. The number of neurons in the hidden layer was determined from experiments. The experiment results have proved that a hidden layer of 10 neurons is the most appropriate.

5.4. Summary of ANN-based hybrid methods

In comparison to other approaches to CAPP, hybrid methods can incorporate the strengths of neural networks and other techniques such as expert systems, fuzzy logic and genetic algorithms, and therefore improve the performance in CAPP. The main advantages of ANN-based hybrid methods are the enhancement of adaptability and consistency for dynamic manufacturing environments, and suitable tools to deal with uncertainties utilising expert experience, and thus, increased system intelligence.

6. CONCLUSIONS

ANN techniques can eliminate three principal drawbacks of conventional feature recognition methods:

• the inability to recognise inexact or incomplete features,
• slow execution speed, and
• the inability to learn.

An ANN-based feature recognition system possesses experience to recognise and classify similar features since it is trained and there is no need to predefine almost every instance of a feature as in most conventional systems.

Many of the process planning tasks, such as selecting and sequencing appropriate machining operations, are based on empirical experience which cannot easily be modelled mathematically. ANNs, which can be trained with a set of typical examples, can be regarded as an effective tool for CAPP applications. Neural networks can adapt quickly to a dynamic manufacturing environment. By incorporating with expert systems, genetic algorithms, fuzzy logic rules and other artificial intelligent techniques, ANNs can make CAPP systems more efficient and adaptive.

However, there are certain limitations with the use of ANN techniques for both feature recognition and CAPP. These are:

- a limited range of features and feature intersections that can be recognised,
- a limited range of component types in CAPP applications, and
- a lack of robustness, especially for feature interactions.

In addition, there is a need for pre-processing of the input data and post-processing of the output, and it is a time-consuming process to configure an optimal ANN architecture with a suitable set of examples.

It is also noted that the knowledge base created by an ANN is not directly observable, so the basis for the output in response to any given input cannot be verified or examined directly. Further, although good at interpolation between adjacent training data sets, the results for input data sets outside the training data range can be fundamentally unreliable.

In spite of the limitations and modest results of current research on the neural network techniques for feature recognition and CAPP, their potential is clear. However, there is a need for further work, in particular on tackling the limitations:

- Solving problems of interacting features through incorporating new training methods as well as conventional techniques, such as heuristic algorithms.
- Extension of the domain of features that can be recognised.
- Efficient utilisation of expert experience to improve the performance of neural networks, especially for CAPP.
- Further development of ANN-based techniques, which can be applied to more CAPP tasks.

7. REFERENCES

1. Gurney, K, *An Introduction to Neural Networks*, UCL Press, 1997.
2. Prabhakar, S. and Henderson, M. R., "Automatic form-feature recognition using neural-network-based techniques on B-rep of solid models", *Computer Aided Design*, Vol. 24, No. 7, pp. 381–393, 1992.
3. Cichocki, A. and Unbehauen, A., *Neural networks for optimization and signal processing*, Chichester: Wiley, 1993.
4. Haykin, S., *Neural networks: a comprehensive foundation*, Macmillan College Publishing company, 1994.

5. Nezis, K. and Vosniakos, G., "Recognising 2.5D shape features using a neural network and heuristics", *Computer Aided Design*, Vol. 29, No. 7, pp. 523–439, 1997.
6. Chuang, J. H., Wang, P. H. and Wu, M. C., "Automatic classification of block-shaped parts based on their 2D projections", *Computers & Industrial Engineering*, Vol. 36, No. 3, pp. 697–718, 1999.
7. Hwang, J.-L., "Applying the perceptron to 3D feature recognition", *PhD Thesis*, Arizona State University, USA, 1991.
8. Peters, T. J., "Encoding mechanical design features for recognition via neural nets", *Research in Engineering Design*, Vol. 4, No. 2, pp. 67–74, 1992.
9. Ding, L. and Yue, Y., "A Novel Input Representation for ANN-Based Feature Recognition", *Frontiers in Artificial Intelligence and Applications*, Vol. 82, *Knowledge-Based Intelligent Information Engineering Systems and Allied Technologies*, KES 2002, Part I, pp. 311–315, 2002.
10. Principe, J. C., Euliano, N. R. and Lefebvre, W. C., *Neural and adaptive system: Fundamentals through Simulations*, John Wiley & Sons, Inc, 2000.
11. Chen, Y. H. and Lee, H. M., "A neural network system for 2D feature recognition", *International Journal of Computer Integrated Manufacturing*, Vol. 11, No. 2, pp. 111–117, 1998.
12. Chan, C. C. H., "ANN-based feature recognition and grammar-based feature extraction to integrate design and manufacturing", *PhD Thesis*, University of Iowa, USA, 1994.
13. Srinath, G., "Optimising neural net input for feature recognition", *MSc Thesis*, Arizona State University, USA, 1993.
14. Gu, Z., Zhang, Y. F. and Nee, A. Y. C., "Generic form feature recognition and operation selection using connectionist modelling", *Journal of Intelligent Manufacturing*, Vol. 6, No. 4, pp. 263–273, 1995.
15. Joshi, S. B. and Chang, T. C., "Graph-based heuristics for recognition of machined features from a 3D solid model", *Computer Aided Design*, Vol. 20, No. 2, pp. 58–66, 1988.
16. Zulkifli, A. H. and Meeran, S., "Feature patterns in recognising non-interacting and interacting primitive, circular and slanting features using a neural network", *International Journal of Production Research*, Vol. 37, No. 13, pp. 3063–3100, 1999.
17. Wu, M. C. and Jen, S. R., "A neural network approach to the classification of 3D prismatic parts", *International Journal of Advanced Manufacturing Technology*, Vol. 11, No. 5, pp. 325–335, 1996.
18. Demuth, H. and Beale, M., *Neural Network Toolbox for Use with MATLAB*, The MATHWORKS Inc., 2000.
19. Charalambous, C., "Conjugate gradient algorithm for efficient training of artificial neural networks", *IEE Proceedings–G Circuits Devices and Systems*, Vol. 139, No. 3, pp. 301–310, 1992.
20. Dagli, C. H., Poshyanonda, P. and Bahrami, A., "Neuro-computing and concurrent engineering", In Parsaei, HR and Sullivan, WG (eds), *Concurrent Engineering: Contemporary Issues and Modern Design Tools*, Chapman & Hall, London, pp. 465–486, 1993.
21. Devireddy, C. R. and Ghosh, K., "Feature-based modelling and neural networks-based CAPP for integrated manufacturing", *International Journal of Computer Integrated Manufacturing*, Vol. 12, No. 1, pp. 61–74, 1999.
22. Li, Y., Mills, B., Moruzzi, J. L. and Rowe, W. B., "Grinding wheel selection using a neural network", *Proceedings of the 10th National Manufacturing Research Conference*, Loughborough, pp. 597–601, 1994.
23. Mei, J., Zhang, H. C. and Oldham, W. J. B., "A neural network approach for datum selection in computer-aided process planning," *Computers in Industry*, Vol. 27, No. 1, pp. 53–64, 1995.
24. Osakada, K. and Yang, G. B., "Neural networks for process planning of cold forging", *Annals of the CIRP*, Vol. 40, No. 1, pp. 243–246, 1991.
25. Gu, Z., Zhang, Y. F. and Nee, A. Y. C., "Identification of important features for machining operations sequence generation", *International Journal of Product Research*, Vol. 35, No. 8, pp. 2285–2307, 1997.
26. Santochi, M. and Dini, G., "Use of neural networks in automated selection of technological parameters of cutting tools", *Computer Integrated Manufacturing Systems*, Vol. 9, No. 3, pp. 137–148, 1996.
27. Park, M. W., Rho, H. M. and Park, B. T., "Generation of modified cutting condition using neural network for an operation planning system", *Annals of the CIRP*, Vol. 45, No. 1, pp. 475–478, 1996.
28. Le Tumelin, C., Garro, O. and Charpentier, P., "Generating process plans using neural networks", *Proceedings of 2nd International Workshop on Learning in Intelligent Manufacturing Systems*, Budapest, Hungry, 1995.
29. Shan, X. H., Nee, A. Y. C. and Poo, A. N., "Integrated application of expert systems and neural networks for machining operation sequencing", *Neural Networks in Manufacturing and Robotics, ASME*, PED-vol 57, pp. 117–126, 1992.
30. Sakakura, M. and Inasaki, I., "A neural network approach to the Decision-making process for grinding operations", *Annals of the CIRP*, Vol. 41, No. 1, pp. 353–356, 1992.

31. Fausett, L., *Fundamentals of Neural Networks: Architectures, Algorithms and Applications*, Prentice Hall International, Inc, 1994.
32. Knapp, G. D. and Wang, H. P., "Acquiring, storing and utilising process planning knowledge using neural networks", *Journal of Intelligent Manufacturing*, Vol. 3, No. 5, pp. 333–344, 1992.
33. Park, M. W., Park, B. T., Rho, Y. M. and Kim, S. K., "Incremental supervised learning of cutting conditions using the Fuzzy ARTMAP neural network", *Annals of the CIRP*, Vol. 49, No. 1, pp. 375–378, 2000.
34. Chen, C. L. P. and LeClair, S. R., "Unsupervised neural learning algorithm for setup generation in process planning", *Proceedings of International Conference on Artificial Neural Networks in Engineering*, pp. 663–668, 1993.
35. Roy, R., Chodnikiewicz, K. and Balendra, R., "Interpolation of forging preform using neural networks", *Journal of Materials Processing Technology*, Vol. 45, Nos. 1–4, pp. 695–702, 1994.
36. Dong, J. X., Tang, X. Q. and Wang, S. C., "Inference mechanism for CAPP tool based on artificial neural network", *Proceedings of 1st Congress on Intelligent Manufacturing*, Puerto Rico, pp. 994–1002, 1995.
37. Giusti, F., Santochi, M. and Dini, G., "COATS: an expert module for optimal tool selection", *Annals of the CIRP*, Vol. 35, No. 1, pp. 337–340, 1986.
38. Ming, X. G., Mak, K. L. and Yan, J. Q., "A hybrid intelligent inference model for computer aided process planning", *Integrated Manufacturing Systems*, Vol. 10, No. 6, pp. 343–353, 1999.
39. Kandel, A. and Langholz, G., *Architectures for Intelligent Systems*, CRC Press, Boca Raton, FL. 1992.
40. Medsker, L., Liebowitz, J., *Design and Development of Expert Systems*, Macmillan, Basingstoke, 1994.
41. Dereli, T. and Filiz, H., "Optimisation of process planning functions by genetic algorithms", *Computers & Industrial Engineering*, Vol. 36, pp. 281–308, 1999.
42. Chang, P. T. and Chang, C. H., "An integrated artificial intelligent computer aided process planning system", *International Journal of Computer integrated Manufacturing*, Vol. 13, No. 6, pp. 483–497, 2000.

NEURAL NETWORK SYSTEMS TECHNOLOGY AND APPLICATIONS IN PRODUCT LIFE–CYCLE COST ESTIMATES

KWANG-KYU SEO

This chapter describes an approximate estimation method for the product life cycle cost (LCC), called an approximate LCC estimation method, which allows the designer to make comparative LCC estimation between the different product concepts. The proposed approach provides the approximate and rapid estimation of product LCC based on high-level information typically known in the conceptual phase. The product attributes at the conceptual design phase and LCC factors are identified and the significant product attributes are determined by statistical analysis. An artificial neural network (ANN) is trained on product attributes and the LCC data from pre-existing LCC studies. This approach does not require a new LCC model.

1. INTRODUCTION

The ability of a company to compete effectively on the increasingly competitive global market is influenced to a large extent by the cost as well as the quality of its products and the ability to bring products onto the market in a timely manner. In order to guarantee competitive pricing of a product, cost estimates are performed repeatedly throughout the life cycle of many products. In the early phases of the product life cycle, when a new product is considered, cost estimate analyses are used to support the decision for product design. Later on when alternative designs are considered, the best alternative is selected based on its estimated life cycle cost (LCC) and its benefits. Manufacturers usually consider only how to reduce the cost the company spends for material acquisition, production, and logistics. In order to survive in the competitive market environment especially resulted from the widespread awareness of global environmental problems and legislation, manufacturers now have to consider reducing the costs of the entire life cycle of a product. The costs incurred during life cycle are mostly committed by early design decisions.

Studies reported in Dowlatshahi (1992) and by other researchers in design suggest that the design of the product influences between 70% and 85% of the total cost of a product. Therefore, designers can substantially reduce the LCC of products by giving due consideration to life cycle implications of their design decisions. The research on design method for minimizing the LCC of a product also becomes very important and valuable.

The need for sustainable development has begun to change the way many companies design products. Generally, product designers are being asked to judge the cost of the products to be developed. Not only is this an additional task for designers, but it is also necessary something they are qualified to do. Therefore, the cost models created by cost estimators should be integrated with traditional design models, making the parametric cost results available on demand. However, the use of detailed parametric models is not well suited to early conceptual design, where ideas are diverse and numerous, details are very scarce, and the pace is swift. This is unfortunate because early phases of the design process are widely believed to be the most influential in defining the LCC of products. Therefore there is a need for a method that directly addresses the issue of providing cost information to the designer irrespective of the design context in which the cost information is used.

The lack of estimation methods for the life cycle cost in early design phase motivated the development of a method. The proposed method has to be developed to offer good prediction of product LCC in response to design decisions and design guidelines for reducing product LCC.

This chapter describes a research to develop an approximate LCC estimation method for use in the conceptual design. The proposed method allows to the approximate and rapid estimation of the LCC based on high-level information typically known in the conceptual phase. An artificial neural networks (ANNs) is trained on product attributes and the LCC data from pre-existing LCC studies. The product designer queries the trained artificial model with new high-level product attribute data to quickly obtain an approximate LCC for a new product concept.

2. BACKGROUND

2.1. General product development

The process of product design or product development is interdisciplinary, time consuming, and involves many tradeoffs. Product design includes every technical aspect of the product, from the purchasing of components to manufacturing, assembly, service, and obsolescence. A successful product not only performs well for the company through high profit, low investment time, and improved future capability, but it also must be valued by the customer and follow government regulations.

Ulrich and Eppinger (1995) define five stages of product development for an engineered, discrete, physical product: concept development, system-level design, detail design, testing and refinement, and production ramp-up. The process begins with a mission statement and ends with product launch. It should be noted that the end of the development process might change in the future with the inclusion of another stage—product take-back—as governments worldwide contemplate mandatory product take-back laws. However, such an inclusion, although it will likely influence a company's value structure, would not alter the key activities within the previous five stages.

Fundamentally important to the concept development process is that a great many decisions have been made by the end of the phase—everything from deciding the targeted market to selecting the most-likely-to-succeed concept for further development. A concept is described in terms of its form, function, and features. The concept that continues beyond this phase will also carry with it a set of specifications, an analysis of competitive products, and an economic justification of the project.

The conceptual phase of product design is the most influential of all phases. It becomes important to have the product objectives represented during this phase. If the cost is appropriately included, cost requirements can then be used in a test for concept feasibility along with other requirements, such as performance specifics and function. This means the designers must be able to evaluate the approximate cost performance of a wide range of solution concepts early in the design process.

Decisions that emerge from the conceptual phase are also most likely never to be changed to any significant degree. This resolved decisiveness is due to the large amount of resources—time, manpower, and money—needed to start over or make a change once a certain path has been chosen and ship deadlines are approaching. It is essential to include the cost early to prevent cost mistakes, which may not be corrected or mitigated later, from occurring. There are many good things that can come out cost estimation in conceptual design. However, there are also several limiting factors to the phase as well.

Time is probably the least plentiful resource for the development cycle as a whole (Ulrich and Eppinger 1995). It can mean the difference between a product and a successful product by beating competition to the shelf. Therefore, time saving support tools are crucial throughout the product development process. In conceptual design, though, lack of information is as much a problem as lack of time. Without information no type of cost, environmental, or other functional performance evaluation can even begin.

Traditional product designers are not necessarily qualified to evaluate the objectives when they design the products. However, designers are recently being asked to assess the objectives, especially LCC, of the products they are developing. In response, many different methods have been developed in attempting to estimate the cost concerns into the product development process.

3. AN APPROXIMATE ESTIMATION METHOD FOR THE PRODUCT LIFE CYCLE COST USING ANNS

3.1. The concepts

In this section, the possibility of an approximate estimation method for the product LCC, called an approximate LCC estimation method, is investigated and validated.

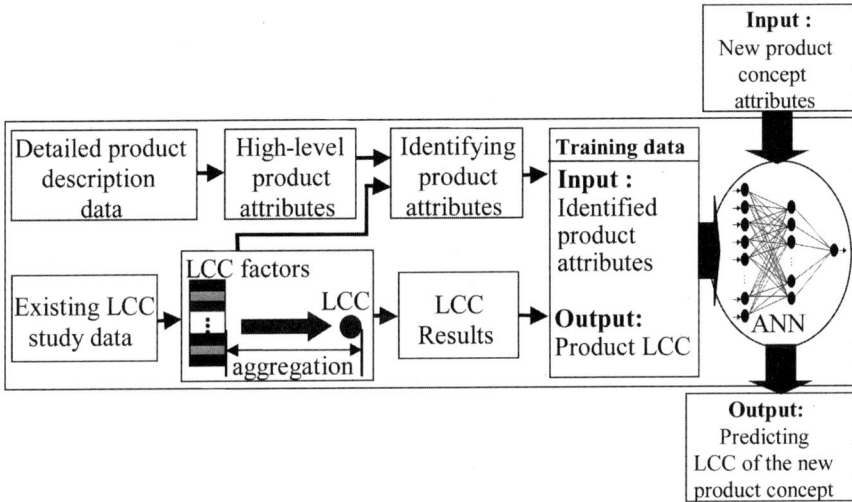

Figure 1. Training process of an approximate LCC estimation method.

The proposed method provides the useful LCC estimation of products in terms of product attributes related with LCC factors. The LCC factors and high–level product attributes are introduced and identified by correlation test between them.

An approximate LCC estimation method based on ANNs is a different approach from other LCC methods. It has the flexibility to learn and grow as new information becomes available, but it does not require the creation of a new model to make as LCC prediction for a new product concept. Also, by supporting the extremely fast comparison of the cost performance of product concepts, it does not delay product development.

Learning algorithms train ANNs using the identified high–level product attributes and the corresponding LCC factors. Through this training, the ANN is adapted to emulate existing LCC studies and generalize trends between products. This is illustrated in Figure 1.

The product designers query an ANN model with high–level product attributes to quickly obtain an approximate LCC for a new product concept. Designers need to simply provide high–level attributes of new product concepts to gain LCC predictions based upon trends inferred from real products and LCC studies used as training data.

However, the approximate LCC estimation model is not envisioned as a replacement for traditional detailed LCC models, but as a complement to them. In the early design stages the learning LCC leverages previously conducted detailed LCC studies to provide rapid feedback on a wide variety of concepts. In later design stages, when a smaller range of variations is under consideration, detailed parametric LCC models can be used. Results from the detailed LCC models are then added to the training database as new training material for the approximate LCC estimation model.

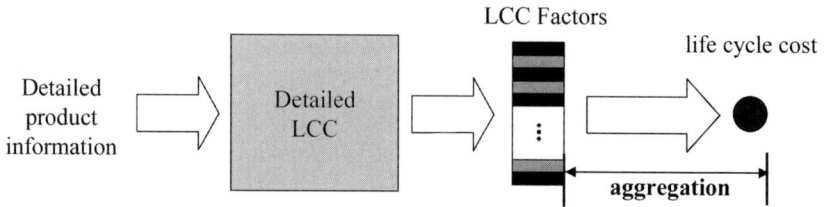

Figure 2. The aggregation scheme for the LCC.

There are three components of the approximate LCC estimation model: a meaningful set of product attribute inputs; a useful set of LCC factor outputs; an appropriately trained LCC model based on ANNs.

The product attribute as inputs must be meaningful to designers and consist of only product attributes typically known during conceptual design. The LCC factors as outputs should also be in a form useful to cost estimators and designers in different contexts. Therefore, LCC factors would provide the most flexibility as different schemes can be applied subsequently. The LCC training data must represent a range of products and contain many complete input samples of product attribute data and corresponding outputs of LCC factors. Data transparency should be maintained with any LCC by fully stating any assumptions, estimations, or uncertainties. Finally, the structure of the approximate LCC estimation model must be chosen, trained, and validated. In application, the approximate LCC model must be fast and provide reasonable LCC estimates.

Given these observations, there are three key areas that must be investigated in order to evaluate the learning LCC concept. Firstly, the feasible LCC factors to predict the LCC must be established. Secondly, a list of reasonable product attributes must be identified and correlated with LCC data to create a set of meaningful attributes. Thirdly, it must be established that an approximate LCC model can be trained to effectively emulate LCC results. The LCC training data will be developed in the course of gathering information to evaluate the three areas.

3.2. Development of the life cycle cost factors

The first issue is to establish the feasible LCC factors for use in training the approximate LCC estimation model based on ANNs. In order to identify the LCC factors, all the costs incurred in the product's life are investigated and enumerated. The LCC of a product is determined by aggregating all the LCC factors as shown in Figure 2.

The total cost of any product from its earliest concept through its retirement will eventually be borne by the user and will have a direct bearing on the marketability of that product [Wilson 1986]. As purchasers, people pay for the resources required to bring forth and market the product and as owners of the product, people pay for the resources required to deploy, operate and dispose of the product. The product

Table 1 The list of the life cycle cost factors

Life cycle phase	LCC factor
Design	market recognition, development
Production	materials, energy, facilities, wages, salaries, waste, pollution, health damage
Usage	material, energy, maintenance, transportation, storage, breakage, warranty service, packaging, waste, pollution, health damage
Disposal/Recycling	disposal/recycling dues, energy, waste, disposal, pollution, health damage

LCC can be decomposed into some cost factors (Fabrycky and Blanchard 1991). This decomposition is by no means the most comprehensive and representative of all products or any product. The cost factors considered would depend on the stage in which we want to use the model, the kind of information to be extracted from the model, the data available as input to the model and the product being designed. While the LCC is the aggregate of all the costs incurred in the product's life, it must be pointed out that there are differences between the cost issues that will be of interest to the person designing the product and the firm developing the product in the LCC analysis.

Table 1 provides a list of cost factors for product life cycle that was adapted to the feasible LCC factors useful for predicting the product LCC (Alting, 1993). In this chapter, the life cycle energy and service costs are shown as examples to estimate the product LCC.

3.3. Development of product attributes

This section focuses on the determination of the set of design properties, or product attributes, which all products possess, that will allow the approximate LCC estimation model to fulfill its functional requirements. Three rules were applied as follows.

(1) the attribute values must be known, or easily quantified in conceptual design;
(2) the set must not be so large as to create excessive complications in the neural network architecture of the approximate LCC estimation model;
(3) and the attributes should be independent of each other, yet fully represent the elements of the LCC factors.

To identify the product attributes to interact with the approximate LCC estimation model based on ANNs, an extensive list of possible descriptors was compiled. Narrowing of the list occurred in several phases: grouping the general attributes, identifying whether the attributes are known in conceptual design, and identifying relationships among attributes and between attributes and the LCC factors to eliminate redundancy and ensure completeness. Especially, maintainability attributes are also identified to estimate the service cost of usage phase.

Table 2 Organizational groupings of the identified product attributes

Group name	Associated product attributes
general design properties	durability, conductivity, strength, degradability
elementary design properties	material content, recycled content
functional properties	mass, volume, performance, intended application
economic properties	potential sales volume, product liability, average selling price, regulatory compliance, price, manufacturing cost
manufacturing properties	assemblability, process
operational properties	lifetime, use time, energy source, mode of operation, power consumption, in use flexibility, upgradeability, serviceability, modularity, additional consumables
distribution properties	distribution mass, distribution volume, means of transport, transport distance
end-of-life properties	Recyclability, reusability, disassemblability

3.3.1. General product attributes

The second issue is to define product attributes for use in training and querying the approximate LCC model. The attributes need to be both logically and statistically linked to elements in the LCC factors, and also be readily available during product concept design. The attributes must be sufficient to discriminate between different concepts and be. They must also be easily understood by designers and cover the scope of the product life cycle. These criteria were used to guide the process of systematically developing a product attribute list.

With these goals in mind, a set of candidate product attributes, based upon the literature and the experience of experts, was formed (Alting and Legarth 1995; Brezet and Hemel 1997; Clark and Charter 1999; Fiksel 1996; Hanssen 1999; Eisenhard 2000; Sousa, Eisenhard and Wallace 2001). Experts in both product design and cost estimation discussed as candidate attributes derived from the literature. After product attributes were identified, they were grouped for organizational purposes developed by Hubka and Eder (1992) as shown in Table 2.

If the designer was able to specify or estimate an attribute in an appropriate qualitative or quantitative sense, the attribute was deemed specified. If the designer could not specify the attribute, but could typically rank order concepts, the attribute was deemed ranked. If an attribute could not be specified or ranked, but the designer could provide a yes or no type of answer, the attribute was deemed binary. For example, the designer might know that a concept will contain polymers, but not be able to specify or rank the amount used. If the designer could typically provide no information about an attribute, it was deemed unknown. Finally, if an attribute did not apply to the class of products designed by the participant, the attribute was categorized as not applicable (Eisenhard 2000).

3.3.2. Maintainability attributes

Service of usage phase can be defined as the combination of all technical and associated administrative actions intended to keep an item or system in, or restore it to a state in

Table 3 Identified maintainability attribute for products

Accessibility	Standardization	Diagnosability
Interchangeability	Simplicity	Tribo-concepts
Reasemblability	Redundancy	Ergonomics
Modularity	Identification	

which it can perform its required function. The main purpose of service activity is to reduce the adverse effects of breakdown and to increase the availability at a lower cost, in order to increase performance and improve the dependability level. We focus on service after occurring breakdown of a product or system. Maintainability is adapted as the parameter representing service for a product.

Maintainability is an important aspect of life cycle concerns and plays significant role during the usage phase of a product. It is the design attribute of a product or system which facilitates the performance of various service activities, in particular, inspection, repair, replacement and diagnosis. These activities for a good serviceable product should not only be performed in quick possible time but also with optimal personnel and support equipment (Wani and Gandhi 1999). Moreover, design characteristics of a product or system which facilitate maintainability will be effective if due recognition is given to the factors which support system service during the usage phase. It is indispensable to perceive all the aspects of maintainability right from the design stage of the product in systematic way. This emphasis is to develop methodology to evaluate the maintainability of product at design stage qualitatively or quantitatively.

Maintainability attributes for electronic products, in general, are identified and they are referred as attributes ascribed to the characteristics of the product serviceability. They are also considered as the product attributes at the early product design stages. The identified maintainability attributes (Utez 1983; Takata et al. 1995; Vujosevic et al. 1995; Paasch and Ruff 1997; Wani and Gandhi 1999) are presented in Table 3. They are also estimated by an appropriate qualitative or quantitative sense.

3.3.3. Determining the final product attributes using statistical analysis

In this section, the final product attributes are determined to estimate the product LCC in the approximate LCC estimation model based on ANNs. In order to determine the product attribute, the correlation tests were performed between the candidate product attributes and the LCC factors. This step was to eliminate redundancy and ensure complete life-cycle coverage within the attributes set.

In this study, the cost of life cycle energy consumption and service were the important elements of LCC factors defined previously was shown, as examples, to predict the LCC. Product attributes and detailed LCC data were compiled for use in analysis of descriptor redundancy and life-cycle coverage.

Based upon these data, the candidate attribute set was again refined and then tested for first order relationships with the LCC factors. Bivariate Pearson product-moment correlations were computed and correlation tests to 95% statistical significance were performed between quantitative attributes and the data of LCC factors for various products. Linearity and bivariate normality in the data were assumed in checking for trends.

The Pearson correlation coefficient, r, is computed by

$$r = \sum_{i=1}^{N} \frac{(x_i - \bar{x})(y_i - \bar{y})}{(N-1)s_x s_y} \tag{1}$$

where N is the number of data points and x and S_x are, respectively, the mean and standard deviation of variable x, and likewise for variable y. If the correlation significance, or p-value, was less than 5% (0.05), then independence was rejected and x and y show linear correlation.

In order to identify the qualitative attributes, bivariate Spearman rank correlation tests were computed and correlation tests to 95% statistical significance were performed between qualitative attributes and the data of LCC for various products. Spearman's method works by assigning a rank to each observation in each group separately. Then calculate the sums of the squares of the differences in paired ranks (d_i^2) according to the following formula:

$$r_s = 1 - \left\{ \frac{6\left(d_1^2 + d_2^2 + \cdots + d_n^2\right)}{n(n^2 - 1)} \right\} \tag{2}$$

where r_s is Spearman rank correlation coefficient and n is the number of observations.

This first order examination required careful interpretation and grouping of products. For example, the data in Table 4 suggest that many product attributes are strongly correlated with many of the LCC factors (the life cycle energy cost) as expected. Insight gained about product attributes through the analysis will later be proposed as a structure for specializing the approximate LCC models to improve results.

Mass and power consumption were most strongly correlated with the LCC factor (the life cycle energy cost) and disassemblability, additional consumable and energy source were strongly. The affect of qualitative attributes on the LCC factor was assessed visually through scatter plots. Additionally, it is believed that some correlations were not apparent because of potentially non-linear relationships between attributes. The product attributes strongly correlated with the LCC factors are used to predict the product LCC in the approximate LCC estimation model.

Table 5 show the final list of 21 product attributes chosen for use to predict the life cycle energy cost in the approximate LCC estimation model. The analysis provided a basis for belief that the attribute list could span the elements in the LCC factors.

Sampling data with product attributes and corresponding the service cost from actual historic service activities were also collected for different electronic products. Based upon these data, the identified product attribute set was again refined and then tested for first order relationships with the service cost. Bivariate correlations were computed and correlation tests to 95% statistical significance were performed between

Table 4 An example of correlation coefficients and tests: product attributes vs. LCC factor (the life cycle energy cost)

The list of product attributes	The coefficient of correlation
Mass	0.9656
Lifetime	−0.1092
Use time	−0.3760
Operation mode	0.2320
Additional consumable	0.6035
Energy source	0.6658
Power consumption	0.9890
Modularity	0.4610
Durability	0.0933
. . . . . .	. . . . . .
Upgradability	−0.0100
Serviceability	0.5807
Flexibility	−0.0295
Post consumable material	−0.0060
Reusability	−0.0455
Recyclability	−0.0325
Disassemblability	0.7730

Table 5 Product attribute list used in testing the approximate LCC estimation model for the life cycle energy cost

Product attributes	Unit	Level of information
mass	kg	quantitative, specified
ceramics	% mass	quantitative, specified
fibers	% mass	quantitative, specified
Ferrous metals	% mass	quantitative, specified
non-ferrous metals	% mass	quantitative, specified
plastics	% mass	quantitative, specified
paper/cardboard	% mass	quantitative, specified
chemicals	% mass	quantitative, specified
wood	% mass	quantitative, specified
other materials	% mass	quantitative, specified
assemblability	dimensionless	qualitative, binary
process	dimensionless	qualitative, specified
lifetime	hours	quantitative, specified
use time	hours	quantitative, specified
mode of operation	dimensionless	qualitative, specified
additional consumable	dimensionless	qualitative, binary
energy source	dimensionless	qualitative, specified
power consumption	watt	quantitative, specified
modularity	dimensionless	qualitative, binary
serviceability	dimensionless	qualitative, binary
disassemblability	dimensionless	qualitative, binary

quantitative attributes and the data of the service cost for various products as shown in Table 6.

The product attributes strongly correlated with the service cost are used to predict the product service cost. Finally, 24 product attributes for the service cost are chosen as shown in Table 7 and used as inputs in ANN models.

Table 6 An example of correlation coefficients: product attributes vs. service cost

Product attributes	The coefficient of correlation
mass	0.49
lifetime	0.43
usetime	0.61
operation mode	0.61
energy source	0.05
power consumption	0.02
⋮	⋮
flexibility	−0.02
upgradability	0.47
modularity	0.51
accessibility	0.56
reassemblability	0.62
simplicity	0.47

Table 7 Product attribute list used in the ANN model for service cost

Product attributes	Unit	Level of information
mass	kg	quantitative, specified
ceramics	% mass	quantitative, specified
fibers	% mass	quantitative, specified
ferrous metals	% mass	quantitative, specified
non-ferrous metals	% mass	quantitative, specified
plastics	% mass	quantitative, specified
paper/cardboard	% mass	quantitative, specified
chemicals	% mass	quantitative, specified
wood	% mass	quantitative, specified
other materials	% mass	quantitative, specified
assemblability	dimensionless	qualitative, binary
disassemblability	dimensionless	qualitative, specified
lifetime	hours	quantitative, specified
use time	hours	quantitative, specified
mode of operation	dimensionless	qualitative, specified
serviceability	dimensionless	qualitative, binary
upgradeability	dimensionless	qualitative, binary
modularity	dimensionless	qualitative, specified
accessibility	dimensionless	qualitative, specified
reassemblability	dimensionless	qualitative, specified
standardization	dimensionless	qualitative, specified
simplicity	dimensionless	qualitative, specified
identification	dimensionless	qualitative, specified
diagnosability	dimensionless	qualitative, specified

4. A CASE STUDY

This section describes the application of the approximate LCC estimation method based on ANNs and shows how the proposed method can be applied to estimate LCC such as life cycle energy and service costs. The structure of artificial neural networks

Table 8 Examples of learning patterns to estimate the life cycle energy cost in the approximate LCC estimation model

Product	Mass (kg)	Ferrous M. (%mass)	Plastics (%mass)	Lifetime (hours)	Use time (hrs) (daily hours)	...	Power consump. (watt)	Energy cost($)*
1	6.49	31.34	59.74	61320	0.01	...	898	515.71
2	1.04	16.19	77.65	26280	13	...	58	20.53
3	0.17	50.33	49.16	43800	7.5	...	0	1.79
4	0.64	22.16	71.09	2160	45	...	13	11.47
5	1.8	22.22	55.56	43800	0.27	...	770.55	709.39
...	...	...	...	...	...	...	...	...
...	...	...	...	...	...	...	...	...
148	81.6	58.33	8.33	122640	0.46	...	500	6358.84
149	49.78	67.08	27.64	87600	24	...	12.5	1467.29
150	1160	67.74	11.98	105120	1.18	...	680.2	85068.47

*Energy cost is total cost of energy consumption during product's life cycle.

for the approximate LCC estimation model is developed. Then, using the identified product attributes as inputs and the LCC as outputs, the LCCs are estimated according to various concepts in early product development.

4.1. Data collection

As mentioned earlier, the feasibility test of the proposed method was conducted by focusing on the total life cycle energy and service costs components of the LCC factors. Sampling data with product attributes and corresponding the life cycle energy cost from the past studies were collected for 150 products and the service costs were collected for 40 different electronic products.

The life cycle energy cost was obtained by total energy consumption during the life cycle of products. The examples of learning patterns to estimate the life cycle energy cost in the approximate LCC estimation model are shown in Table 8.

In order to calculate the service cost, the historic data are collected and failure rate (F_R) as constraint is added in equation (6.1). The equation is useful in determining the service cost of a product.

$$C_{Service} = [L_{Fixed} + (L_T \times L_R) + C_M] \times F_R \qquad (3)$$

Where:

$C_{Service}$ = Service cost ($)
L_{Fixed} = Fixed labor cost ($)
L_T = Labor time (h)
L_R = Labor rate ($/h)
C_M = Consumable material and repair/replacement parts cost ($);
F_R = Failure rate

Table 9 Examples of learning patterns to estimate the service cost in the approximate LCC estimation model

	Inputs								Outputs
Product	Mass (kg)	Ferrous M. (%mass)	Plastics (%mass)	Lifetime (hours)	Use time (hrs) (daily hours)	...	Power consump. (watt)	Modularity (0–4)	Service cost($)*
1	8.17	32.62	61.58	61320	0.01	...	1064	1	6.00
2	1.04	16.19	77.65	26280	0.01	...	58	1	1.79
3	0.18	45.77	32.86	43800	7.5	...	0	1	8.25
4	0.64	22.16	71.09	2160	0.5	...	13	1	1.85
5	1.93	2.85	65.54	43800	0.27	...	616.44	4	2.75
...	...	...	...	...	...	...	...	...	...
...	...	...	...	...	...	...	...	...	...
38	49.78	67.07	27.64	87600	24	...	13	3	18.00
39	40.46	8.83	25.81	87600	3.2	...	616	3	6.54
40	35.01	24.24	51.75	121764	24	...	19	4	12.57

*Service cost is mean cost of product service during usage phase.

In equation (3), L_{Fixed} refers to fixed labor cost when a service representative visits a customer site. The labor time, L_T, is the service time such as Mean Actual Repair Time (MART) or Mean Actual Maintenance Time (MAMT) associated with repairing or replacing the individual components that fulfill the primary function. The cost of the replaced parts or materials is the mean replacement cost of products and represented by the value C_M. The failure rate, F_R, is obtained by the reliability information of products. In this study, I use constant and independent failure rates which are appropriate for earlier conceptual design phase.

The above equation (3) only reflects the costs borne by the company that produces the product. In short, the equations provide an internal view of service. The equations do not reflect the cost or hardship experienced by the customer. Therefore, the company needs to examine more service policy from the customer's point of view.

Sampling data with product attributes and corresponding the service cost were collected for 40 different electronic products. The examples of learning patterns to estimate the service cost in the approximate LCC estimation model are shown in Table 9.

4.2. Development of training algorithms

4.2.1. Backpropagation algorithm

There are different models of neural networks. General details about artificial neural networks can be found in Rummelhart et al. (1994). Taxonomy of the types of artificial neural networks can be found in Beardon (1989). We employ a connectionist, feedforward backpropagation neural network.

Since the predictive capability of neural networks is typically nonlinear, it is appropriate to explain that feedforward neural networks perform a kind of nonlinear regression in which a multilayer network is trying to find a low-order representation in the weights between the network layers. That representation itself is, in general, a nonlinear function of the physical input variables that allows for the interactions of relationships among many input variables at one time. Thus, the inputs become dependent on one another through network interaction and ultimately, generate nonlinear estimations as output variables.

Backpropagation (BP), selected for my design, is a neural networking algorithm in which activation is passed forward through the network and the output unit activations are compared with a teaching vector. These represent the input/output pairs. The comparison of input/output pairs results in error scores, which are used to propagate changes back down through the layers of weights. Weights represent the numerical strength of the connections or links between a node and its neighbors in a neural network and can have either positive or negative values. These weights represent the "intelligence" of the network—the essence of its predictive capability.

The role of an activation function is to combine the input being broadcast to a node from other nodes in a network. A typical activation function compresses the network activation impinging on a node between predetermined limits—usually a value between zero and one. A sigmoid, or s-shaped, activation function on the basis of its excellent predictive capabilities demonstrated in the previous studies.

During the learning process, the sigmoid unit is roughly linear for small weights (a net input near zero) and gets increasingly nonlinear in its response as it approaches its points of maximum curvature on either side of the midpoint. Thus, at the beginning of learning, when weights are small, the system is mainly linear and seeking a linear solution. As the weights grow, the network becomes increasingly nonlinear and begins to move toward a nonlinear solution to the problem. This linearity property makes the units more robust and allows the network to reliably attain the same solution in repeated experimentation. Thus, two different training sessions, using the same input data and randomly initialized weights, should consistently predict the same results.

The ability to train multilayer networks is an important step toward building intelligent applications. Neural networks must learn their own representations because it is not possible to program them by hand. The optimization of neural network parameters is critical in order to achieve the best possible predictive ability.

Five different parameters can be adjusted in the creation of a backpropagation neural network: hidden units, number of layers, learning rate, momentum and number of epochs. The number of hidden units refers to the number of nodes plus a threshold node which are to be placed between the input and output vectors. Layers represent the number of layers of hidden units between the input and output vectors. Learning rate is the numeric value by which the weights between the input, hidden, and output layers are adjusted. Momentum is a parameter, which can increase the pace of learning, potentially reducing the amount of time that it takes to train the network. The number of epochs refers to the number of times a data set is applied to the neural network for training, tuning, and testing.

4.2.2. Development of training algorithm with backpropagation

In order to decide the structure of backpropagation neural network, the convergence rate of error was checked by changing the number of hidden layers, the number of nodes in each layer and by adjusting learning rate h, and momentum term a. Here, h and a are constants whose values are between 0 and 1.

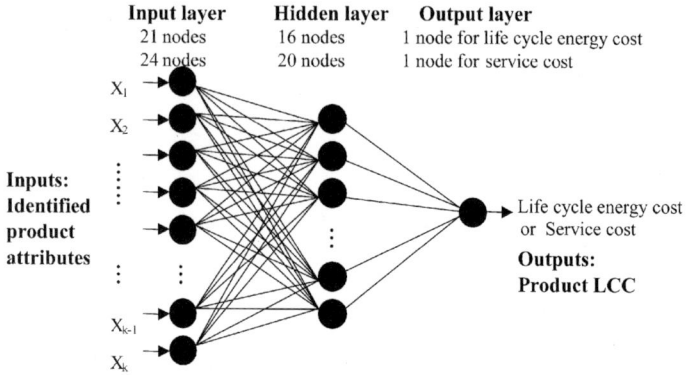

Figure 3. Structure of the backpropagation neural network to estimate the product LCC.

More than 50 experiments were performed to determine the best combination of the learning rates (h), momentum term (a), number of hidden layers, number of neurons in hidden layers, learning rules and transfer functions. Figure 3 shows the structure of the developed BP neural network, which consists of an input layer with 21 or 24 nodes, a hidden layer with 16 or 20 nodes, and an output layer with one node. The most popular learning rules, generalized delta rules and a sigmoid transfer function were used for the output node.

4.3. Testing and the results

The artificial neural network with backpropagation algorithm for the approximate LCC models was implemented in C++. The training of the backpropagation neural network took 2,688 seconds for life cycle energy cost with 140 learning patterns on a 500 MHz Pentium III processor. When η and α were 0.6 and 0.1 respectively, the number of iteration was 60,000, and the mean square error was 0.00014. The ANN runs its learning cycle by reading a text file containing the training data. Once model learns, users can set the model inputs (product attributes) to values corresponding a product concept. The approximate LCC model based on ANNs then immediately provides the predicted LCC output.

The training for service cost took 102 seconds for 30 learning patterns. When η and α were 0.6 and 0.25 respectively, the number of iteration was 5,000 and the mean square error was 0.00062.

The trained neural network was evaluated using products with known LCC results. The approximate LCC estimation model was estimated in two different ways: absolute accuracy and ability to generalize trends. Ten different products were used in the estimation.

The results of LCC prediction and accuracy comparisons are provided. The results of life cycle energy cost prediction and accuracy comparisons for the ten products

Table 10 Comparison of the life cycle energy cost of products as predicted
by the approximate LCC estimation model with the actual LCC

Product	Actual LCC ($)	Predicted LCC ($)	Relative error (%)
1. Vacuum Cleaner	596.21	570.99	4.23
2. Mini Vacuum	20.53	19.36	5.72
3. Radio	24.15	23.24	3.75
4. Heater	2893.56	3241.37	−12.02
5. Coffee Maker	464.37	488.61	−5.22
6. Washing Machine	6358.84	6365.83	−0.11
7. Refrigerator (S)	313.41	306.3	2.27
8. Refrigerator (L)	2221.19	2193.87	1.23
9. TV	2935.2	3020.91	−2.92
10. LCD TV	2895.17	2880.69	0.5
Ave. absolute error			3.79
Max. absolute error			12.02

*Training sample size is 140, ** Test sample size is 10.

Table 11 The predicted results of product service cost (SC)

Product	Actual SC ($)	Predicted SC ($)	Relative error (%)
1. Vacuum Cleaner	6	6.02	−0.38
2. Mini Vacuum	1.79	1.75	2.08
3. Radio	9.46	9.44	0.12
4. Heater	3.23	3.22	0.15
5. Coffee Maker	2.83	2.81	0.97
6. Washing Machine	22	22.01	−0.02
7. Refrigerator (S)	12.38	12.38	0
8. Refrigerator (L)	16	16.01	−0.02
9. TV	6.54	6.68	−0.06
10. LCD TV	12.57	12.59	−2.11
Ave. absolute error			0.59
Max. absolute error			2.11

*Training sample size is 30, ** test sample size is 10.

are provided in Table 10. Those of service cost for ten products are provided in
Table 11.

Secondly, the ten products were used to test the approximate LCC estimation model's
ability to generalize and predict trends correctly for a given product concept. The
characteristics of each test—case product were held constant, with the exception of
the attribute for which trends were being assessed—mass and power consumption.
The life cycle energy cost is only shown as an example for ability to generalize trends.

The mass and energy consumption results for the washing machine shown in Figures 6 and 7, are representative in illustrating trends as predicted by the approximate
LCC estimation model. Results produced in trying to assess trends with respect to
mass and energy consumption for the washing machine were generally good.

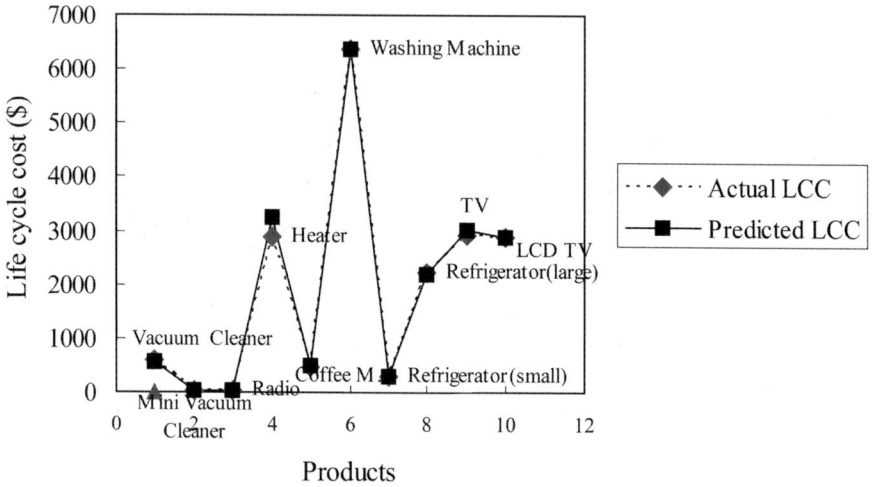

Figure 4. Comparison results of the LCC of products in Table 9.

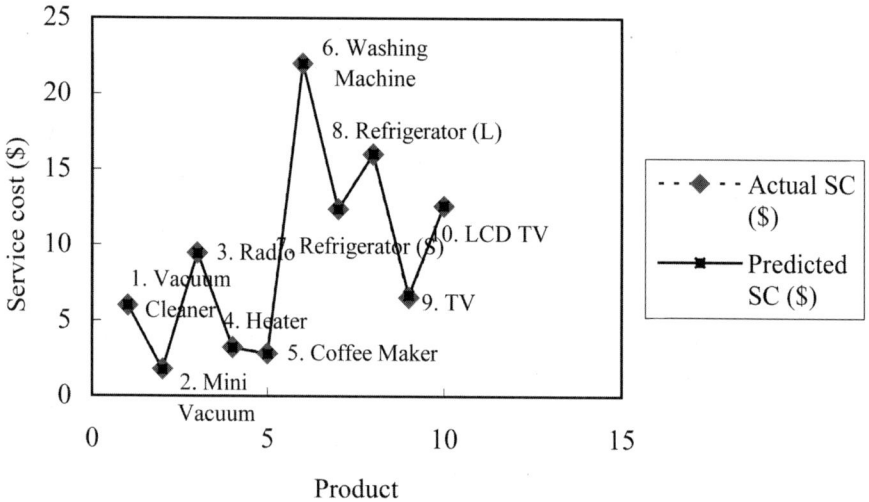

Figure 5. Comparison results of the service cost of products.

4.4. Discussion

In order to test the capability of the trained ANN, ten another samples were used as the test set which had not been used in the training. The results of the product LCC predicted by the ANN model for ten products are provided in Tables 10 and 11. In

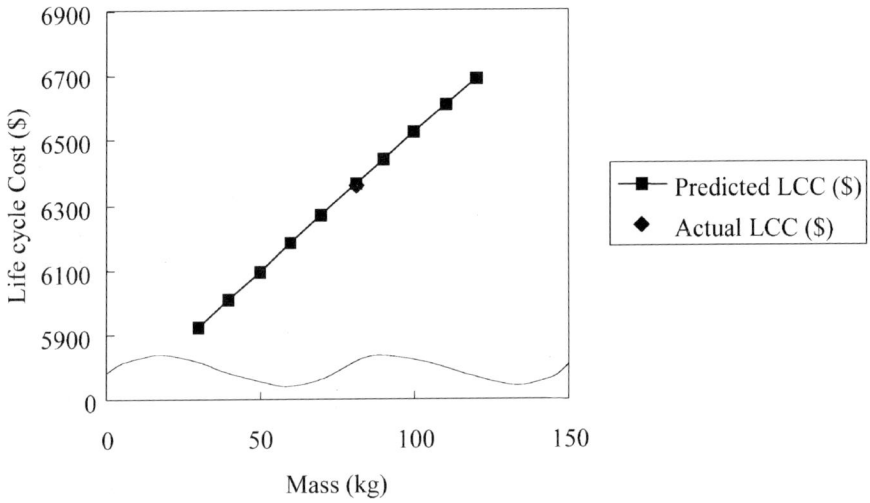

Figure 6. Results of mass trends for the washing machine.

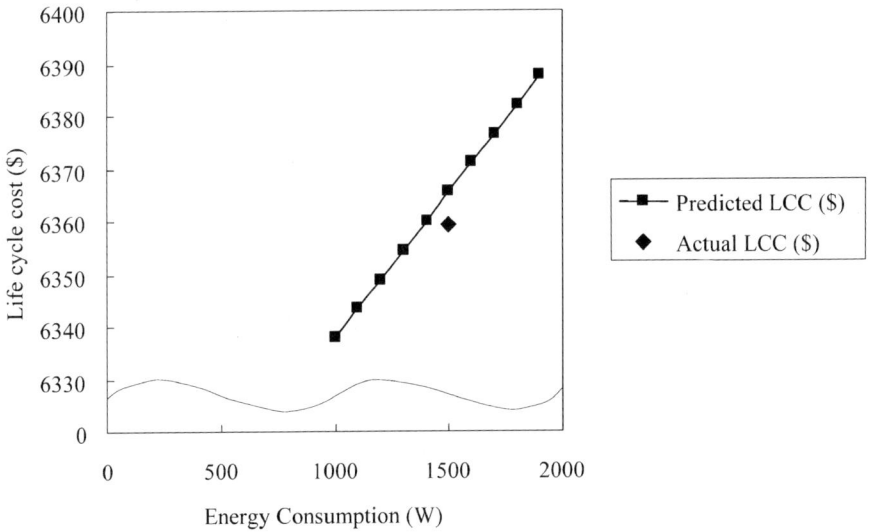

Figure 7. Results of energy consumption trends for the washing machine.

these Tables, some observations from the testing results are summarized as follows:

(1) Among ten testing samples, it can be found that the percentage errors of the samples are within ±6% except for the life cycle energy cost of the heater (12%). This is considered as a very good LCC estimation at the early design stage.
(2) The maximum deviation of LCC estimate from the actual LCC is about 12% which is acceptable for practical use.
(3) The performance of the trained ANN is consistent in the training, validation and testing samples.

During the early conceptual design stages of product development, available data are limited and the cost analyst must depend primarily on the use of various parametric cost estimating techniques in the development of cost data. The accuracy of a LCC model deviated from an actual LCC is typically between −30 and +50% (Creese and Moore 1990), so the proposed method based on ANN shows better product LCC estimation and gives the guidelines for the cost-effective design decisions in conceptual design phase.

The prediction results of trends for the other products were generally good too. The approximate LCC estimation method to predict the product LCC is somewhat generalized since the results of trend experiment were shown to be satisfactory. This generalization can be extended to the product LCC according to various product attributes and diverse products.

The two advantages of the approximate LCC method are summarized as follows:

(1) The product attributes include the cost aspects related to products. Extracting such product attributes can be easily done by a product designer. Detailed information for cost estimation is not required.
(2) The ANN based method can help better conceptual design through evaluating the costs of different design alternatives.

5. CONCLUSIONS AND FUTURE WORKS

Life cycle engineering as an approach to the development of a product has been recognized as an effective way to compete in the current global market. One aspect of life cycle engineering is LCC analysis. The growing demand on producers to develop products that are inexpensive to acquire, use, and dispose of has necessitated that the LCC of products be considered during the design of the product. For designers, estimating the LCC of a proposed product during its development phase is required for a number of reasons including:

(1) Determining the most cost efficient design amongst a set of alternatives,
(2) Determining the cost of a design for monetary purposes.
(3) Identifying cost drivers for design changes and optimization.

In this regard, LCC analysis should not only be seen as an approach for determining the cost of the product but also as an aid to design decision making.

It has been recognized that the design process needs cost models that:

(1) Take into account the complete life cycle of products.
(2) Can be used at the very early stages of design.
(3) Can provide information to designers in a timely manner and in a form that can be understood and used.

The product LCC is mainly determined by early design decisions. But, at early conceptual design stages designers do not know the costs incurred in subsequent life cycle phases. Thus, the estimation method for minimizing the product LCC should be able to offer sufficient prediction of the product LCC in response to design decisions and design guidelines for reducing the product LCC.

The lack of estimating methods for early conceptual design motivated the development of the approximate LCC estimation concept. This chapter has described the approximate LCC estimation method for predicting the product LCC, especially focused on the life cycle energy and service costs, in conceptual product design. Three areas critical to the preliminary validation of the approach were developed: model outputs in the form of the LCC factors; model inputs in the form of a compact, meaningful, and understandable set of product attributes; and the ability to predict the product LCC using the ANN model.

The LCC factors for the approximate LCC estimation model were investigated and they were able to be used to predict the product LCC. A list of meaningful product attributes needed for inputs to the approximate LCC estimation model were made and related with elements of the LCC factors. A set of product attributes was identified, and tested for first order relationships with elements in the list of LCC factors.

Finally, LCC data and product attributes were collected for products, and the approximate LCC estimation models based on ANNs were trained to predict the product LCC, and then tested. The learning LCC models for ten products with known LCC results were successfully tested to assess performance in two categories: absolute accuracy and the ability to predict trends associated with changes for a given product concept.

It is apparent that the approximate LCC method based on ANN is feasible for estimating the cost incurred in subsequent phases of the product life cycle based on design decisions at early conceptual design stages. The proposed method can be used to estimate the product LCC and gives the guidelines leading to cost-effective design decisions in the conceptual design phase.

There are some future works as follows.

Firstly, the various product attributes for LCC factors are identified and further tests using more data are needed to determine to what extent the ANN model can provide reasonable predictions for product attributes and to test for another LCC factors.

Secondly, in order to learn the proposed method faster and more effectively, "learning space" has to be narrowed, or filtered, in a preliminary stage. For example, a classification of products into general categories will lead to more specific relationships between product attributes and LCC factors. The reasonable product groups according to product categories can provide the predicted LCC more accurately by using the product attributes related with the product groups.

REFERENCES

Alting, L., 1993, Life-cycle design of products: a new opportunity for manufacturing enterprises. In Concurrent Engineering: Automation, Tools, and Techniques, A. Kusiak (ed.) (New York: Wiley), 1–17.

Alting, L., and Legarth, J., 1995, Life cycle Engineering and Design, *Annals of the CIRP*, 44/2: 569–580.

Beardon, C., 1989, Artificial Intelligence Terminology: A Reference Guide, Halstead Press, New York.

Blanchard, B. S., 1979, Life cycle costing—a review, Terotechnica, 1, 9–15.

Breset, H. and van Hemel, C., 1997, Ecodesign, a Promising Approach to Sustainable Production and Consumption. Paris, France: United Nations Environmental Program (UNEP) Industry and Environment.

Clark, T. and Charter, M., 1999, Eco-design Checklists for Electronic Manufacturers, Systems Integrators, and Suppliers, of Components and Sub-assemblies. http://www.cfsd.org.uk

Creese, R. C. and Moore, L. T., 1990, Cost modeling for concurrent engineering, *Cost Engineering*, 32(6) June, 23–27.

Dowlatshahi, S., 1992, Product design in a concurrent engineering environment: an optimization approach, *Journal of Production Research*, 30(8), 1803–1818.

Eisenhard, J. L., 2000, Product Descriptors for Early Product Development: An Interface between Environmental Experts and Designers, M.S Thesis, MIT.

Fabrycky, W. J. and Blanchard, W. J., 1991, Life-Cycle Cost and Economic Analysis (Englewood Cliffs, NJ: Prentice Hall).

Fiksel, J., 1996, Design for Environment: Creating Eco-efficient Product and Processes (New York: McGraw-Hill).

Gershenson, J. and Ishii, K., 1993, Life-cycle design for serviceability. In Concurrent Engineering: Automation, Tools, and Techniques, A. Kusiak (ed.) (New York: Wiley), 363–384.

Hanssen, O. J., 1999, Sustainable Product Systems—Experiences Based on Case Projects in Sustainable Product Development, *Journal of Cleaner Production*, Vol. 7, pp. 27–41.

Hubka, V. and Eder, W. E., 1992, Engineering Design: General Procedural Model of Engineering Design (Zurich, Switzerland: Heurista).

Ishii, K., 1995, Life-cycle engineering design. Design for Manufacturability, *ASME*, DE-81, 39–45.

Paasch, R. K. and Ruff, D. N., 1997, Evaluation of failure diagnosis in concepts design of mechanical systems, *Trans. of ASME: J. of Mech. Design*, 119(1), 57–67.

Porter, M. E., 1985, Competitive Advantage: Creating and Sustaining Superior Performance, New York, The Free Press.

Rich, E. and Knight, K., Artificial Intelligence, McGraw-Hill, New York, 1991, pp. 487–509.

Rummelhart, D., Durbin, R., Golden, R., and Chauvin, Y., Backpropagation: the basic theory, Backpropagation Theory, Architectures, and Applications, 1995: 1–34.

Rummelhart, D., Widrow, B. and Lehr, M., The basic ideas in neural networks, *Communications of the ACM*, Vol. 37(3), 1994: 87–92.

Sousa, I., Eisenhard, J. L. and Wallace, D., 2001, Approximate Life-Cycle Assessment of product Concepts Using Learning Systems, *Journal of industrial Ecology*, 4/4: 61–81.

Takata, S., Hiraoka, H., Asama, H., Yamoka, N. and Saito, D., 1995, Facility model for lifecycle maintenance system, *Annals of the CIRP* 44/1: 117–121.

Tarelko, W., 1995, Control model of maintainability level, *Reliability Engineering and System Safety*, 47/2: 85–91.

Utez, H., 1983, Maintainability of production system, *Maintenance Management International*, 4, 55–68.

Ulrich and Eppinger, S., 1995, Product Design and Development (New York, NY: McGraw-Hill, Inc.)

Vujosevic, R., Raskar, R., Yeturkuri, NV., Jothishankar, MC. and Juang, S.-H., 1995, Simulation, animation and analysis of design disassembly for maintainability analysis, *International Journal of Production Research*, 33(11), 2999–3022.

Wani, M. F. and Gandhi, O. P., 1999, Development of maintainability index for mechanical systems, *Reliability Engineering and System Safety*, 65(3), 259–270.

NEURAL NETWORK SYSTEMS TECHNOLOGY IN THE ANALYSIS OF FINANCIAL TIME SERIES

RENATE SITTE AND JOAQUIN SITTE

As human nature strives for wealth and comfort in life, the ways of attaining wealth have changed through time. In the dark ages the focus was on turning material into gold, but nowadays the efforts go into managing and manipulating trades enabling profitable growth in different economic strata. For decades, financial time series predictions have been the target for profitable trade. Those who succeeded are reluctant to share their secrets. Thus successful applications of times series prediction techniques are unlikely to be found in the scholarly literature of the field. We cannot promise a pot of gold, but we will explain financial time series, with emphasis in using neural networks for their prediction, as a technique which has brought significant improvements not only to time series predictions but also enabled new technologies in many other areas. Neural Networks are particularly attractive for the prediction of financial time series because they do not require any kind of model knowledge about the relationships between variables [1]. In this chapter we shall review different approaches to financial time series. We present this material in a way that is understandable to a wide and interdisciplinary audience.

We start with an introduction of financial time series in their wider context, providing the background to their modeling and the applicability of neural networks. The next section provides an overview of time series, their components, and modeling techniques. This is followed by a tutorial on neural networks specific for financial time series. Then comes a section on data preparation. It explains in detail the steps required for the preparation of time series data as input for neural networks. This is done with the purpose to show newcomers to the field that neural networks are not difficult to apply. Finally a section updating the review of financial time series applications compiled in Zhang's earlier work [2]. For the sake of completeness, an appendix explaining financial derivatives can be found at the end of this chapter.

INTRODUCTION AND CONTEXT

In general, a time series is a collection of data of some variable that changes over a time, and is recorded, typically at regular time intervals, for example the monthly rainfall of a region, or the yearly yield of a farmed produce. Financial time series are those that record an event related to finances, for example the daily exchange rates between two currencies, or the daily closing value of a specific stock.

The changing values of financial time series are the result of complex phenomena. The effect of such phenomena is visible as a blend of slopes and bumps in a time series plot. The most noticeable variations are the trend, the cyclic and the periodic variations, and the day-to-day variations. The trend is an identifiable long-term gradual variation in the time series. It is usually predicted by extrapolation. The cyclic and periodic variations follow either seasonal patterns or the business cycles in the economy. Short term and day-to-day variations appear to be random and are difficult to predict, but they are often the source for financial trading gains and losses.

There is a still the unresolved controversy that dates back to the beginning of the century, whether the short term variations of certain financial time series behave like a random walk, or not [3] [4]. If they were a random walk, any attempt to predict would be futile. Despite this controversy, the so-called *charting* methods remain popular among financial speculators, in particular on stock markets. Chartists assume that past values of the time series contain most of the information required to predict its future behavior.

In explaining and predicting stock value fluctuations, two hypotheses have emerged. One is the so-called efficient market hypothesis [3], which states that current asset prices always fully reflect the available information. This means that there is no publicly available information, such as a history of past values, that will allow the holder of such information to obtain sustained above market average returns. A corollary of the efficient market hypothesis is that short-term price variations follow a random walk and are thus unpredictable.

The second hypothesis states that the prices are not only determined by previous values, but also by other external or unknown variables. This hypothesis interprets fluctuations as the result of delayed or incomplete information that influences the stock market prices. External phenomena such as political turmoil or climatic changes influencing agricultural yield, may affect subsequent stock market prices. Accurate predictions are difficult because it is not possible to model, quantify, or even know a priori such external phenomena.

Because of their potential for pecuniary gain the prediction of financial time series has been and continues to be a topic of intense research. However it is also a subject shrouded in secrecy for the simple reason that whoever finds a method that consistently produces correct predictions will not want this method become known to others. Disclosure of such knowledge is likely to rapidly evaporate its financial value. In agreement with the "efficient market" hypothesis, any technique that leads to sustained above-average returns will upon divulgation be factored into the marked and thus will be neutralized.

Time series prediction is usually based on an extrapolation, and even slight deviations can lead to wrong decisions, missed opportunities and financial losses not just for an individual, but for a whole economic system. Predictions tend to hold only for very short periods, but financial systems require often long term strategies and early decisions. Short and medium term prediction of events in the environment is essential to the success of any human endeavor. The capacity of predicting what will happen reflects our level of *understanding* of the processes unfolding in our environment. Understanding means having established causal relationships between events that associate the later occurrence of an effect with an earlier occurrence of the cause. The scientific method is the tool for establishing causal relations. The scientific method induces causal relations from the quantitative analysis of observations. Such an analysis aims at establishing a causal relationship between the quantities being observed (dependent or output variable), other observable quantities (explanatory or input variables) of the process. The causal relationships found in this procedure form the model of the observed process.

Prediction of the behavior of economic systems by detailed modeling of the dynamics is a big and difficult task because of the size and complexity of most economic systems of interest and the lack of full understanding of the causal laws in action. Despite the scarcity of widely accessible and reliable economic models there is a great variety of financial and economic data that characterizes various aspects of economic and financial systems and that are recorded at regular intervals resulting in many economic and financial time series. These time series are widely used for making policy and business decisions and the disclosure of the next value in the series is awaited with great expectation. Without reliable models there is no way to obtain the next new value in the series other than waiting until its time has arrived. It is needless to say that the correct prediction of future values, ahead of their occurrence, can lead to substantial pecuniary rewards, hence empirical methods that allow the prediction of economic and financial time series are in great demand.

When a causal dependency on other explanatory variables is not known or hard to establish, it is tempting to try to predict future values of a time series based exclusively on its past values. In its strict sense this is the problem of time series prediction. The justification for it is that variation over time of the data is a reflection of the unknown, dynamics of the system and that future states of the system will depend on its past states, if the system is deterministic.

Traditionally, stochastic models, based on statistical analysis of time series, were used for predictions [5]. In more recent times attention has focused on Neural Networks (NN) methods [6] [7] [8] for the prediction of financial time series. This was because in the meantime the deficiencies and critiques of linear models in financial applications have become well known [9]. Artificial neural networks have the advantage of ease of use. Subsequently alternative modeling approaches using Neural networks, Fuzzy Logic, Evolutionary Computation, and Chaotic Dynamics have been designed.

There was skepticism in the 1990s about the whether neural networks provide an improvement over linear and traditional techniques. Sufficient evidence has now accumulated to overcome the skepticism. An intuitive example of a modulated sinusoid is described further down in the Time Delay Neural Networks section. This example shows very convincingly that no "intelligent" analysis is required, yet the neural network is capable of producing an astonishing result. In general, neural networks approach treat both, the linear and non-linear processes, in the same way.

It is necessary to assess the predictive performance and the range of validity of the neural network predictions prior to their use. It is also scholarly practice to report the findings of such exercise. Although numerous papers have been published reporting results of applying neural networks to the prediction on various financial time series the value of these publications is diminished because they lack the discipline of comparing the proposed method to one or more accepted reference techniques, or to a "benchmark" problem. In many cases the authors use their own variants of a neural network technique without justifying clearly the need of the variant, and even worse very often the crucial details of the technique used are not described in the paper making it very laborious or almost impossible for another researcher to reproduce the reported results. A scholarly example of the few exceptions of this weakness is Walczak's study of the effect of the size of the training set on the accuracy of the prediction of currency exchange rates, with well-specified neural nets [10].

It is often stated in neural networks papers that neural networks methods are superior to statistical methods for time series prediction, as for example the statistical formulations of linear predictors. However, as time series prediction have evolved over the years using a variety of techniques, some of them based on statistics and probability, we cannot – as it is often wrongly done – suggest a separation into statistical models and neural network models. Clearly statistical methods can also be applied with neural networks as the volatility prediction papers show. Here we refer to earlier methods as *traditional methods*.

The tutorial about neural networks later in this chapter is not "yet another neural networks review". It focuses on recent insights on the applicability of Time Delay Neural Networks (TDNN) and Feed Forward Neural Networks (FFNN) in particular, and recognizes their link with dynamic systems, providing strong theoretical support. Zhang et al. did a comprehensive review of the state of the art of forecasting with neural networks up to around 1996. Their review focused on Multilayer Perceptron (MLP) networks because it was the neural network type predominantly used for forecasting. In the years since 1996 the understanding of MLPs and their training has matured and other networks, particularly recurrent neural networks have gained importance in the prediction of time series. Therefore we will only summarize the state of MLP for time series prediction and will present in more detail recent developments relevant to the prediction of financial time series.

Also, since the last review in the mid 1990's, interests have moved beyond the simple predictions of the next value in the time series, to the assessment of the volatility, requiring extensions of the techniques. This translates into precision estimates of the prediction, in other words, predicting the mean square error (MSE) of a prediction. This is where statistical methods come into play again. The prediction of volatility is essential for risk management, in particular in relation to the trading of financial derivatives. Financial derivatives are briefly explained in the appendix at the end of this chapter.

TIME SERIES AND THEIR TECHNIQUES

This section provides an overview to time series and its related operations and techniques. It focuses specifically on those topics that are relevant for the understanding of neural networks applied to financial time series. First the time series and its components are explained. Then the related operations such as detrending and index calculations are summarized. For additional readings about time series, its theory, methods, and statistical techniques, or economics the reader is referred to literature that is specific to these topics [11] [12] [13] [14].

Modern financial systems are a man made invention. One must see money as a tradeable good just as any other consumable. We exchange money – real or virtual – for goods, including money itself, but the time of trade is not limited to one single event. The time gap between the start of a trade, i.e. handing in one good, and finalizing the trade, i.e. paying back in currency or other good can be anything between immediately and up to decades apart, with very different socio-economic conditions. The value of our traded goods rises, falls and fluctuates, in a continuous dynamic way. These movements are often influenced by natural phenomena such as good crops and abundance of produce offered on the markets, triggering progressions of wealth, or the opposite of it, in times of shortage and natural disaster. Likewise they are also influenced by human interests in modes and fashions of consumerism, be it in food, leisure, or knowledge and technical innovations in semiconductors, communications, biotechnology, or any others. In financial time series, the main interest is on forecasting, but neither nature nor technology nor the next fad of consumerism can be forecast easily and accurately. Neither can their concurrent effect and that of many other factors on the financial situation be predicted.

So, why would one wish to forecast financial markets situation? Because, by knowing, when a good becomes more scarcely and more desirable, one can wait and sell it for a higher price, than in times of abundance and competition. Conversely, one might not be able to endure further decline in prices without incurring in loss. In the end, it boils down to predicting the next change in abundance, scarcity or fashions. However, just predicting is not enough, the predictions must be very accurate as well. Decisions based on accurate predictions are rewarded with gains, wrong or inaccurate predictions lead to wrong decisions and loss.

Modern economics is based on the assumption that the ability of prediction is not necessarily the result of one or another individual's premonition abilities, but that the knowledge is embedded in the data of the system, in the form of response by consumers and brokers to earlier patterns of market situations. The prediction ability consists then, in finding the right data and an algorithm that is able to tap into that information and predict from it the next change.

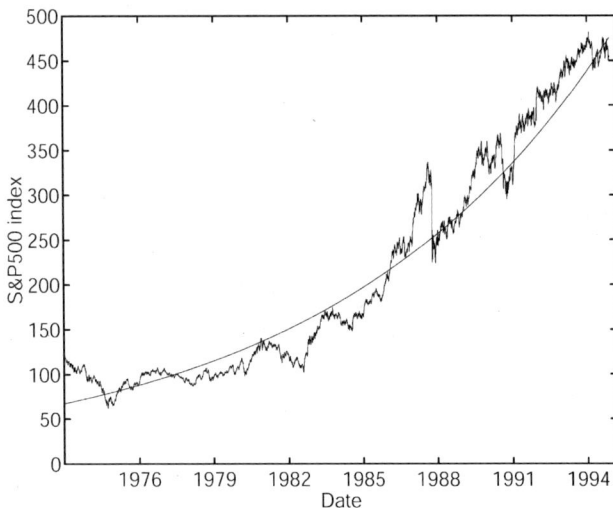

Figure 1. Example of a financial time series: The daily closing values of the S&P 500 stock market index.

Financial time series

A time series is a collection of values of a variable observed at specific times, and arranged in chronological order, for example the value of stock market shares at closing time as shown in Figure 1. The time series is an ordered set of observations

Observation	y_1	y_2	$\ldots$	y_n
Time step	t_1	t_2	$\ldots$	t_n

Typically, when the variable is sampled at fixed time intervals the time is omitted and the series is given as a ordered list of values of the variable $y_1, y_2, \ldots y_n$ which are only the observed values of the variable y at times $t_1, t_2, \ldots t_n$. What makes time series different from other series is that they often follow a complex pattern that for which a simple formula or set of equations is not known. More often than not, a time series is the result of several overlapping phenomena, who may be known through their effect, but whose nature is uncertain. For whatever reason, the purpose of knowing the governing rules and equations of a time series is to predict its future behavior or parts of it, based on past observations.

Components of financial time series:

Time series, financial time series in particular, often exhibit easily recognizable features. As mentioned in the introduction their effect is visible as a blend of slopes and bumps in a time series plot. They are the characteristic components or variations of a time series. Four main components can be distinguished: the trend, the periodical variations, the cyclical variations and the short-term fluctuations. They are illustrated in Figure 2.

1. *The trend* is a gentle long-term component (also known as secular variation). It refers to the overall shape of the time series plot, for example following a linear growth, exponentially rise, logistic, or other. Sometimes it can be difficult to distinguish the overall shape of a time series from other variations in the time series. Therefore the length or scope of a time series should be sufficiently long to ensure that the trend can be derived from the time series data.

2. *Cyclical variations* are medium or long-term oscillations meandering around the trend. These cycles can be periodic or aperiodic, i.e. variable period. If they are periodic, then the duration of a cycle must be more than one year to be considered a cyclic variation, else it would be a seasonal variation. An example are the business cycles with the four alternating phases of prosperity, recession, depression and recovery, which are not subject to a calendar year. For good observations, a financial time series should include at least two economic periods, e.g. two complete business cycles or more.

3. *Seasonal variations* are very regular cycling patterns, typically with annual recurrence. For example annual rain patterns, or animal population growth in spring, automotive car production, or seasonal sales.

4. *Short-term fluctuations* are short time, quite irregular variations with "noise like" appearance, or sudden jumps that are attributed to random events such as disasters, failed crops, or political events. In stock market time series they are called day-to-day variations. They are difficult to predict but *they* are the source of stock trading gains and losses and the aim for predictions with lucrative rewards.

These components are not completely independent to each other, nor are they exclusive to financial time series. Cyclic variations can influence the trend, the seasonal variations, and the random variations. Conversely, strong seasonal variations can influence the cyclic variations, and these in turn affect the trend. Likewise the random variations through wars, natural disasters, or outbreak of epidemic diseases can affect any other component.

Two main ways of compositions of a time series have emerged that are widely accepted; they are based on the assembly of a time series' components, which are either added or multiplied.

$$Y = T + C + S + I \tag{0.1}$$

$$Y = T \times C \times S \times I \tag{0.2}$$

where Y is the observed value, T the trend, C the cyclic variation, S the seasonal variation and I the irregular or random component respectively. Each component

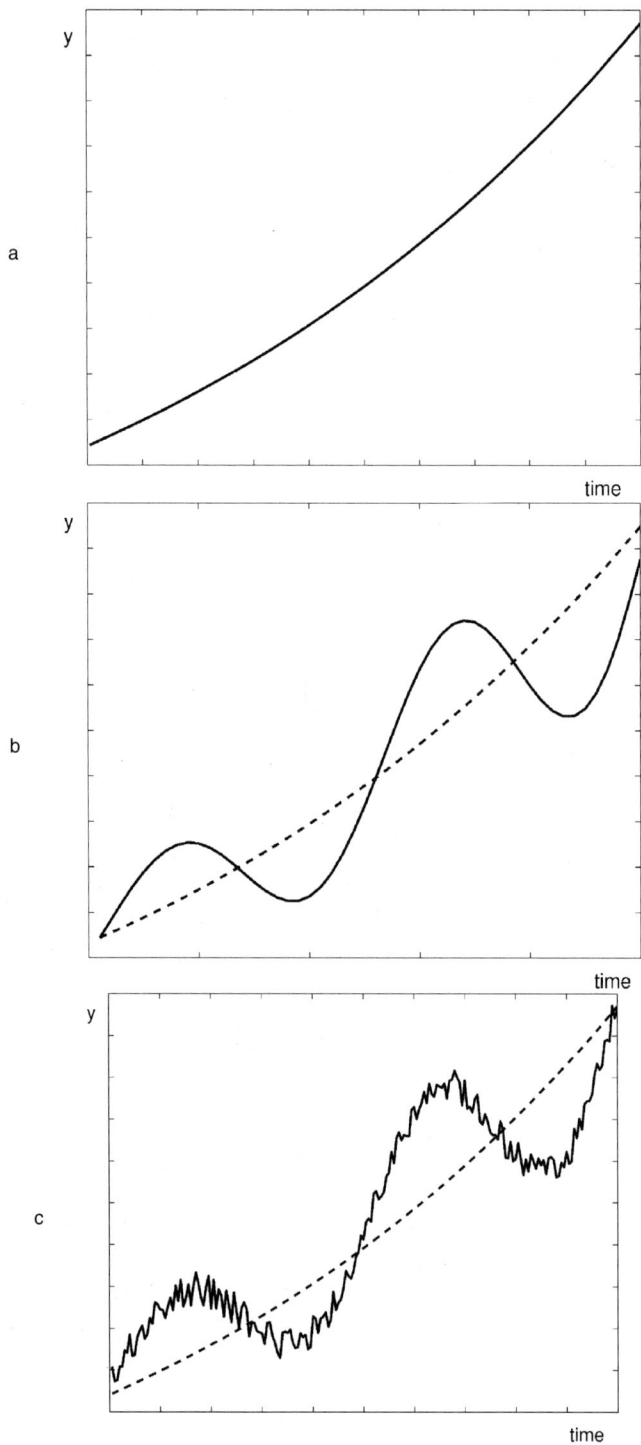

Figure 2. The different components of a Time Series: (a) the trend, (b) the cyclical and the periodical variations and (c) the short-term variations.

varies on a different time scale. The choice of operation however depends on the data and the intention of the model.

The purpose of the analysis of time series is to decompose the series and separate the component of interest for whatever purpose of the study. For example after obtaining the trend, predictions can be made by extrapolating the trend function for short period predictions of a nation's economy. For each component in the time series, a different model is applied. In general, these models are obtained by fitting the data to a specific model.

Analysis of time series

If our level of interest on the time series is on the larger components, such as the trend or the cyclic variations, the smaller fluctuations appear as irrelevant noise that do not contribute to predictions. To the contrary, they would lead to overfitting the model and distort the result. We eliminate all the small variations by smoothing the function. There are several methods of smoothing data, and their suitability depends on the type of data. In the context of financial time series the most popular is that of the moving average (or running average). Other variations of smoothing algorithms are the *weighted moving average* and *weighted smoothing*.

The moving average

The moving average is a technique that is used for several purposes in financial time series analysis. It is used to smooth the data, that is, to even out the random short-term fluctuations, and for detrending. A weighted version of the moving average is used for linear prediction in the autoregressive moving average (ARMA, ARIMA) technique.

A moving average consists in generating a new series based on the piecewise averages of small successively overlapping groups of the original data. The new series is then used for forecasting. A moving average of a series is obtained—for instance for a run-period of 3, by taking the average of elements $[a_1,a_2,a_3]$, $[a_2,a_3,a_4]$, $[a_3,a_4,a_5]$ . . . and so forth. A higher run-period value smoothes the series more, a lower value smoothes less. For higher values, in the limit it tends to the centroid of the function. This means, that by using a larger run-period, the prediction is affected by increasing error caused by over or underestimating. While this would be rarely desirable, a typical run-period of 3 or 5 is sufficient for time series predictions. For a time series whose progress in time we wish to predict, this is a more appropriate data preparation, than simply averaging non-overlapping groups. Moreover, by simply averaging in non-overlapping groups the time series is reduced, and with it valuable information is lost.

Trend estimating and detrending

The process of separating the trend from a time series is called detrending. The rationale for identifying the trend and separating it can vary. It can be either because of one's interest in the trend itself, or to remove its masking effect on the other components that comes from its dominant effect on the time series. What remains after removing the trend we obtain what is called the *residuals*. Removing the trend allows better

Table 1 Examples of non-linear functions for trend fitting

Gompertz function

$y = ka^{b^x}$

Logistic function

$y = \frac{1}{k+ab^x}$

Exponential function

$y = e^x$

Logarithmic function

$y = \log x$

Second order polynomial

$y - a + bx + cx^2$

observation of the other variations. This is particularly important in the application of neural networks, which would rather pick up the trend, than the lesser variations when they are the focus of interest. Despite the fact that detrending has been practiced for decades, there are also claims that one should not remove the trend in time series analysis, because it is considered to contain information that is somehow correlated to the other time series' movements, and that would be lost otherwise [15].

The simplest way for estimating the trend to be removed is by fitting a function to the original time series data points, using the least squares method. The functions to fit can be linear or non-linear functions. Table 1 shows some examples of non-linear trend recommended by L. Chao of [16].

There are various methods for detrending. The two most widely used ones are by estimating the trend by curve fitting; the other is by using the moving average.

DETRENDING BY CURVE FITTING. This method consists in fitting a function using the least squares method and then subtracting it from the original data points. In the selection of the fitting function, caution must be taken not to use higher polynomials, although they may give a better fit. The reason is, that in doing so, one might overfit, by including and subtracting with the fitted curve not just the trend but also the cyclic or even seasonal variations. The resulting time series may be devoid of desired information.

DETRENDING WITH THE MOVING AVERAGE. This method is suitable when the trend is not known and beyond the interest of the case. Detrending is done by either subtracting the local average from each data point, or by dividing each data point by the local average. In recent research we have found that this method of detrending can introduce correlations to the data [17]. Figure 3 shows how increasing the run-periods increases the autocorrelation. Detrending by subtraction does not introduce correlations. At this time however, it is not known whether other methods of detrending also might introduce correlations, nor is it known to what extent they would do so.

Day to Day Autocorrelation

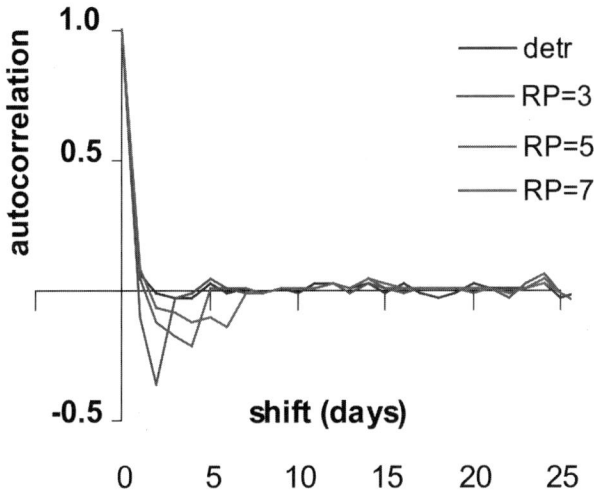

Figure 3. Comparison of day-to-day autocorrelations for different run-periods and the detrended cost series of the S&P 500.

Another method for detrending is done by taking differences between successive samples of (stock) sample values as

$$\Delta y(t) = y(t) - y(t - 1) \tag{0.3}$$

This eliminates constant and slowly changing trends, including seasonal variations.

Another alternative for trend removal is by taking the logarithm of the quotient of successive values

$$\Delta y(t) = \log \frac{y(t)}{y(t - 1)} \tag{0.4}$$

Seasonal indices

The seasonal variations are expressed by their seasonal index. These are sets of numbers whose values are relative i.e. as a percentage to the monthly movements. On average these 12 numbers must add to 100%, but their *index values* must add to 1200% for one year, or be correspondingly adjusted if necessary. Several well documented data filtering techniques or more traditional calculations for those indices are available in the literature. All have the common purpose of removing or adjusting the seasonal fluctuations. There is however, growing controversy about removing those fluctuations, because they are likely to be part of the sought information when using neural networks for predictions time series. Another source of concern is the large period used in moving averages techniques. Some of the techniques to calculate indices use periods of up to 12 months per moving average data point.

Cyclic movements

Cyclic movements can be obtained by dividing the time series by the seasonal and trend components ST as expressed in equation (0.2), leaving only the CI component of the time series. By smoothing the time series then by any means, for example the moving average, the cycling movements remain, although they are affected by a slight error introduced by the smoothing operation. Again as a caution it must be stressed that the cyclic movements may contain information that affects the time series to the extent that removing them would equate of throwing away decisive information for the prediction. In general, any decomposition of a time series either in factors or additions has the risk of splitting some important information.

Prediction

The prediction of a time series is a case of learning from experience. The only information available for prediction are the previous observations of the quantity to predict. Specifically, the time series prediction problem consists of predicting the value $\hat{y}(t_{n+1})$ of an observation to be made at a future time t_{n+1} following a sequence of n similar observations $y(t_1), y(t_2), \ldots, y(t_n)$ made at past times $t_1, t_2, \ldots, t_n$.

The notion of a predictor helps in concisely formulating the prediction problem. A predictor is an operator $P(\bullet)$, that acting on a set of past values of the series returns a prediction for the value of the series at a future time:

$$\hat{y}(t + 1) = P(y(t), y(t - 1), \ldots, y(t - (n - 1)))$$
(0.5)

Predictors fall into two main classes: linear predictors and non-linear predictors. The theory of linear predictors is well developed, but of limited applicability because of the prevalence of non-linear phenomena, particularly in economy and finance.

Some common predictors are

- The moving average. The justification for using moving averages is that the noise masks the value of the data but that the noise will cancel on average. Because the function is slowly varying, the average of the last m points is a good predictor for the next value without noise.
- Slope extrapolation. Special case of a linear predictor that only uses the two most recent observations. It only works when there is no noise.
- Local curve fitting. Least mean square fitting of a function that can be non-linear, to the last m observations and extrapolation the fitted function to the next time.
- Artificial neural networks

Models of time series

According to the definition, a time series would be just the sequence of an observed set of numbers ordered along a time scale. However, a variety of time series can be distinguished either in the way the time series is observed, or in the phenomenon whose observations are recorded.

It is important to recognize differences between types of time series to be aware of their limitations and nature. While most of the characteristics described here are common to financial time series, the apparent similarity of time series is at times misused as the following example demonstrates. It is common practice to use the sunspots and Mackey–Glass time series for benchmarking newly developed forecasting methods. The problem arises from the fact that these time series differ in character from the typical financial time series, The sunspots and Mackey–Glass series do not have long term trends, are highly cyclical and are not very noisy, while financial TS which have growth, have only modest periodic variations and are high in noise. In the end, the comparison is somewhat pointless, because the series are so different that to use them for benchmarking equates to comparing apples and pears.

Univariate vs. multivariate modeling

A crucial distinction comes from the number of variables that are considered in its modeling as either univariate or multivariate. A time series is *univariate* when it is modeled with only one time dependent set of data observations. A time series is *multivariate* when additional variables are recorded in association with the time series main observations. For the prediction, the recorded data are expected to be correlated. Here is an example: the daily recorded cost of stock market shares at closing time is a univariate time series. If we maintain also a record the volume, and use both, the cost and the volume to predict next day's cost, then a multivariate model is being used. It is important to notice that our recording (or the lack of it) of additional data sets does not warrant that the time series by its nature actually depends on any of the other recorded variables. Whether it does or not depend on other variables can be found out easily with a correlation test. The choice of modeling as univariate or multivariate is ours, and consequently this includes the ease and accuracy of the prediction.

Linear vs. non-linear modeling

First of all we have to distinguish between two different ways of referring to "linear" (or non linear) in time series. One of them refers to the overall shape; witch may be exponential due to the dominating trend. The other is the model, that is, the equations that are used for the prediction, which may or may not be linear.

When referring to the overall shape, the linearity is dictated by the shape of the trend. It is a condition of the data, which in financial time series typically is exponential. Usually after detrending, the data points of the time series lay scattered around a flat line.

When referring to the prediction, linearity is an important distinction that affects the choice of the model.

THE ARMA/ARIMA MODEL. The Auto-Regressive-Moving-Average (ARMA) is perhaps the most important linear model for time series with noise. They belong to the statistical estimation models. Observations in a time series can be affected by noise to the extent that it affects the values before or during observation. The ARMA models are used to estimate the most likely value of the prediction (mean and variance) in the presence of noise. The presence of noise links the linear models with statistical estimation theory.

With *additive* noise the observation $y(t_n)$ will be sum of the data $a(t_n)$ and the noise $\varepsilon(t_n)$

$$y(t_n) = a(t_n) + \varepsilon(t_n) \tag{0.6}$$

Time series that appear *noisy* pose a special challenge and therefore noise removal (smoothing) is often the first step in extracting information from a time series. The theory of noise removal is also well developed in the area of signal processing [18]. A method that removes noise is called a filter. The input to a filter is the noisy data and the output of the filter is a data with reduced noise.

The theory of linear predictors also draws on the theory of linear filters used in signal processing. A linear filter is nothing more than a weighted sum of the M most recent values of the signal.

$$\hat{y}(t) = \sum_{k=1}^{M} a(k) y(n - k) \tag{0.7}$$

In the signal processing literature the set of coefficients $a(k)$, $k = 1 \ldots M$ is called the *finite impulse response* (FIR) of the filter. Because as time passes the filter moves along the series always covering the most recent values linear filter is also called a *moving average*.

Replacing $\hat{y}(t)$ with $\hat{y}(t + 1)$ turns the linear filter expression (0.7) into a linear predictor, of course with different coefficients. The ARMA moving average predictor with orders p, q is obtained from the linear predictor by adding a linear term of the errors ε_t of each of the observation.

$$\hat{x}(n) = h_0 + \sum_{i=1}^{p} h(i) x(n - i) + \varepsilon_0 + \sum_{j=1}^{q} \theta(j) \varepsilon(n - j) \tag{0.8}$$

When $q = 0$ then the model becomes an autoregressive (AR) model of order p. When $p = 0$ the model becomes a moving average model of order q.

The generalization of the ARMA model to non-stationary time series is the ARIMA (Autoregressive Integrated Moving Average) model. We will not discuss linear models any further and refer the interested reader to one of several excellent books written on the topic [12].

Stochastic vs. chaotic modeling

Our next distinction is between chaotic and stochastic time series. According to Menna and Rotundo, the most marked difference between stochastic and chaotic time series is the number of variables that characterize the system; they propose a method for choosing the model either way. The assumption is that irregularities in the data can come from some deterministic chaos and the presence of an attractor, or by a stochastic process [19].

STOCHASTIC MODELING. The following explanation relies heavily on Granger and Watson [11]. Consider a discrete time stochastic process, with variable y_t. We are at time t and wish to predict about y_{t+h}. The proposition y_{t+h} will be based on whatever information available at time t; we call it I_t. Given the set of information I_t, anything that can be inferred about y_{t+h} is contained in the conditional distribution of y_{t+h} given I_t. Because each prediction step is based on the current information, a small inaccuracy in the information, results in a slightly inaccurate prediction, which in turn, will be part of the information for the next one. Therefore, it is difficult or impossible to predict several time steps ahead. This happens to a lesser extent, if each time we can critically assess how far off the prediction was made. With this we can acquire a confidence band for a single step prediction. We call this a *point forecast*; it is simply one single value y_{t+h}. The best point forecast of y_{t+h} is the one that is as close as possible to the actual event, that is, with minimal error in the prediction. Let $f_{t,h}^y(I_t)$ be the forecast of y_{t+h} based on the information set I_t. The error of the forecast is then

$$\varepsilon_{t,h}^y(I_t) = y_{t+h} - f_{t,h}^y(I_t) \tag{0.9}$$

From statistics we know that the linear minimum error is the mean square error (MSE).

Based on this, as a coarse approximation we can estimate the of the time series prediction as

$$y_{t+1} = (\text{function of } \tilde{y}_t) + \varepsilon_{t+1} \tag{0.10}$$

where $\tilde{y}_t = (y_t, y_{t-1}, \ldots)$. In a statistical approach, a time series would be modeled as the joint distributions of all the possible probabilities of the occurrence of the event in observation. It is clear that we can not determine all the possible probabilities of all the variables that can influence the financial system, hence for practical reasons a linear time series is modeled as the first and second order moments, of what in theory would be all possible joint distributions. These moments are the well known mean and the variance or covariance for univariate or multivariate distributions respectively.

A quick reminder: the moment generating function $m(t)$ for a discrete variable y with density $f(y)$ is defined as the expectancy E of e^{ty}

$$m(t) = E(e^{ty}) = \sum_y e^{ty} f(y) \tag{0.11}$$

The rth moment is obtained by differentiating r times with respect to t.

This can be extended to the case of many variables, whose formulations can be found in statistics books. In time series, however, the interest is in the specific case of the mixed moments, where the covariance is the most important one to us. It is clear that if the variables are not correlated, their covariance equals zero. The mean and covariance function of the variable y_t are defined as

$$\mu_y = E(y_t) \tag{0.12}$$

$$\varphi_{x,y}(r, s) = Cov(x_r, y_s) = E[(x_r - \mu_x)(y_s - \mu_y)] \tag{0.13}$$

where r and s are integers. The covariance is always calculated between two variables only. The auto-covariance is the covariance of a variable with its own lagged value. The mean function and the covariance are sufficient to determine and predict a time series by statistical methods. Statistical predictions are calculations that in one or another way are based on the mean and covariance in a variety of refinements and escalating complexity.

Several important concepts are required in time series. One of them is that of *stationarity*. From a qualitative point of view one can see a stationary time series as if it was produced seamless in one cast, while a non-stationary time series appears segmented into noticeably different periods [20]. A time series Y_t is *weakly stationary* (or covariance-stationary) if its mean and auto-covariance functions are independent of time. It is *strictly stationary* if it depends on the intervals separating the dates only, but not on the date itself. Stationarity plays an important role in studying time series with statistical methods. Neural networks deal implicitly with the statistics of the data, and stationarity of statistical distribution of the time series data will improve prediction. Preliminary stationarity tests are not required. Another important concept is that of *ergodicity*. In the simplest possible explanation, an ergodic state is a positive recurrent aperiodic state [21]. That is, that after some time span the same conditions or events re-appear, but the time between the re-appearances is irregular. Financial time series exhibit *ergodic behavior* in the sense that some patterns are repeated in the same way, or very similar, as in the past. The concept often refers to the increasing amount of information that becomes available, as time progresses in the time series, when it is modeled as a stochastic process.

CHAOTIC MODELING. Holyst, Zebrowska and Urbanowicz have modeled financial time series as a combination of stochastic and chaotic series [22]. This is important, as it seems to be pioneering work in investigating the "chaosity" of financial time series, showing that financial time series can contain a chaotic component. Their result leads to the important conclusion that underlying deterministic process may be identified form the time series data and thus short term prediction of that component may be possible. Until now financial time series were assumed to be driven by stochastic processes.

A quick review of concepts from chaos theory will be helpful for understanding this type of model. A chaotic system is a deterministic system that is highly sensitive to initial conditions. Minute changes in initial conditions give different results, which is known as the butterfly effect. The sequence of states or trajectories become aperiodic for a certain range of system parameters, but would be periodic outside those intervals. In the aperiodic intervals the system is said to be in *chaotic regime*. Two chaotic time series can be very different pointwise as for example two trajectories around the same attractor, but be produced by the same dynamical system. Chaotic systems exhibit *ergodic behavior* re-visiting every point in an interval (or arbitrarily close to a point) with varying periodicity. Modeling time series using chaotic models is becoming popular and has several advantages. Time series have their seasonal regularities, as well as aperiodically recurring movements, the cyclic movements. One should notice that, the modeling of chaotic time series can only be based on artificially created models, regardless whether the time series originated from real events or not. Chaos theory, like mathematics in general, is an artifice. What this means is that one would not be able to derive a model empirically, based on the observations, as it is usually done in science, rather create or design a model that fits, knowing that it will be affected by error. While there is wide agreement that there is no conclusive evidence of chaos in financial data, detecting chaotic structures in financial data is complicated by the large noise component [23].

Chaotic time series are often used as benchmarks for financial time series [24] [25]. As indicated earlier, this can be misleading if the time series are considerably different such as the sun-spot time series and a financial time series, which have substantially different noise and trend components. Nevertheless, when the intention is to gauge the predictive ability of neural networks by benchmarking them on similar time series it certainly helps to assess the confiability of the prediction.

For the purpose of predicting financial time series using neural networks, the presence or absence of chaotic components is not really relevant for predicting purposes. The neural networks would be applied in the same way as any other financial time series. While the neural network can predict the time series to whatever its ability to predict, the weights of the network cannot be mapped to specific parameters of time series that are suspected to be chaotic. Indeed the neural network's weights can never be mapped to a time series, chaotic or not, because the networks are structurally different from the phenomena that produce the time series, although both may exhibit the same behavior.

Switching time series

Our last special time series are the *switching time series*. This type of time series originates from different sources. The series is generated by non-stationary processes, as the combination of several, alternately activated sources [20] [26]. A typical feature of switching time series is that their elements are observable, but their sources are not observable, and may even be unknown. The challenge is then to predict when a change (switching) occurs, and identify the source. In financial time series their elements stem from different market phases. Other examples of switching time series are computer network routing, medical and biological applications, video segmentation or handwriting recognition.

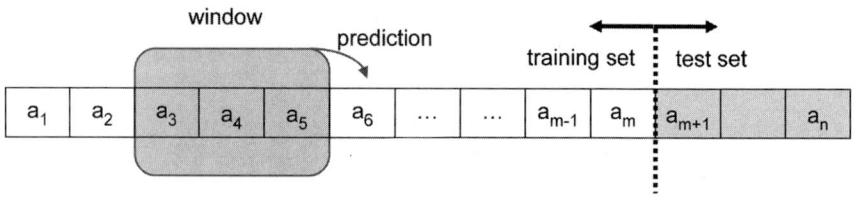

Figure 4. The training and testing partitions of neural networks.

NEURAL NETWORKS FUNDAMENTALS

The idea of using artificial neural networks to predict time series dates back to 1964 when Hu [27] used the adaptive linear neuron for weather forecasting. Research on artificial neural networks languished until the mid 1980s when there was a strong renaissance of interest in neural networks, propelled by enormous growth of cheap computing power.

In the 20 years since the explosive rebirth of interest in artificial neural networks the mathematical foundations of the field have been clarified and artificial neural networks techniques have been applied and tested widely. A core body of knowledge has taken shape and neural networks have gained their place in the toolboxes of engineers, scientists and economists for data analysis and modeling of complex systems.

Neural networks are useful for two reasons: First, they are generic mathematical constructs with a large number of parameters, called weights, that can be adjusted to represent almost any multivariate function and a wide range of dynamic systems. Second, given a set of sample points of an unknown function, there are algorithms for finding the weights such that the neural network approximates the unknown function. Thus artificial neural networks are a data driven technique for modeling.

For the purpose of illustration consider the application of a feedforward neural network to time series prediction. There are three phases: the training phase, the testing phase and the out-of-sample prediction phase. In the training phase, sections (a window) of equal length of time series data are shown to the neural network, together with its expected prediction. For the testing phase, the neural network is shown new sections of data, and its prediction is compared to the value known from the data. This is illustrated in Figure 4. The testing phase provides a measure for the confidence of the prediction. Finally in the out-of-sample prediction phase the window with the most recent values of the series is shown to the network to obtain the prediction for an unknown future value of the series. Experience shows that predictions of several steps ahead become increasingly unreliable, thus it is preferred to train the networks for one-step-ahead prediction. Predictions several steps ahead can be made iteratively by successively incorporating the prediction in the input window. However this will amplify the small error in the next value prediction, and the prediction will go off course.

This section introduces the fundamental concepts for understanding the use of neural networks for the prediction of time series. It is written with the non-specialist reader in mind. The mathematics is confined to the minimum needed to convey the concepts correctly. To keep the exposition brief we refrained to provide detailed accounts of the artificial neural network training algorithms, as computer program libraries with a wide range of training algorithms are widely available. Correct use of these programs does not require understanding the full derivations of the training algorithms.

Artificial neural networks

Artificial neural networks are computational constructs inspired by the facts and hypotheses about information processing in natural systems (animals). Animal brains are surprisingly homogeneous in their structure. Under the microscope the cerebral cortex appears as a network of a large number of very similar cells, called neurons that connect through filamentary ramifications to many other neurons.

Each neuron cell has many inputs from other neurons and combines the incoming signals into a single output that is distributed by a long fiber, called the axon, to many other neurons. Signals travel through the neuron in only one direction: from inputs to output. Neuron input and output fibers touch at points called synapses. It is believed that the synapse modulates the signal transmission between nerve cells and that gradual modification of the synapse characteristic result in learning. All neurons appear to do the same type of computation; the differences between neurons are only in the number and characteristics of their synapses.

Following the above model, artificial neural networks consist of many interconnected simple computing elements called artificial neurons. An artificial neuron has many inputs, each characterized by a weight factor that corresponds to the synapse characteristic in natural neurons. "Learning" occurs by modifying the weights for specific inputs. Although inspired by nature, the artificial neuron is a highly simplified mathematical abstraction of a natural neuron. In fact it is not yet certain that it captures the essence of the computation of a natural neuron. Regardless of this ANNs have very useful mathematical properties.

Like natural neurons, artificial neurons are meant to operate concurrently and thus artificial neural networks should be massively parallel computing structures. However hardware implementations of neural networks are not yet widely available and therefore for most applications ANNs are simulated as mathematical models on conventional sequential computers.

Despite the predominant sequential digital simulation of ANNs, parallel signal flow diagrams of ANNs are helpful and widely used for thinking about and understanding the parameterization of the neural network algorithms. Figure 5 shows the flow diagram representation of a so-called feedforward neural network.

There are many different neural net types depending on the kind of neuron being used and how they are interconnected. The two main types of neural networks applicable to time series prediction are feedforward and recurrent neural networks. A range of proven mathematical theorems supports the computational capabilities of each type. Feedforward neural networks can represent almost any kind of continuous multivariate function while recurrent networks are able to mimic almost any dynamic

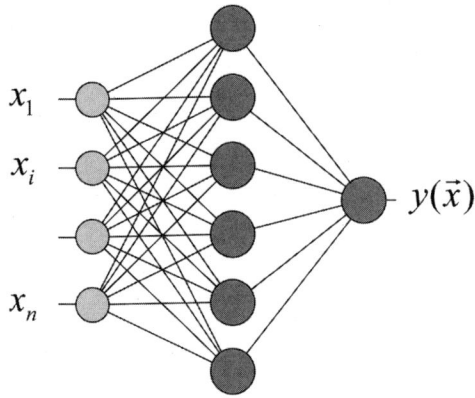

Figure 5. Flow diagram representation of a sample feedforward neural network. Signal flow is from left (input) to right (output). The larger circles represent neurons. Each of the incoming lines to a neuron has an associated weight factor. The smaller circles on the left side are distribution points for the incoming signals.

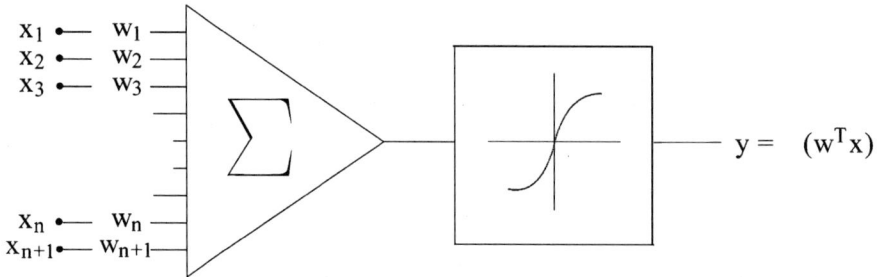

Figure 6. Diagram of a generic artificial neuron.

system. Before going further into neural networks we should first take a look at the artificial neuron by itself.

The single neuron element

Neurons are multiple-input single-output devices. The most widely used artificial neuron is the generalized McCulloch-Pitts neuron illustrated in Figure 6.

The McCulloch-Pitts neuron calculates the weighted sum of its m inputs and then applies a sigmoidal (s-shaped) function $\sigma(\bullet)$ to the sum to produce the output.

$$y(\vec{x}) = \sigma\left(\sum_{i=1}^{m} w_i x_i - b\right) = \sigma(\vec{w}^T \vec{x} - b) = \sigma(h(\vec{x})) \tag{0.14}$$

where $\vec{x}$ is a vector of real numbers, $\vec{w}$ is a vector of weight coefficients characteristic of each neuron and b is the (constant) bias.[1]

The linear discriminant

$$h(\vec{x}) = \sum_{i=1}^{m} w_i x_i - b = \vec{w}^T \vec{x} - b \qquad (0.15)$$

is an *affine* transform of the input space R^m onto the real numbers R. A sigmoidal function is any function $f : R \rightarrow R$ that is bounded and monotonically increasing. In practice either the logistic sigmoid

$$\sigma(h) = \frac{1}{1 + e^{-kh}} \qquad (0.16)$$

or the hyperbolic tangent sigmoid

$$\sigma(h) = \tanh(h) = \frac{1 - e^{-kh}}{1 + e^{-kh}} \qquad (0.17)$$

are almost always used, depending on whether the output should be unsigned or signed. The reason for choosing the sigmoid is that the derivative is simple to compute from the value of the function

$$\sigma'(h) = k\sigma(h)(1 - \sigma(h)) \qquad (0.18)$$

This is useful, as we shall see later, when *training* neural nets. With the sigmoidal transfer function the output of the neuron becomes a non-linear function of its inputs. The neuron output is always between 0 and 1, or -1 and 1 in the case of the hyperbolic tangent sigmoid. The input to a neuron can have any real value, however when it comes from another neuron then it will be limited to the output range of the preceding neuron.

The expression (0.14) for the output of the artificial neuron does not involve time. For many applications of neural networks, such as pattern classification, time is not relevant and the McCulloch-Pitts neuron can be thought of producing its output instantaneously after applying the input. This approximation is even valid for time series prediction. The reason is that values in a time series correspond to discrete moments in time separated by time intervals that are large compared to whatever time the neuron needs to calculate its output.

A more realistic view is that there is some propagation delay of the signal through the neuron. Thus once the input is held stable the output will stabilize at the value of

---

[1] We use vector notation to simplify the mathematical expressions. Vector notation makes it easier to describe operations on large collections of numerical data. A weighted sum is the same as the *scalar* or *dot* product of two vectors; they are a vector of weight coefficients and the data vector. All vectors are by default assumed to be column vectors. Using the rule of matrix multiplication the dot product can be written concisely as the product of the transpose of the weight vector (row vector) times the data vector (column vector).

expression (0.14) after a certain delay Δt. By measuring time in multiples of Δt the output of the neuron at the next time step is

$$y(t + 1) = \sigma(\vec{w}^T \vec{x}(t) - b) \qquad\qquad (0.19)$$

This describes the artificial neuron as a discrete time device. The time dependent behavior of McCulloch-Pitts neuron can be modeled more accurately by a differential equation, which describes how the output changes continuously with time. However, we do not require this level of detail for time series prediction.

Another way of looking at the generalized McCulloch-Pitts neuron is as non-linear extension to linear filters. Linear neurons, that is, neurons with a linear instead of a sigmoidal transfer function are identical to adaptive linear filters widely used in digital signal processing. A linear filter is adaptive when used in conjunction with an algorithm that modifies the weight coefficients to meet some performance criteria. In an artificial neuron it is always assumed that the weights will be modified with training or learning procedure.

Feedforward neural networks

Neural networks like the one in Figure 5 are called *feedforward* because the signal flow is always in one direction from network inputs to network outputs. FFNN are made up of several layers of neurons. The outputs of the previous layer are the inputs for next layer. The outputs of any layer only feed into the next layer but never into the same layer or previous layers. The layers before the output layer are called *hidden* layers. The first layer receives external inputs. In Figure 5 the smaller circles on the left side are not neurons; they are input distribution points from which the neurons in the first layer take their inputs.

Inputs are always supposed to be held constant long enough to let the signals propagate through the network and allow the outputs to stabilize to new values. Transient behavior is not of interest. Feedforward nets represent static mappings of inputs to outputs and there is no explicit reference to time.

There are two important types of feedforward neural networks that are relevant for time series prediction: Multilayer Perceptrons (MLPs) and Radial Basis Function (RBF) networks and their generalizations. Both types of feedforward neural networks are general multivariate function approximators. We will discuss the MLP networks first not only because historically they were studied first, but also because the RBF networks were developed to overcome some deficiencies of the MLP networks that one needs to understand first.

An m-input feedforward neural network takes as input m-dimensional vectors and produces an p-dimensional output of real numbers. For time series prediction and many other applications the required output is a single scalar quantity ($p = 1$). Thus the feedforward network implements a function $f : R^m \rightarrow R$. Neural networks contain a large number of parameters in the form of connection weight coefficients, which gives them their flexibility. Finding appropriate values for a large number of parameters is usually a complex undertaking. The special usefulness of feedforward neural networks arises from the existence of so called *training algorithms* by which the weights of a feedforward neural network can be found so that its output reproduces the value of a function, to any desired degree of accuracy, at a given set of sample points.

The multilayer perceptron

The most widely used feedforward neural network is the Multilayer Perceptron (MLP) named after the neural network computer Rosenblatt built at Cornell University in 1957 [28].

The MLP consists of at least two layers of generalized McCulloch-Pitts neurons. The MLP networks are remarkable because they are universal function approximators [29]. The *Universal Approximation Theorem* establishes the mathematical capabilities of an MLP with one hidden layer of sigmoidal neurons and one linear neuron in the output layer.

Let $\sigma(\bullet)$ be a non-constant, bounded and monotone increasing continuous function. Let I_p be the p-dimensional unit hypercube $[0, 1]^p$ and let $C(I_p)$ be the space of continuous functions on I_p. Then, for any given function $f \in C(I_p)$ there exist values of M, v_i, b_i, w_{ij} such that the function

$$y(x_1, x_2, \ldots, x_p) = \sum_{i=1}^{M} v_i \sigma \left(\sum_{j=1}^{p} w_{ij} x_j - b_i \right) \tag{0.20}$$

converges uniformly to $f(x_1, x_2, \ldots, x_p)$.

The function $y(x_1, x_2, \ldots, x_p)$ is precisely the expression of the output of a feedforward neural network with p inputs, M neurons in the first layer and one neuron in the second layer. In vector notation the same expression is:

$$y(\vec{x}) = \vec{v}^T \sigma (\mathbf{W}^T \vec{x} - \vec{b}) \tag{0.21}$$

where W is the matrix of weight coefficients. By virtue of the theorem an MLP should never need more than one hidden layer to represent a continuous function with any desired degree of accuracy. Furthermore the neuron in the output layer is a linear neuron, that is, the weighted sum of the output of the hidden layer neurons is not fed into a sigmoidal transfer function.

Another way of looking at the MLP expression (0.20) is that the network implements an expression of the unknown scalar function of p variables as linear combination of a set of p-dimensional basis functions, which are the sigmoid functions.

An important point to keep in mind is that the Universal Approximation theorem is an existence theorem, it guarantees the existence of such an approximation, but it does not tell how to find the values of the parameters. We will return to this matter later.

Use of feedforward neural networks

The Universal Approximation theorem tells us that we can represent any continuous multivariate function on a bounded domain as an MLP feedforward neural network. This is useful whenever all we know are the values of a multivariate function at a set of sample points and we would like to know what values the (unknown) function takes at points not in the sample. If we can find the parameters of an MLP that reproduces the known values at the sample points we can evaluate the MLP at any other point and take the result as the value of the unknown function at that point. This is precisely the problem of non-linear multivariate regression.

The problem of multivariate non-linear regression is: Given the set of possibly noisy values $(y_1^*, \vec{x}_1)$, $(y_2^*, \vec{x}_2)$, ..., $(y_q^*, \vec{x}_q)$ of a function on a set of sample points find a function $y(\vec{x}_1)$ that *best* fits the given values. The mean square error (MSE) over the sample points is most often taken as a measure of the best fit. The hypothesis is that the best fit function will also produce good estimates of the unknown function values at points other than those used in fitting (out-of sample estimate). The mean square error minimization principle can be applied to finding the parameters W, $\vec{v}$ and $\vec{b}$ for an MLP with a fixed number M of neurons in the hidden layer. Straight application of gradient descent minimization of the sum of the squares of the errors over the sample set with the function (0.21) leads to the most widely known algorithm for *training* an MLP, namely the *backpropagation* algorithm[2]. Nevertheless, the backpropagation algorithm suffers from slow convergence, and it sometimes fails to converge to the lowest error value. This behavior is a direct consequence of applying gradient descent to an error surface that is far from being a nice parabolic surface for which gradient descent works best. The error surface it the sum of the square of the errors over all training samples, considered as a function of the network weights. In fact the error function looks like numerous stepped terraces crisscrossed by deep and narrow ravines. Clearly, a gradient based method will tend to become stuck on terraces where the gradient is very small. Although the scarcity of true local minima had already been demonstrated in the late 1980s, it is still frequent to find in the literature references to the back propagation algorithm as being susceptible to get stuck in local minima.

During the 1990s much effort was dedicated to improving the convergence of MLP training algorithms. Many improvements to the backpropagation algorithm were proposed and different approaches of error minimization were explored. The most successful are the so-called *second order* algorithms derived from Newton's method for function minimization, and line search algorithms such as the conjugate gradient algorithm. These algorithms are much more complex than the simple backpropagation algorithm but their performance is substantially better. Today the backpropagation algorithm is rarely used. Libraries of improved neural networks training algorithms are widely available; such as for example the Matlab neural networks toolbox.

---

[2]The name backpropagation was given to the algorithm because it works like successive application of a single layer network training algorithm from the output layer backwards to the preceding layers. Unfortunately there is some widespread confusion between training algorithms and network structure. Some authors refer to feedforward networks as "backpropagation networks," which is clearly incorrect as backpropagation is not the only training algorithm for feedforward networks.

Even with a good training algorithm the approximation given by the neural network is by no means unique. Several factors see to that. First, training usually starts from an initial weights estimate, usually a set of small random numbers. Thus repeating training from another initial position will often end up on a somewhat different solution. Second, error optimization algorithms work with a fixed number of neurons in the hidden layer. Thus it is necessary to try different numbers of neurons in the hidden layer before a satisfactory solution can be found. In most cases increasing the number of neurons in the hidden layer will decrease the final error. Putting too many neurons in the hidden layer not only increases training time but also carries the danger of overfitting. Overfitting occurs when the fitted function also fits the noise of noisy data, in this case the error on the training sample is low but it will be much higher on samples that are not from the training set. Overfitting essentially consists in the network *memorizing* the sample set. Finally, even if we avoided overfitting, training a network with a different sample is likely to produce again a somewhat different result. Due to all these factors statistical inference techniques should be applied to the prediction of out-of-sample values. We will discuss this later in the context of validation.

Localized response neurons

The convergence problem of MLP training can be traced back to the shape of the error surface, which in turn is a direct consequence of using sigmoidal McCulloch-Pitts neurons. This is because the logistic sigmoid function tends fairly quickly to the limiting value of 1 as the argument grows in the positive direction. This asymptotic value stretches out to infinity. Matching a set of function values requires the correct combination of the neuron outputs to add up to the value at that point. With the neuron output being non-zero over a half of its domain (the input space), on average, probably half the neurons in the hidden layer contribute to the function value at any one point. Thus the training will have to modify the weights of about M/2 neurons at each training point. Fitting at the next point may destroy the setting at the previous point. A careful juggling is required to reach the simultaneous fitting at all points. In fact in the limit of the sigmoid becoming a step function it has been shown that MLP training is of np-complete complexity [30].

This problem can be overcome by using neurons that have an non-zero output only in a finite volume in input space. Initially multivariate Gaussian functions were used relying on the fact that general function approximation theorems have long been known for Gaussian functions. The output of a symmetric multivariate Gaussian neuron is:

$$y(\vec{x}) = e^{-\frac{\|\vec{x} - \vec{r}\|^2}{2k^2}} \tag{0.22}$$

The Gaussian is centered at the position $\vec{r}$ in the input space, and the neuron output decays with increasing Euclidean distance $\|\vec{x} - \vec{r}\|$ between the input vector $\vec{x}$ and the center $\vec{r}$. In other words the equipotential surfaces of a RBF are hyperspheres.

The position vector $\vec{r}$ of the center of the Gaussian together with the width k of the Gaussian constitute the adaptable parameters of this neuron.

RBF feed forward networks

Networks of radially symmetric localized response neurons are called Radial Basis Function (RBF) networks, for the reason that other than Gaussian radially symmetric functions can and have been used. We will however limit our discussion to Gaussian neurons.

In an RBF network each neuron has its own position in input space. The network output is a linear combination of the output of all the neurons:

$$y(\vec{x}) = \sum_{j=1}^{m} v_j e^{-\frac{\|\vec{x}-\vec{r}_j\|^2}{2k_j^2}} \tag{0.23}$$

The structure of the RBF network is similar to the MLP in that it has a hidden layer of non-linear neurons and a single linear neuron in the output layer.

Training the network implies positioning neurons at the right points in space and giving them the right width such that the added outputs produce a function with a RMS errors on the training data. With this scheme only neurons in the neighborhood of a data point contribute to value at that point. As expected RBF networks train much faster than MLP networks, sometimes up to a hundred times faster. Also, quite importantly, training can be incremental. The error can be reduced by adding another neuron to an already trained network. This cannot be done with an MLP, where changing the number of neurons in the hidden layer requires completely retraining the network.

RBF networks however suffer from another problem, namely the so-called "curse of dimensionality" which makes the number of required neurons grow with the power of the input space. The cause of this is easy to visualize. To represent a function over a domain of input space it is necessary to cover that volume with overlapping RBF neurons. It is like filling a volume with spheres. The number of equal sized spheres that fit into multidimensional cube grows with the power of the dimension of the cube. For example if 9 (3^2) non-overlapping discs (2D spheres) fit in a square of side d, to fill a cubic box of side d with spheres of the same diameter we need 27 (3^3) spheres, and so on.

A function that would suffer most from the dimensionality curse is one that changes sign regularly along every dimension, like an egg carton. The space would have to be filled with contiguous RBF functions of alternate sign. Fortunately many functions of interest have a more benign behavior. Often they oscillate slowly allowing one, or a few, basis functions of the same sign, to cover a large volume in input space, thus pushing back the onset of the curse of the dimensionality. However, as long as the basis functions are radially symmetric the problem does not go away completely even in the case of benign functions.

The corresponding universal approximation theorem for RBF networks requires an RBF neuron for each data point in the sample. This can lead to large networks. The power of local response networks is to use fewer, hopefully much fewer neurons than data points to beat the curse of dimensionality. An obvious strategy is to start out with a small number of neurons and use an error minimization method to adjust the width and centers of the basis functions such as to obtain the lowest error. If the error target is not achieved then more neurons can be added successively centered at the positions where the largest errors occur. Often the initial centers for the neurons are picked at random form the sample set.

A variety of procedures have been used for training RBF networks. Often the positions of the centers are determined and the adaptation of the width and amplitudes, the vs and ks in (0.23), are optimized in separate steps. A clustering technique is used to place the centers, and then a gradient method is used to find the widths and amplitudes that give the lowest error.

There are potential improvements to the simple RBF networks that have yet to be fully utilized. The function fitting capability of a multivariate Gaussian node is enhanced if its equipotential surfaces are ellipsoids with arbitrary orientation, instead of spheres. A linear coordinate transformation in the form of a metric matrix $M_j(\vec{x} - \vec{r}_j)$ that expands and rotates the axes achieves this purpose. Substitution into (0.22) gives

$$y(\vec{x}) = e^{-\frac{\|M_j(\vec{x}-\vec{r}_j)\|^2}{2k^2}} \tag{0.24}$$

and (0.23) becomes the output of a generalized Gaussian network

$$y(\vec{x}) = \sum_{j=1}^{m} v_j \, e^{-\frac{\|M_j(\vec{x}-\vec{r}_j)\|^2}{2k_j^2}} \tag{0.25}$$

This generalization increases the number of parameters per neuron that characterize the shape of the function from one to the square of the input dimension.

It is also possible to combine sigmoid functions in such a way that they create a localized function similar to ellipsoidal Gaussian neurons but with even greater representation capability. These Local Cluster Neural Networks (LCNN) also have a matrix of dimension equal to the input space that characterizes the shape of the local cluster function [31]. However studies have shown that the number of required local cluster neurons decreases drastically in comparison with the number of required spherical neurons for a given level of accuracy more than compensating the increase of number of parameters per neuron.

Moreover, LCNN networks as well as ellipsoidal Gaussian networks can be trained effectively by optimizing the centers and the function shape parameters at the same time with an optimized gradient descent algorithm.

Time delay neural networks

Time series prediction can be cast into a multivariate regression problem suitable for solution with a feedforward neural network. When a conventional feed-forward neural

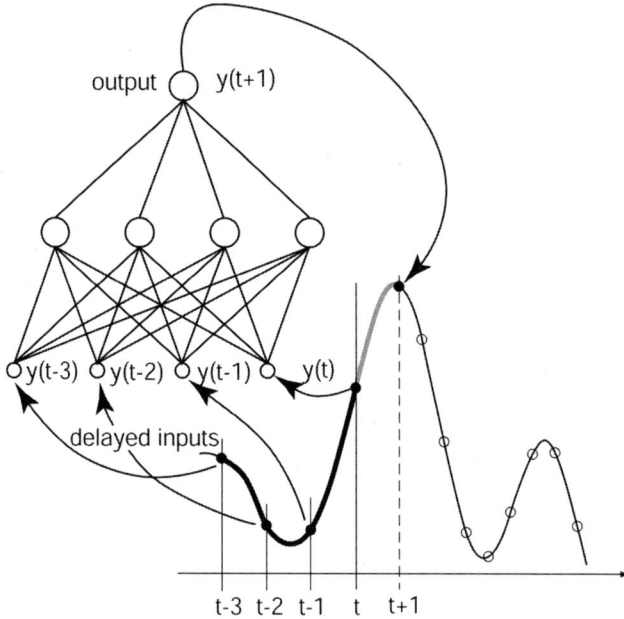

Figure 7. Diagram of a Time Delay Feed Forward Network with one hidden layer, where the input is a sequence of recent values of the time series.

net is used for time series prediction it is called a Time Delay Neural Network (TDNN) [32][33].

In multivariate regression each input to the feedforward neural network receives the value of one of the independent variables. In a time series we do not have independent variables, we only have a sequence of values. However the idea behind using a feedforward NN for time series prediction is simple. To similar *patterns* of the m most recent values of the time series there should correspond similar values of the next data in the series. Thus there should be a mapping of the vector of m most recent values, now considered as independent variables to the next values. This mapping that can be learned by a feedforward NN. Thus the feedforward network becomes a predictor as defined in equation (0.5).

It is necessary to prepare the time series data in a special way for input into a TDNN. An input sample for the TDNN consists of a *window* containing a chosen number m of successive values of the time series. The most recent value in the window is called the current value $y(t)$ and the preceding values are called the delayed values, $y(t-1), y(t-2), \ldots, y(t-m-1)$, as shown in Figure 7.

Every *window* of n values $y(t), y(t-1), \ldots, y(t-n-1)$ into the time series record is an input vector for the neural network that will output a prediction $\hat{y}(t+1)$ for $y(t+1)$.

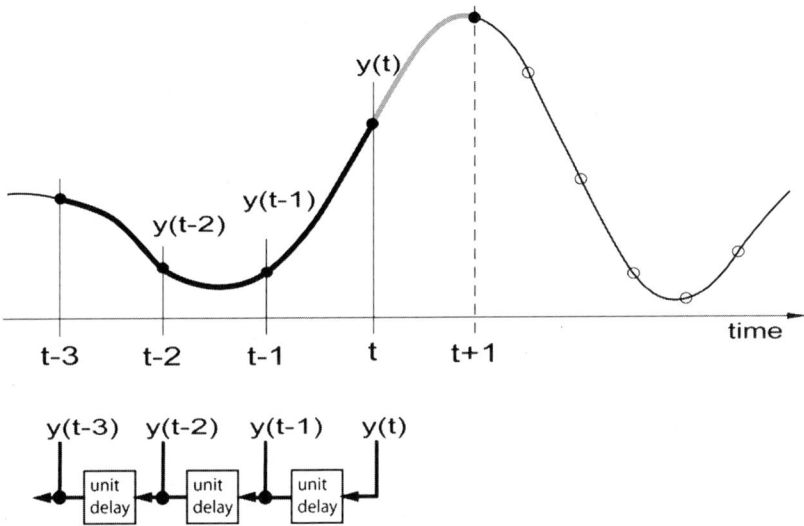

Figure 8. Illustration of the working of a tapped delay line. The most recent time series datum is fed into the delay at one end (right). Data remain in each delay stage for one time step (unit delay) after which all data are simultaneously shifted to their next (left) delay stage as the next new datum comes in. The result is a window of the most recent values of the time series available on the taps between the delay stages.

An alternative view is to feed the time series signal into a tapped delay line consisting of a sequence of unit delays with the neural network connected to points in between the delays as shown in Figure 8. The delay line acts as a short-term memory for the recent values of the series. In this fashion the time series is applied to the first input and then propagates through the delays from one input to the next. The effect will be that the network input window sweeps over the values of the time series moving the window one position at each time step.

The method just described for using feedforward networks for time series prediction was initially purely empirical but has later found a theoretical justification by Takens' embedding theorem [34]. Takens' embedding theorem has to do with creating a multidimensional state variable form the observation of a time series of an observable quantity of a dynamic system. The state variable of dimension d is simply created by associating with each time t, a state vector $\vec{x}$ consisting of the segment $y(t-1), y(t-2), \ldots, y(t-d)$ of the time series.

Although dynamic systems are governed by differential equations it is also possible to describe a dynamic system by a mapping of state $\vec{x}_t$ at a time $t = k$ to the state $\vec{x}_{k+1}$ at $t = k + 1$

$$\vec{x}_{k+1} = f(\vec{x}_k) \qquad (0.26)$$

Repeated application of f creates a trajectory in the systems state space.

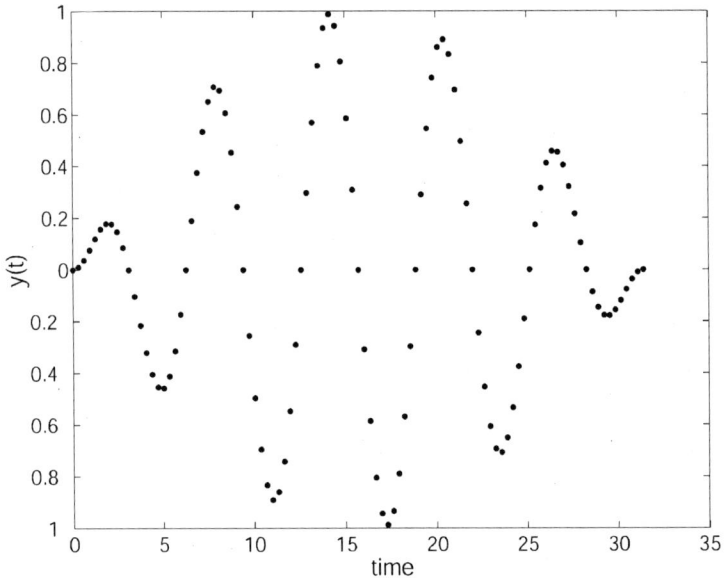

Figure 9. Time series obtained from the modulated sine function $y(t) = \sin(t)\sin(t/10)$.

Let $x(1), x(2), \ldots$ be the first coordinate of a trajectory of a dynamic system corresponding to the mapping f that has an attractor of dimension m. Takens' theorem says that if $d \geq 2m + 1$ then the time-delay vectors

$$\vec{x}(k) = (x(k + d), x(k + d - 1), \ldots, x(k)) \tag{0.27}$$

will accurately reconstruct the attractor of the dynamic system corresponding to f. More precisely if the attractor A is a m-dimensional manifold then the points $\vec{x}(k)$ give an embedding of A in R^d.

Thus it is possible to interpret the time series as a one-dimensional projection of the mapping f [35]. The task of the neural network is to learn one component of the mapping $f : \mathrm{R}^d \leftarrow \mathrm{R}^d$

$$x_1(k + 1) = f_1(\vec{x}(k)) \tag{0.28}$$

Figure 9 shows the (noiseless) time series generated from the function $y(t) = \sin(t)$ $\sin(t/10)$. The trajectory in a state space of dimension $d = 3$ generated from the time series is shown in Figure 10 and Figure 11. Clearly the attractor is of dimension $d = 2$ embedded in three dimensions.

Figure 12 shows the result of training a TDNN network with 8 hidden units and a window of 4 time steps to predict one step ahead for the modulated sinusoid time series. The network was trained with the first 20% of the data after which it could

State space trajectory (d=3)

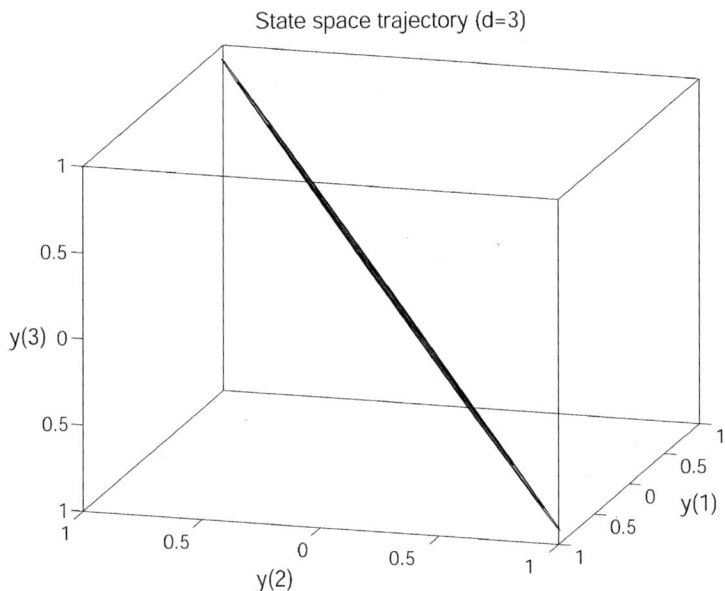

Figure 10. View of the attractor for a modulated sine time series, embedded in a three-dimensional state space. The view shows that attractor in profile demonstrating the it is indeed two-dimensional.

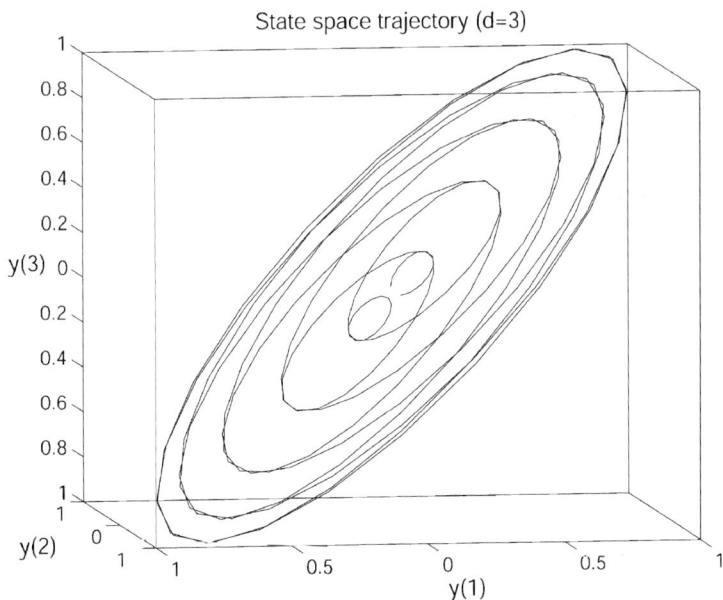

State space trajectory (d=3)

Figure 11. Front view of the attractor for the modulated sine time series showing details of its two-dimensional structure.

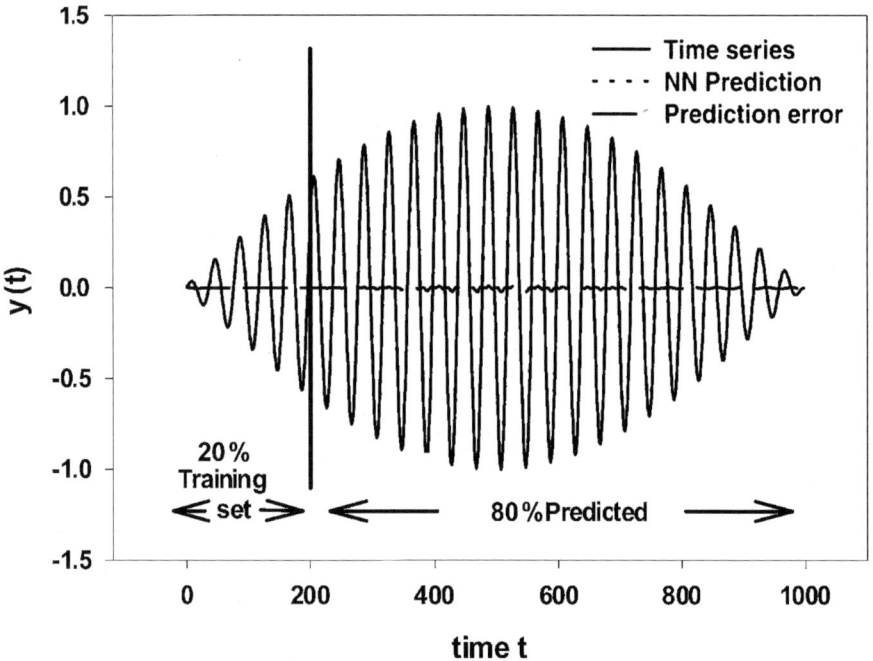

Figure 12. TDNN prediction of a modulated sinusoidal time series. The network was trained on the first 20% of the data and was used to make one-step-ahead prediction on the rest of the data. In this figure the prediction totally overlaps with the time series, showing only one solid line.

accurately predict the next value for the remaining 80% of the data. Without having *seen* a sample of the time series where the amplitude decreases, it was able to capture the shape of the modulation envelope from an initial segment of the time series. In this figure the prediction totally overlaps with the time series, showing both curves as one solid line. The horizontal curve in the middle of the figure is the prediction error.

It is also interesting to note that each of the neurons in the hidden layer of TDNN acts as a finite impulse response filter (FIR) feeding into a sigmoid non-linearity. In addition to this, some authors have suggested to replace *each weight* in a FFNN by an FIR filter, that is, a sequence of delays and associated weights. The comparative study by Bone et al. suggests that FIR synapses are a complication that is not justified by the results [36].

One of the design parameters for a TDNN network is the size of the time window. Too big a window will increase the computational effort without any improvement in prediction accuracy. Too small a window may not capture the correlations that exist in the data. The optimal window size is data dependent and there are no theoretical principles for determining the optimal window size a priory. Trials have to be made with different sizes to find the smallest size that gives a desired prediction accuracy. The size of the time window determines how far back in time the series is remembered.

Recurrent networks

In recurrent neural networks there are no restrictions on the interconnection between the neurons. The output of a neuron may feed into any other neuron in the network including itself. A feedback loop occurs when there is a connection from the output of a neuron to one of its own inputs, either directly or through a chain of neurons in the network; hence the name recurrent. In the case of a direct connection one of the inputs to the neuron at time t is its output at time $t - 1$, which is caused by the inputs to the neuron at time $t - 1$. Since the inputs at time t contain the output of the neuron at time $t - 1$ the neuron's output at time t is affected by the neuron's output at all previous times. The dynamics of a network with recurrent connections implicitly provides a *memory* of previous inputs to the network. The immediate consequence for time series prediction is that there is no need for a delay line on the inputs of a recurrent neural network for making the history of earlier inputs bear on the current output.

The feedback loops in recurrent networks cause a complex dynamic behavior of the networks that is far from being completely understood. Despite of the complex dynamics it has been possible to prove that recurrent neural networks can approximate almost any dynamical system, discrete [37] or continuous [38].

Because of the great diversity of the possible interconnections patterns there are many different types of recurrent neural networks. We will limit the discussion to some of the simpler recurrent neural networks that have been applied to time series prediction.

The elman net

A simple way of constructing a feedback network is to add feedback loops to the MLP as proposed by Elman [39]. Elman adds a set of *context* units that buffer the output of the hidden layer units, as shown in Figure 13. The context units feed again into all of the hidden layer units in the same way as the input units. In this way the output of the hidden units is applied in the next time steps to the hidden units along side with new input.

At each time step the input to the network consists only of the current value of the time series. Contrary to the normal FFNN, the training data for the time series has to be presented to the network in sequence. At a given time the output of the context units is dependent on the sequence of values previously presented to the network. Instead of feeding back the outputs from the hidden layer the network output can also be feed back to the hidden layer via a context unit, or one context unit for every output in case there are more than one output. This form of feedback network, proposed by Jordan, is known as a Jordan network [40].

Training recurrent networks

Recurrent neural networks require more complex training algorithms than feedforward networks. However the Elman and Jordan networks can still be trained with the same algorithms as the FFNN. This is not the case for the more general recurrent

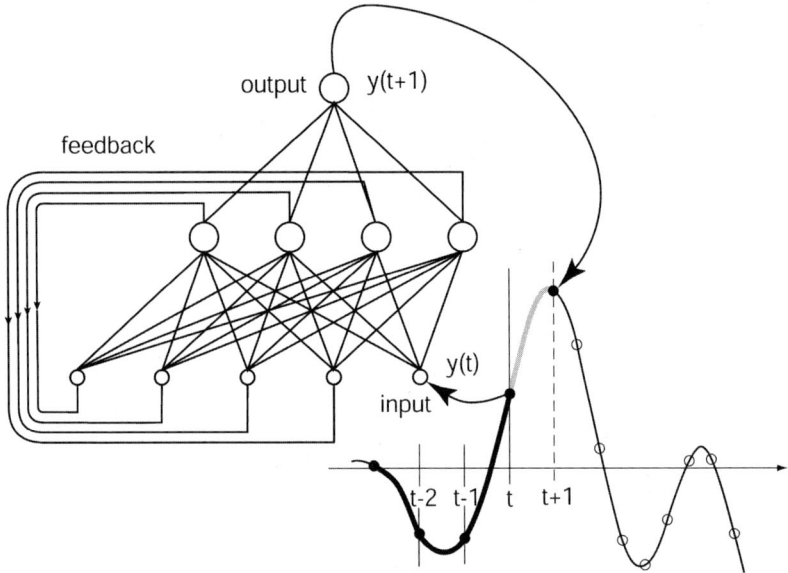

Figure 13. The Elman net captures the temporal context by feeding the output of the hidden layer units back to the *context* input units.

networks. There are two main algorithms for training recurrent neural networks: Backpropagation-through-time (BPTT) and real-time recurrent learning (RTRL). As fully recurrent networks appear not to have any advantages over the TDNN or Elman and Jordan, partially recurrent networks, we will not explain these algorithms here.

Relative performance of different neural network architectures

In a comparative study of the performance of TDNN, Jordan and Elman networks for predicting chaotic time series Mandziuk and Mikolajczak [24] found that there was little difference between the performance of Jordan and Elman networks. The best performance was obtained for TDNN networks with two hidden layers.

Support vector machines

A variant of feedforward neural network algorithms with roots in statistical learning theory known as Support Vector Machines (SVM) have received much attention in recent time because of their good performance in classification tasks. The idea behind support vector machines is to the decision surface by mapping the input space into a high dimensional feature space. This idea can also be applied to regression. In this case the time window data will be approximated by a linear function in higher dimensional space. The fitting criterion is the usual least square error and the neural network is called a LS-SVM.

Contrary to the popularity of SVM for classification the application of SVM to regression is still in its infancy. Van Gestel et al. have used LS-SVM to estimate the error (volatility) in the one-step-ahead prediction of the US short-term interest rate and the DAX30 index [41]. The advantage of the LS-SVM formulation is that expressions for the error can be obtained and the Bayesian inference framework can be applied to the estimation of the error.

Validation

From the earlier description of using feedforward neural networks for regression it might appear that all we need to do is to train a neural network with a set of example input-output pairs until it reproduces the output corresponding to each input with desired accuracy. Once this has been achieved we can obtain the unknown function value for any other input (out-of sample input). The problem with this procedure is that we have no indication about the trustworthiness of the network's answer for out-of-sample inputs. Note that only when we are certain that the data contain no noise can we expect to obtain negligible small RMS error on the training set.

The first step towards obtaining some indication of the accuracy on out-of-sample network outputs is to set apart some of the available input-output examples for testing the network performance. The data in this test set are not used for training. The desirable situation is that the RMS error of the network output on the test set and the error on training set are roughly the same. An error on the test set that is significantly larger than the error on the training set indicates that the network is been tuned too closely to the particular values of the training set. One solution to the problem of overtraining is to set apart a third set from the available data, the so-called *validation* set. During training the error on the validation set is monitored and training is stopped when the error on the training set drops below the error on the validation set. This technique is known as *early stopping*. An alternative is to reduce the number of neurons in the hidden layer of the feedforward network until the error on the training set does not decrease with further training time. It is known that the more neurons there are in the hidden layer, the more accurately the network can fit every data point. Essentially what this does is to force the appropriate level of smoothing by limiting the networks capacity of closely following the rapid variations of the data.

The achievable smallest error depends on the combinations of many factors and their possible multiple choices, such as the number of hidden nodes in a feedforward neural network, the parameters of the neuron transfer functions, the particular split of the data set into training and test set, and the parameters of the training algorithm. Furthermore each training session is started with a random initialization of the weights. Therefore for a particular data set, there arise infinitely many training situations, each characterized by a particular combination of choices of the above factors. The consequence is that the output of a neural network, for a particular input can be treated statistically as a random variable. Any output obtained is just one sample from the possible outputs of a population of training situations.

Given all these rather arbitrary decisions one would like to know what confidence can be put on the on the output of a trained neural network. Variances of estimators of characteristics of the population, such as the mean, can usually be inferred from a set of samples if the underlying probability distribution is known[3]. In the case of neural networks this probability distribution is not known.

The bootstrap technique allows the estimation of variance and other measures of error of an estimator without having to know the underlying probability distribution. Bootstrapping is a method for statistical inference where empirical sample distributions are generated for statistical analysis. The bootstrap technique applied to an available sample of *n elements* consists of drawing a large number of bootstrap *replicas* of the sample, each obtained by drawing with the same likelihood and with replacement, *n* elements of the original sample. The estimator is calculated for each bootstrap sample and from this the variance of the estimator is calculated with respect to the average of the estimator over the bootstrap samples.

For example, consider the RMS value of the error of prediction of a time series by a neural network. An estimate of the variance could be obtained by applying the bootstrap technique to the sample of RMS of values obtained by training the network *n* times with randomly initialized weights.

Bagging is the idea of the bootstrap method applied to the training set. Multiple Bootstrap replicas of the training set are created and used for training. The output of all the networks is averaged to obtain the output value for a given input vector.

Cross-validation

The common practice for evaluating the performance of a neural network in an regression or classification is to split the available set of input–output data pairs into three sets: the training set, the validation set and the test set. The training set is used for fitting the weights (training) of the network, the neural network performing best on the validation set is used to test how well the network reproduces the output for inputs not used in training (test set). An alternate method is a jackknife technique that consists of using all except one input-out pair for training, and using the remaining pair for testing. This is done for many times always leaving out a different pair.

DATA PREPARATION FOR NEURAL NETWORKS

The preparation of the data for time series analysis depends much on what the focus of interest is, and the granularity or level of resolution required. If the focus interest is on a monthly or yearly resolution, then it is covered by the indexes and seasonal movements techniques, and things like trend or random fluctuations should be removed or smoothed. Larger scale economies would rather be interested in trends or cyclic movements. Much of the preparation depends on the techniques to be applied.

When using statistical methods much of the data is preprocessed. In this process some of potential information is removed, intentionally or not. This is done under the assumption that the lost information is not relevant. This happens to a much lesser

---

[3] An *estimator* for a characteristic of the population is the value for the characteristic, i.e. a parameter computed on a sample, if the sample is sufficiently large, which in turn depends on the variance. The sample mean is an estimator for the mean of the population.

scale when using neural networks. Still, to obtain good results with neural networks the input data have to meet some requirements.

Results can be biased by the transformations that are required for pre-processing the data. While the choice of pre-processing depends on the data, the widely practiced and recommended pre-processing of the data such as detrending with a moving average can introduce autocorrelations in the data, which in turn can affect the predictions [17]. A systematic analysis to gauge possible correlations introduced to the data among the variety of time series analysis techniques is yet to be done.

The time series data preparation suitable for input to neural networks comprises four steps

- Detrending
- Smoothing
- Normalizing and scaling
- Structuring the data.

Detrending

Given their importance, detrending and smoothing alternatives were explained earlier. Detrending is important for neural networks especially when the trend is strongly increasing or decreasing. Otherwise the neural network would predict just the dominant trend, and not the other features that we might be interested in. The reason is that neural networks have a finite output range, which is determined by the neuron transfer function used. For sigmoidal neurons this range is either $(0, 1)$ or $(-1, 1)$, for Gaussian functions it is $(0,1)$. Although these values can be scaled up or down when linear neurons are used in the output layer, which is mostly the case, the output range will always be finite. In practice the number of data points in a time series will be finite and consequently the values of the series will be bounded. It is customary, but not necessary to normalize the data, i.e. scale the data to the range $(0, 1)$ or $(-1, 1)$.

For time series that do not have a strong trend component, like for example the sunspot series no scaling of the data is required. However for series with a pronounced trend the finiteness of the output range will cause the network to become insensitive to the variations in the time series in the region where the values are small compared to the regions where the values are large. This is particularly pronounced when the time series has an exponential trend, which is often the case with financial series such as stock indices. In such cases it is necessary to remove the trend, at least partially to obtain a series that does not have pronounced differences in the range of variation of the values across the whole time span of the series. This also applies when the values of the series are large in relation to their variations. In this case the series has a large constant trend that should be subtracted.

Smoothing

The other preprocessing operation commonly applied to time series is smoothing. Neural networks, when used properly (see the discussion of overfitting earlier in this chapter), do not require strong noise filtering capabilities and smoothing of the data. However if short-term variations are not of interest smoothing the series may help to reduce the time required for training.

Normalizing and scaling the data

Normalizing or scaling the data is common practice in data analysis for several reasons, for example to easy comparison among different data sets. For neural networks normalization is only required when the output neurons have a sigmoidal transfer function, which is mostly the case when the purpose is classification. With a sigmoidal transfer function in output neuron it is advisable that the output values avoid the saturation regions of the sigmoids. By scaling them to be between $(-0.8, 0.8)$ or between $(0.2, 0.8)$. [6] [24].

Normalizing and scaling can be done in the following way.

$$NV = \frac{DV - md}{MD - md} \times (UppN - lowN) + lowN \qquad (0.29)$$

DV	Data value
NV	Normalized value
MD	Maximum data value
md	minimum data value
UppN	upper normalized boundary
lowN	lower normalized boundary

In time series prediction, linear transfer functions are preferred for the output neurons. Scaling is not necessary in this case, as the weight adaptation in training can undo any scaling.

Structuring the data

So far the research on time series prediction with neural networks indicates that perhaps the best predictive capability for time series is achieved with time-delay feed-forward neural nets. For such a network an input an input sample consists of a *window* containing a chosen number m of successive values of the time series. The most recent value in the window is called the current value $y(t)$ and the preceding values are called the delayed values, $y(t - 1)$, $y(t - 2)$, ... $y(t - m - 1)$, as shown in Figure 7.

Each input to the network will correspond to a specific delay. It is convenient to think that each input to the feed-forward neural network is connected to the next by a delay line. In this fashion the time series is applied to the first input and then propagates through the delays from one input to the next. The effect will be that the network input window sweeps over the values of the time series. At each time step the network senses one current value and the corresponding set of delayed values. From these inputs the net will be trained to predict a future value of the series. In a one-step-ahead prediction this value is the next value $y(t + 1)$ in the series.

c1	c 2	c3	...	...	...	...	
c2	c3	c4	...	...	...		...
c3	c4	c5	...	...		...	...
...	...	Price Training	data		...	Test	data
v1	v2	v3	...	...	...	...	...
v2	v3	v4	...	...	...	...	...
v3	v4	v5	...	...	...	...	...
...	Volume	Training	data		...	...	...
p1	p2	p3	...	prediction		...	...

Figure 14. Schematic diagram for the neural network input data preparation, shifting left by one position in each row.

The data input set is based on detrended, normalized and scaled time series. We have to train the network by telling it that on input of small section of time series (the window), $(y(t-m), y(t-m+1), \ldots, y(t))$ it must predict $y(t+1)$.

For practical purposes, we can think of the input data as a large data array A of m (the window size) rows, and $N-m$ columns, where N is the size of the time series. For the case of a one-day ahead prediction, the data block is arranged such that the first row contains the data $y(1)$ to $y(N-m+0)$. The second row is shifted by one data point and contains the data $y(2)$ to $y(N-m+1)$. Consecutive rows are always shifted by one place, until the last row which starts with $y(m)$ to $y(N-1)$ or less. The last few elements of data have to be discarded to fill all columns after shifting the data to the left in one position in each row, as shown in the diagram in Figure 14. Each data input vector will be a column of size m of the array A. We can think now of another row that contains the data points $y(m+1)$ to $y(N)$. This row will contain the expected predictions that the network must learn for each of the columns above. For a multivariate data set, the matrix A would be appended with another set of rows with the same structure as A, but with data values from the other variable, and so on. For each variable, another block of rows is appended. The order of the two or more layers of blocks is not relevant.

For recurrent networks this step is not needed as only one value, the most recent one, of the series is required as input for the prediction. However these data have to be input to the network in the correct time order, both when training and when predicting. This is because the output of a recurrent network not only depends on the current input but also on what has been input to the network before. In contrast, the data vectors for the TDNN are independent can be input in any order. That is the output of the network only depends of the input vector (window) and not what has been input before.

The last thing that remains to do, is to decide how much of the data will be training data, and how much will be testing data. This has been explained in the neural network section under *Validation*.

Time series and neural networks applications

This section focuses on recent applications of neural networks to financial time series reported in the literature. Neural networks can be used in financial time series for different purposes. The design factors of a neural networks such as the architecture, the input variables, the amount of training data, the span of the prediction, all have a significant impact on the predicting performance of the NN. In this section we look at the purposes of the application, the type of network used, and the performance achieved. The aim is to provide insight into what has been done, to be able build upon previous expertise and to open new windows of research to the research community or newcomers to this area.

The predominant application has been the one-step ahead prediction of the time series. Recently several researches have extended the use of neural networks to the prediction of the volatility of asset prices.

Time series forecasting with neural networks has started only a bit over two decades ago. An extensive and elaborate survey was compiled by Zhang et al. in 1996, summarizing the then state of the art of forecasting with ANNs [2]. Zhang et al. include in their work not only financial time series, but also environmental science time series, such as river flow, sunspots, transport time series such as air traffic, and others, such as student performance. Based on the findings of the works surveyed, they concluded that the popular FFNN has several weaknesses. One of them is that the training parameters of the neural network play a critical role in the performance of the network, and that the neural network's learning rate depends on the complexity of the data. A range of modified backpropagation emerged and improvements in the predictive performance were achieved. The improvements were achieved in particular due to introduction of improved optimization algorithms.

Zhang et al. then suggested a future introduction of optimization techniques such as genetic algorithms, simulated annealing, or other optimization algorithms to facilitate the search of an appropriate objective function that works well for the prediction. Expansion of neural networks to Fuzzy neural networks or wavelet neural networks was also deemed as promising. However so far these techniques did not have the expected impact.

The conclusion from Zhang et al. exhaustive survey was that for the cases of the financial time series covered in their survey, the ANNs outperformed statistical models' predictions. In some cases of weekly, monthly and hourly exchange rate time series the performance was better in at least one order of magnitude, in others it performed only marginally better, but monthly or weekly data were better predicted than annual data. The stark differences in performance could be attributed to possible inadequate choice of network, and inappropriate or lack of data preparation.

In the following years, since Zhang's et al. compilation in 1988, many applications of time series and neural networks have been reported. However, not as many as one could wish do belong to the financial time series. While most of the research done thereafter, consistently agrees that the predictive performance of neural networks is higher than traditional methods, the focus is now on improving those methods and expanding to modeling complex events such as multivariate, switching, and chaotic time series.

Types of applications

To make the discussion about applications and neural networks performance more specific and meaningful, we have grouped the applications into three groups:

- Forecasting
- Multivariate models
- Switching time series
- Chaotic time series

Within these groups we look at the performance of both, using sole neural networks and neural networks combined with other techniques such as Fuzzy neural networks and Genetic Algorithms.

A substantial interest seems to lay in applications of forecasting stock market and currency exchange rates. Additional effort goes into probing for indirect or complex information that can be contained in a time series, and which is reflected in the prediction. In those cases the time series is then modeled as a multivariate time series, rather than a simple predicting the future by looking at the past. Modeling the time series as a multivariate series means that there is correlation in the data, with the aim of extracting this implicit information it to aid in decision taking.

Forecasting stock market indices and currency exchange rates

Forecasting is based on the motivation to produce predictions of future events as accurate as possible, based on information of past events, for financially beneficial purposes.

Reported work on financial time series prediction using neural networks often shows a characteristic one step shift relative to the original data. This seems to imply a failure of the neural network, because a shift corresponds to a random walk prediction. To investigate this Sitte & Sitte set up a comprehensive, systematic analysis of different time delay Neural Networks (TDNN) and Elman neural networks applied to the detrended S&P 500 time series [7][42]. Systematic short-term correlation experiments were done with networks trained to predict one day ahead to detect a mapping of previous values on current values if such a mapping is supported by the data. To find the best performing predictor, the input to the neural networks was varied for each prediction run by changing the window size, ranging from one day to up to a month back in time. The networks were trained on the first 60% of data, with weights initialized randomly, and tested on the remaining 40%. In another group of experiments the neural networks were arranged by systematically changing the combinations of window size and number of nodes in the hidden layer between 2 and 32 each. For the Elman recurrent networks the number of context units was progressively increased from 2 to 16. All the networks were trained and tested on the same portion of the data set. Finally, to investigate the influence of the size of the training set on the prediction capability of the networks the proportion of the data used for training were changed by incrementing the training proportion in steps of 10%. For each of the experimental runs three RMSE errors calculated separately for both, the training set and test set; the recorded errors were the random walk prediction error, the TDNN prediction error, and the difference between the neural networks prediction and the random walk prediction. Calculations of the autocorrelation between the data shifted for up to 50 days revealed that there are no short-term correlations in the data.

The result from these systematic experiments were be summarized as follows [7] [42]:

• For all parameters tried, both, the TDNN's and Elman nets' best prediction was the random walk prediction
• Increasing the window size or the number of nodes in the hidden layer of TDNNs, or more context units in Elman networks had no effect on the prediction performance.
• Increasing the training set did not improve the predictions
• The randomness of the residual time series was supported by statistical tests

Prediction errors for several low order polynomial extrapolations were also calculated, but their predictions were significantly worse than the random walk predictor.

In essence this research indicated that the random walk prediction behavior is not a limitation of the network, but may be a characteristic of the time series. It is consistent with findings of decades of statistical analysis. One should be aware that the S&P 500 index is a special case in that it is an average of a large number of stocks and therefore the deviations of individual stocks from the economy's exponential growth have been averaged out. The economic environment affects individual stocks differently and many do not track the overall exponential growth of the economy.

These results do not exclude the possibility of other tools being able to extract more information, for lucrative purpose, as the purpose of this study was not to find a "better way" to predict stock markets, but to study the predictability of neural networks.

A different stock market prediction was sought by Plikynas et al. in their work on neural networks applied to forecasting stock exchange indices [43]. The particular interest was to investigate the construction of compound models that include macroeconomic data due to their possible influence on the indices for better predicting Lithuania's National Stock Exchange (LNSE) indices. To do this, measures to estimate the accidentness of index movements derived by using analysis for entropy and correlation. The data were then preprocessed by filtering out model input variables such as LNSE indices, macroeconomic indicators, Stock Exchange indices of other countries such as the USA—Dow Jones and S&P, EU—Eurex, Russia—RTS. Different backpropagation ANN learning algorithms with variable configurations, iteration numbers and data form-factors were applied to find the best approximation and forecasting capabilities. A linear discriminant analysis was used to compare the autoregressive, autoregressive causative and causative trend model performance of the ANN. The results from this study have shown a high sensitivity to ANN parameters. In particular the NN-MLP method achieved one or two orders of magnitude higher prediction performance than the simple autoregressive trend model. It is anticipated that with the appropriate optimization techniques, the neural networks could outperform the multidimensional linear regression.

The work of Pantazopoulos et al. [44] uses an elaborate neurofuzzy approach to aid in trading strategies involving stocks and options. The options trading strategy is based on neural networks predictors from the daily prizes of movements of the index, which can be *up, down,* or *same.* Trading strategies are tested on their profitability using historical data of the S&P 500. The prediction is typically a few days ahead. The returns reported on the simulated trades appear extremely high. It is unclear from their paper how the neural networks were trained. Two methodologies were set up. One methodology is set up for the stock trading strategies with a FFNN with two hidden layers and a single output layer. For the other methodology a set of three neural networks with recurrent connections, with three outputs each, were used. The fuzzy part consisted in training the networks with three values representing the center, and the upper (center $+\alpha$) and lower (center $-\alpha$) limits of a triangular membership function. The outputs of the trained networks are then combined into crisp value using a fuzzy (centroid) average. Neither the motivation of this complicated procedure nor a comparison with a standard method were given.

Tino, Schittenkopf and Dorffner, compared Markov models and Elman recurrent networks for the prediction of volatility of DAX and FTSE stock index for the purpose of options trading [45]. They quantized the volatility to two levels, up and down. The reason being that earlier studies by the same authors showed them that predictors operating on continuous time series performed worse than those operating on quantized series. The two possible input symbols were coded as a pair of digits one position for each value, that is (1,0) and (0,1). The networks also had two outputs, one for each of the two quantized values. The performances of the predictors were evaluated by the average profit per day obtained by a trading strategy based on the predictions. They found that the Elman net never performed much better than the simpler Markov models. They also found in a separate study that TDNN never outperformed the Markov models.

Walczak has investigated the effects of different sizes of training sample sets on forecasting currency exchange rates [10]. This work demonstrates that, given an appropriate amount of historical knowledge, neural networks can forecast future currency exchange rates with 60 percent accuracy, while those neural networks trained on a larger training set have a worse forecasting performance. In addition to higher-quality forecasts, the reduced training set sizes reduce development cost and time. Different training sets are used with training data spanning between 1 and 21 years. Best performers were with 1 to 5 years training data, with neural networks with three input values, one hidden layer with five nodes and one single output value.

Kodogiannis and Lolis developed improved models to forecast currency exchange rates, for one and multiple step ahead predictions [46]. They compared several models on conventional neural networks prediction using MLP, RBF, Dynamic neural networks such as autoregressive neural networks (ARNN) and memory Elman (M.ELMAN) and Neurofuzzy systems. Results compared with real data revealed that Adaptive Fuzzy Logic Systems have a slightly better performance than MLPs or Elman nets.

Hu and Tsoukalas predict the volatility of the European Monetary System (EMS) exchange rates, by using a combination of four conditional volatility models and an neural networks [47]. The input data spanned 15 years for the US dollar and 10 European currencies. The prediction capability was tested and compared on out of sample predictions. The neural networks used was an MLP with one input layer with four input nodes, one hidden layer with four nodes, and one output layer with one node, and additionally 5 bias nodes. Inputs were normalized to the (0, 1) range. The RMSE and RMAE were recorded. The prediction results were mixed, for the EMS currency rates as a managed float regime, the one for the conditional volatility models predicted better, but for crisis times the neural network predicted better, in the sense that it had consistently lower RMSE than the other models.

Singh compares the forecasting performance of a non-NN long memory pattern recognition system with the performance of neural networks [48]. The pattern recognition system uses conventional pattern recognition models. The introduced concept is based on the observation that most financial markets have a long memory, in the sense that whatever occurs today, affects the future forever. Singh claims that such long-term data correlations cannot be detected with predictors that use only a short portion of historic data to predict. A comparison is performed with tests using data from the DAX, FTSE, FRACAC, EOE and S&P 500 series for a duration of eight years. Two neural networks are developed, one to predict the up or down change in direction, the other for predicting the index returns. Each of the neural networks has five inputs, and one output. The nodes in the hidden layer were incremented stepwise to find optimum. For training 90% of the data was used, and 10% for testing. Training is done with the backpropagation algorithm. The result of this study is that in general the proposed pattern recognition system comes close to an neural networks in predictive performance, but still requires further refinement.

Multivariate models

There are two ways in which time series can be modeled: univariate or multivariate. One is in the way we have always been told to distinguish between uni and multivariate models, that is by having one or more than one variable. For example, if we model a time series as the cost of stocks, then it is univariate, but if we model it with cost and volume, it becomes multivariate. Another, perhaps less intuitive way is associated with neural networks. It consists in taking a window, that is a set of, say, three or five successive readings of the time series data points at a time. These lots of three or five or whatever number of data points can be interpreted as a multidimensional vector, and would input to a neural network with three (or five) input nodes. However, these

Volume Predictions

(a)

Cost Predictions

(b)

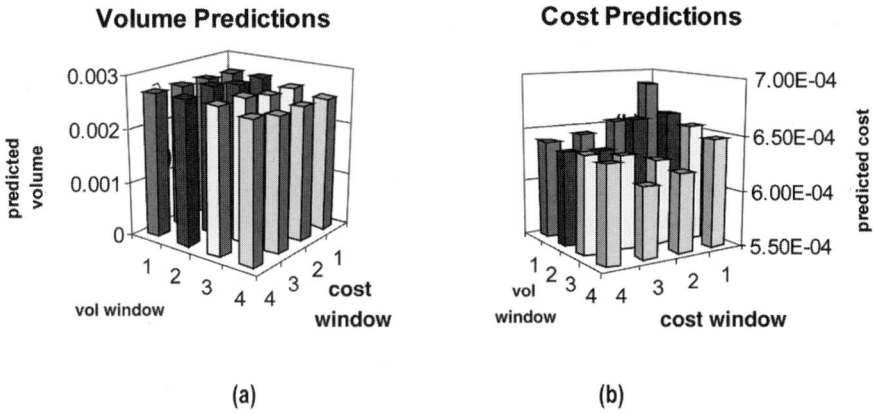

Figure 15. (a) Volume prediction errors and (b) cost prediction errors, both based on varying combinations of volume and cost training window sizes between 1 and 4.

windows could come from one single data set, or from different data sets, for example a window of five data points could be made up of - say three data points from cost and two data points from volume at closing time.

In a follow up to earlier work [7] [42] investigations of the S&P500 time series predictions by Sitte & Sitte were expanded from a univariate to a multivariate time series model by including both, cost and trading volume [17]. To do this the TDNN was trained on earlier values of both, volume *and* cost, but predicting either the volume, or the cost only. Several sets of combinatorial experiments were performed by varying the training window size from 1 to 4 days of volume data, and 1 to 4 days of cost data.

Fluctuations in the volume grow with the average volume. So, for the volume-cost experiments we de-trended with a moving average by dividing each original data point by the moving average at that point. After finding that the moving average introduced an autocorrelation, different moving average periods between 3 and 7 were tested and compared these with the prediction of the time series de-trended by subtraction. While detrending the time series by subtracting the trend does not introduce autocorrelations in the data set, detrending with a moving average does introduce some correlations. Despite this, the volume-cost predictions still make better predictions than a random walk. In the volume-cost experiments the TDNN were trained with both, volume and cost, and predicted either volume or cost, the errors on the test set were systematically 20–25% lower than the random walk errors. While this could be attributed to the introduction of correlations by the running average data preparation, the results show that there are also contributions by the volume data, slightly improving the cost prediction. This becomes apparent by comparing the two histograms in Figure 15. In both cases the TDNN were trained with exactly the same data: volume and cost. The histograms show the test error for different combinations of window size proportions. The left figure shows the volume prediction for the next day, and the right figure shows the cost prediction the for the next day. If the correlations were due to the data preparation only, both figures would be qualitatively equal. However, they are not, as one shows very little variation while the other clearly shows variation. It gives evidence that the volume prediction is little affected by the size of the volume or cost windows, while the cost predictions are indeed affected by these parameters.

These figures also demonstrate that there is information in the volume that affects the cost, because there is a decrease in the test error as the volume window size increases. Conversely there is also an effect of the cost on the prediction, because the error decreases as the cost window sizes increases. In comparison the random walk errors for this set of experiments were 4.4×10^{-3} for the volume predictions and 8.2×10^{-4} for the cost predictions.

A word of caution: there is no point in comparing the values of the volume test prediction errors with the values of cost prediction errors, because the absolute value of the errors depends on the data set. The comparisons become meaningful only in comparing trends within either class, and comparing those trends between the classes.

Another application looks at energy forecasting. Given a lack of consistently successful elasticity forecasting methods, Nasr et al. set up a set of experiments to estimate gasoline demand using neural networks [49]. A set of four different neural networks configurations provides for modeling the gasoline consumptions as both, univariate and multivariate models. The first is a univariate model that uses gasoline consumptions only. The second forecasts gasoline consumption as a function of price. The third model includes the car registration as a determinant of gasoline consumption. The fourth model combined all three time series. The neural network parameter values and number of hidden nodes vary according to the modeling of the gasoline consumption time series, in any of the four models, i.e. between 1–4 hidden layers. The neural networks were trained with a backpropagation algorithm. RMSE and MAD are the indicators of the prediction performance. The data set used was a time series of seven years that was split into five years for training, one year for testing and two last years for evaluation of the prediction performance. Between 1 to 10 input values are used, either from one single variable such as price only, or various values for the 3 variables, for example gasoline consumption, price and car registration. This research found that multivariate models gave better results than others, with approx 23% improvement over the univariate model for this application.

Burgess and Refenes proposed an extension of the neural networks, in which error feedback is provided to the neural network, achieving substantial improvement for volatility forecasting [50]. In a systematic experiment, the effect of the number of estimated parameters either as AR or ME was investigated. The experiment is based on the duality of AR and MA, with either high or low number of parameters involved. A total of 12models were estimated and evaluated for each of the 400 realizations of the target series. The data set used was either generated by Monte Carlo methods of up to 400 data points, or real data from the Spanish Ibex 35 implied volatility series. The windowsize used for inputs was varied from 1 to 3; the models were estimated both with and without error feedback; for each combination both linear models were estimated with no hidden units, and non-linear models, with four hidden units.

Switching time series

The work of Kehagias and Petridis [26] comprises the developed an unsupervised data allocation methodology for on line schemes for the classification and identification of switching time series. A switching time series is generated by a combination of several, alternately activated unknown (non-observable) sources, of any nature, including financial. The non-observability poses a challenge on the learning algorithm. In this case it is solved by separating the learning into a two stage iterative process, in which FFNNs are first trained for separating and assigning each incoming datum to a specific data set corresponding to each source, and a later stage of periodic retraining of the predictor model. The learning task consists in discovering the number of underlying data sources, and predict its output (choice of corresponding model to apply). The proposed data allocation can occur either in parallel or sequentially. The algorithm was tested on a variety of different test data, not necessarily financial, demonstrating the algorithm works efficiently despite various levels of noise.

In a joint project with the Landesbank Hessen-Thuringen and Universities, Heyder and Zayer have developed several mathematical neural network models, to enable daily forecasting of financial time series [20]. To recognize different variations market or phases in the currency exchange rates as a non-stationary time series. The idea is to model the financial series as a switching time series, whose elements are generated by different market phases. Neural networks are then trained to perform as "competing experts", that is to be able to identify to which phase a currently analyzed section of the market belongs. A refinement of the model are the *Annealed Competing Experts*, where not only the phase, but also the corresponding expert is identified. Expert specialization occurs through escalation of the degree of competitivity. The point is then to predict when a change of expert, and hence a change of phase, will occur. The models were then tested in a trading environment to predict the change of phase. The experience shows that it is possible to achieve returns on investment between 6% and 10%. An improvement of almost 2% is achieved with the Annealed Competition of Experts technique over conventional neural networks for currency exchange predictions.

Chaotic time series

In their pioneering work, Principe and Ku applied a time delay neural network with a global feedback loop (TDNNGF), and for comparison a normal TDNN [51]. Both networks had 8 inputs, 14 hidden layer nodes, with sigmoid transfer function, and 1 linear output node. The learning algorithms used were the BPTT or back propagation through time, which is a modified back propagation algorithm, and the real time recurrent learning (RTRL). For the data set 500 samples were generated using a Mackey-Glass system, and further 3000 points were generated by the algorithm.

Mandziuk and Mikolajczak performed an experimental comparison between neural network architectures for short-term chaotic prediction problems (logistic map series)

Table 2 Summary of modeling and ANN parameters in forecasting

Research team	Data type	NN	Training/ test size	# Input nodes	Hidden layer node	# Output nodes	Transf.fun. hidden: output	Training algorithm	Data norma- lization	Performance measure
Burgess 1999 [50]	IBEX 35	FFNN	1 year	1–3	0 to 4	1	sigmoid	gradient descent	n.a.	MSE
Heyder 1999 [20]	currency exchange rates	MLP	n.a.	n.a.	n.a.	n.a.	n.a.	n.a.	n.a.	RMSE
Hu 1999 [47]	currency exchange rates	MLP	15 years	1/4	1/4 + 5 bias	1	sigmoid	BP	0–1	RMSE, RMAE
Kehagias, 2002 [26]	Switching time series	FFNN	various cases	n.a.	n.a.	n.a.	sigmoid	BP	n.a.	
Kodogiannis [46]	currency exchange rates	MLPfuzzy RBF ARRN M.ELMAN	800/200	24 n.a. 4 4	34/18 n.a. 16/8 16/24	6 n.a. 1 1	Gaussian n.a. sigmoid n.a.	n.a.	n.a.	SED, PRE, RMSEE (all three)
Mandziuk 2002 [52]	Chaotic TS (selection)	FFNN, Jordan Elman,	700/200	1- or more	1 & 2 layers 20, 30, 60,100 nodes	1	sigmoid	BP, SNNS	0.2–0.8	RMSE
Nasr 2003 [49]	Gasoline consumption	FFNN	5yrs/2yrs	1–4	1–3	1	n.a.	BP	linear 0.1–0.9	MSE, MAD
Pantazopolis 1998 [44]	S&P 500	FFNN recurrent	3000/n.a.	n.a.	1 or 2	1,3	sigmoid/ linear	BP?	n.a.	trading returns
Plikynas 2002 [43]	LITIN	MLP	2293/644	23	15	1	Log- sigmoid	Grad-des LM others	indices 0–1	RMSE

Reference	Application	Model	Data			Activation	Algorithm	Range	Error measure
Principe 1995 [51]	Mackey-Glass	TDNNGF TDNN	500/3000	8	14	1	sigmoid	BPTT, RTRL	−1, 1	average predition error
Singh 1999 [48]	Selection of 5 financial series	MLP	1900/211	5	n.a.	1	n.a	BP	n.a.	selection of 5 errors
Sitte 2000, 2002, 2003 [7] [17]	S&P 500	TDNN Elman	increm. 10–90%/ 90–10%	2–32	2–32	1	Tangent Sigmoid	LM	linear 0.1–0.9	RMSE
Tiño 2001	DAX FTSE	Markov Models Elman recurrent	1060, 1525	2	2–6	2	Sigmoidal	RTRL	0, 1 binary	profit
Walczak 2001 [10]	currency exchange rates	FFNN	1 to 21 years	3	5	1	n.a.	n.a.	n.a.	n.a.

BPTT   back propagation through time
LM   Levenberg-Marquardt
MAD   mean absolute deviation
MSE   mean square error
n.a.   not available/not applicable
PRE   percent relative error
RMAE   root mean absolute error
RMSE   root mean square error
RTRL   real time recurrent learning
SED   standard error deviation

[52]. It is difficult to make long-term predictions in chaotic time series. MLP, Elman, Jordan nets were used, with one neuron input and first one hidden layer of sizes 20, 30, 60 and 100; then with 2 layers. The data set was not based on real observations, but was generated as a chaotic time series. Results reveal that FF with 2 hidden layers are better predictors than other neural networks, but they are more demanding on training time and often can be early stuck at local minima. Different networks gave different results. The resulting performance may also be subject to the class of chaotic time series.

Table 2 summarizes the modeling and ANN parameters used in forecasting in the works previously explained. This table is laid out in a similar way as the one presented by Zhang et al. to maintain continuity with their earlier work [2].

In conclusion we can say that neural networks outperform statistical linear methods for time series prediction. The research in recent years suggests that the time delay feed forward neural network still are the preferred network for time series prediction as their performance has not been clearly surpassed by other network types such as recurrent networks.

APPENDIX

Financial derivatives

A financial derivative is a contract between to parties where payment is based on an mutually agreed reference. An example are stock market *call* and *put* options. A *call* option gives the holder of the option the right to buy a number of shares at an agreed price (strike price) at some specified future time. The holder of the option is in no obligation to exercise the option in case the share price is below the agreed price, and instead buy the shares on the open market at the lower price. A put option gives the buyer of the option to sell the shares. However is the price of the shares is higher than the agreed price on the date the option is due, the holder of the option may not exercise the option and sell the shares on the market at the higher price.

It is possible for a party to sell a put option without owning the shares subject of the option. In case the buyer of the option decides to exercise the option the seller of the option will have to buy the shares at the higher price and sell them to option holder at the lower price, bearing the loss. The purpose of an option is to transfer risk from the buyer of the option to the seller of the option. The buyer limits the risk to the price of the option.

There is no need for any of the parties to ever own the shares subject to the option. The case of the holder exercising a put option, the seller of the option may simply pay the holder of the option the difference between the agreed price and the price of the shares on the day the option comes due. In this case the option becomes a financial instrument in its own right *dervived* from the price of a certain share. The logical step is to derive an option not from the price of a specific share but instead from another reference such as the S&P 500 stock index. There are many other financial derivatives besides options; some are traded at exchanges and others over-the-counter.

BIBLIOGRAPHY

[1] P. Refenes, Y. Abu-Mostafa, J. E. Moody, and A. S. Weigend, "Neural Networks in Financial Engineering," *World Scientific,* Singapore 1996.

[2] G. Zhang, B. E. Patuwo, and M. Y. Hu, "Forecasting with artificial neural networks: The state of the art," *Int. Journal of Forecasting,* 14 (1998) 35–62.

[3] E. F. Fama, "Efficient Capital Markets: A Review of Theory and Empirical Work", *Journal of Finance,* vol 25, pp. 383–417, 1970.

[4] E. F. Fama, "Efficient Capital Markets II", *Journal of Finance,* vol. 46, No. 5, pp. 1575–1610, 1991.

[5] T. C. Mills, "The Econometric Modeling of Financial Time Series", *Cambridge University Press,* 1993.

[6] G. J. Deboeck, "Trading on the Edge. Neural, Genetic and Fuzzy Systems for Financial Markets", *John Wiley & Sons, Inc.,* 1994.

[7] R. Sitte, and J. Sitte, Analysis of the Predictive Ability of Time Delay Neural Networks Applied to a Class of Financial Time Series, IEEE Transactions on Systems, Man, and Cybernetics, Part C, November 2000, vol. 30, No. 4, pp. 568–572.

[8] A. Refenes, (Editor) "Neural Networks in the capital markets", *John Wiley & Sons,* 1995.

[9] R. B. Harriff, Book Reviews/*Journal of Forecasting* 13 (1997) 143–147.

[10] S. Walczak, "An empirical analysis of data requirements for financial forecasting with neural networks," *Journal of Management Information Systems,* 17 (4): 203–222 SPR 2001.

[11] Handbook of Econometrics, Vol II, Edited by Z. Grilichesand M. D. Intrilligator, *Elsevier Sciences Publishers BV,* 1984.

[12] P. J. Brockwell, and R. A. Davis, "Introduction to Time Series and Forecasting," 2nd Ed., *Springer,* 2001.

[13] P. J. Brockwell, and R. A. Davis, "Time Series: Theory and Methods," 2nd Ed., *Springer,* 1991.

[14] J. D. Hamilton, Time Series Analysis, *Princeton University Press,* 1994.

[15] P. C. B. Phillips, "Challenges of Trending Time Series Econometrics," (Keynote presentation) *International Congress of Modelling and Simulation,* Townsville, Australia, July 2003, D. A. Post (Editor) pp. 945–952.

[16] L. L. Chao, "Statistics Methods and Analysis," McGraw-Hill, Inc. USA, 1974.

[17] R. Sitte, and J. Sitte, Effects of Data Preparation in Multivariate Time Series Predictions, *Proceedings Int. Conference on Computational Intelligence For Modelling, Control & Automation CIMCA 2003,* Vienna, ISBN 1740880684, M.Mohammadian (Ed.), pp. 782–790, 2003.

[18] S.Haykin, "Modern Filters," *Maxwell Macmillan Int. Editions,* 1990.

[19] M. Menna, and G. Rotundo, "Distinguishing between chaotic and stochastic systems in financial time series," *International Journal of Modern Physics C,* vol 13, No. 1, (2002) 31–39

[20] F. Heyder, and S. Zayer, "Analysis of financial time series with neural networks and competing experts," *Wirtschaftsinformatik,* 41(2): 132–137 Apr. 1999.

[21] Hillier Lieberman, Introduction to Operations Research, *Holden-Day, Inc.* 1980.

[22] J. A. Holyst, M. Zebrowska, and K. Urbanowicz, "Observations of deterministic chaos in financial time series by recurrence plots, can one control chaotic economy? *Eur. Phys. J.* B 20, 531–535 (2001).

[23] C. Schittenkopf, G. Dorffner, and E. Dockner, "On Nonlinear, Stochastic Dynamics in Economic and Financial Time Series," *Studies in Nonlinear Dynamics and Econometrics,* 4(3): 101–121.

[24] J. Mandziuk, and R. Mikolajczak, "Chaotic time series prediction with feed-forward and recurrent neural nets," *Control and Cybernetics,* 31(2): 383–406 (2002).

[25] K. Judd, and A. Mees, "On selecting models for nonlinear time series," *Physica D,* 82 (1995) 426–444.

[26] A. Kehagias, and V. Petridis, "Predictive modular neural networks for unsupervised segmentation of switching time series: The data allocation problem," *IEEE Transactions on Neural Networks,* 13(6): 1432–1449, Nov. 2002.

[27] M. J. C. Hu, "Application of the Adaline System to Weather Forecasting," Technical Report 6775-1 Stanford Electronic Laboratories, Stanford, CA, USA, 1964.

[28] F. Rosenblatt, "The Perceptron: A Probabilistic Model for Information Storage and Organization in the Brain", *Psychological Review,* vol. 65, number 6, pp. 386–408, 1958.

[29] K. Hornik, M. Stinchcombe, and H. White, "Multilayer feedforward networks are universal approximators", *Neural Networks,* vol. 2, 1989, pp. 359–366.

[30] S. J. Judd, "Learning in networks is hard", *Proceedings of the First International Conference on Neural Networks,* IEEE, San Diego,CA, 1987, pp. 685–692.

[31] S. Geva, K. Malmstrom, and J. Sitte, "Local Cluster Neural Net: Architecture, Training and Applications", *Neurocomputing,* vol. 20, 1998, pp. 35–56.

[32] K. J Lang, and G. E. Hinton, "The development of the time-delay neural network architecture for speech recognition", *CMU-CS-88-152*, Carnegie-Mellon University, 1988.

[33] A. Waibel, T. Hanazawa, G. Hinton, K. Shikano, and K. J. Lang, "Phoneme recognition using time-delay neural networks", *IEEE Transactions on Acoustics, Speech, and Signal Processing*, vol. 37, pp. 328–339, 1989.

[34] F. Takens, "Detecting strange attractors in turbulence", *Lecture Notes in Mathematics*, vol 898, D. A. Rand and L. S. Young (Ed.) 1981, Springer Verlag, Berlin.

[35] S. Ergezinger, and E. Thomsen, "An accelerated learning algorithm for multiplayer perceptrons: optimisation layer by layer," *IEEE Transactions on Neural Networks*, vol. 6, 1985, pp. 31–42.

[36] R. Bone, M. Crucianu, and J. P Asselin de Beauvill, "Learning long-term dependencies by selective addition of time-delayed connections to neural networks", *Neurocomputing*, vol. 48, 2002, pp. 251–266.

[37] D. R. Seidl, and R. D. Lorenz, "A structure by which a recurrent neural network can approximate a nonlinear dynamic system", *Proceedings of the 1991 International Joint Conference on Neural Networks*(IJCNN) Seattle, WA, USA, vol. 2, 1991, pp. 709–714.

[38] K. I. Funahashi, and Y. Nakamura, "Approximation of Dynamical Systems by Continuous Time Recurrent Neural Networks", *Neural Networks*, vol. 6, 1993, pp. 801–806.

[39] J. L Elman, "Finding structure in time", Cognitive Science, vol. 14, 1990, pp. 179–211.

[40] M. I. Jordan "Serial order: A parallel distributed processing approach," Technical report No. 8604, Institute of Cognitive Science, University of California, San Diego, La Jolla, CA, USA, 1986.

[41] T. Van Gestel, J. A. K. Suykens, D.E. Baestaens, A. Lambrechts, G. Lanckriet, B. Vandaele, B. De Moor, and J. Vandewalle, "Financial time series prediction using least squares support vector machines within the evidence framework," *IEEE Transactions on Neural Networks*, 12(4): 809–821 Jul. 2001.

[42] R. Sitte, and J. Sitte, "Neural Networks Approach to the Random Walk Dilemma of Financial Time Series", *Journal of Applied Intelligence*, APIN Vol. 16, No. 3 (May/June 2002) pp. 163–171.

[43] D. Plikynas, L. Simanauskas, and S. Buda, "Research of neural network methods for compound stock exchange indices analysis," *Informatica*, 13(4): 465–484, 2002.

[44] K. N. Pantazopoulos, Boyd L. H., N. G. Bourbakis, M. J. Brun, and E. N. Houstis, "Financial prediction and trading strategies using neurofuzzy approaches," *IEEE Transactions on Systems Man and Cybernetics Part B-Cybernetics*, 28(4): 520–531, Aug. 1998.

[45] P. Tino, C. Schittenkopf and G. Dorffner, "Financial Volatility Trading Using Recurrent Neural Networks," *IEEE Transactions on Neural Networks*, vol. 12, No. 4, 2001, pp. 865–874.

[46] V. Kodogiannis, and A. Lolis, "Forecasting financial time series using neural network and fuzzy system-based techniques," *Neural Computing & Applications*, 11(2): 90–102, Oct. 2002.

[47] M. Y. Hu, and C. Tsoukalas "Combining conditional volatility forecasts using neural networks: an application to the EMS exchange rates," *Journal of International Financial Markets, Institutions and Money* 9 (1999) 407–422.

[48] S. Singh, "A long memory pattern modelling and recognition system for financial time-series forecasting," *Pattern Analysis and Applications*, 2(3): 264–273, 1999.

[49] G. E. Nasr, E. A. Badr, and C. Joun, "Backpropagation neural networks for modeling gasoline consumption," *Energy Conversion and Management, 44*(6): 893–905, Apr. 2003.

[50] A. N. Burgess, and A-P.N Refenes "Modelling non-linear moving average processes using neural networks with error feedback: An application to implied volatility forecasting," *Signal Processing*, 74 (1999) 89–99.

[51] J. C. Principe, and J. M. Ku, "Dynamic Modelling of Chaotic Time Series with Neural Networks," *Advances in Neural Information Processing Systems* 7: 311–18, 1995.

[52] J. Mandziuk, and R. Mikolajczak, "Chaotic time series prediction with feed-forward and recurrent neural nets," *Control and Cybernetics*, 31(2): 383–406, 2002.

FUZZY RULE EXTRACTION USING RADIAL BASIS FUNCTION NEURAL NETWORKS IN HIGH-DIMENSIONAL DATA

F. ADMIRAAL-BEHLOUL AND J. H. C. REIBER

INTRODUCTION

Rule learning is an increasingly important topic in both machine learning and data mining research. Machine learning concerns the development of algorithms or programs, which learn knowledge or skills while data mining is about the discovery of patterns or rules hidden in the data. Given a set of corresponding input-output values of a system, the challenge consists of identifying and formulating the relations between the input-output values in order to describe the system. To identify such relations, a functional input-output description may be provided. However, when dealing with complex processes, this is generally not feasible. One needs to look for alternative methods. The use of fuzzy models described through fuzzy rules has proven to be successful. Indeed, general knowledge about actions or conclusions can be expressed by a set of fuzzy If-Then rules of a Fuzzy Inference System (FIS).

The basic structure of FIS consists of three conceptual parts: a selection of fuzzy rules (rule base), definitions of the membership functions used in the fuzzy rules (dictionary), and a reasoning mechanism, which performs the inference based on given facts to derive a conclusion (a fuzzy reasoning). In general, one designs a fuzzy inference system based on the past known behavior of the target system. The FIS is expected to reproduce the behavior of the target system, for example a human decision in a specific domain. Although the FIS model has a well-structured knowledge representation, it lacks the adaptability to deal with a changing external environment. The FIS is used only to mimic and not to learn and teach. If learning and automatic rule extraction abilities are required, then neural network concepts are preferred to fuzzy inference systems. Neural Networks (NN) received the attention of the researchers because of their adaptivity and ability to learn. However, the semantic of a NN in terms of the problem to be solved is not explicit; the information is captured by a set of weights, and thus they are considered as black box systems.

J.-S. R. Jang proposed a class of adaptive networks that is functionally equivalent to fuzzy inference systems [1]. He demonstrated that under simple conditions, a Radial Basis Function Network (RBFN) is functionally equivalent to a FIS. While a FIS comprises a certain number of membership functions, a RBFN consists of radial basis functions. Both models produce a center-weighted response to small receptive fields, localizing the primary input excitation.

Under simple conditions, a FIS can be viewed as a neural network and vice versa. This hybridization[1] leads to a neuro-fuzzy model which cumulates the advantages of both models: the adaptivity of NNs and the well-structured knowledge of FISs. The functional equivalence provides a shortcut for better design of both FISs and RBFNs [2–7]. The analysis and learning algorithms for RBFNs are applicable to FIS and the fuzzy modeling procedure could be a good way of initializing a RBFN before training.

The use of fuzzy clustering for fuzzy rule extraction or design of a RBFN has been proposed in the literature [2][8][9]. One generally projects the fuzzy clusters in the domains of the variables leading to a grid partitioning of the domain space. However, this method may lead to a poor characterization of the system to be modeled because of the possible overlapping projections of different clusters. When an accurate model is desired, the method tends to produce a large number of rules making the interpretability of the model difficult.

Figure 1.a shows a case problem where the cluster projections are highly overlapping, assuming that a clustering technique has been able to identify the different ellipsoidal clusters. In the case of axes-parallel ellipsoidal shapes, the projection technique captures the information with a relatively good accuracy (Figure 1.b). However, the correlation between variables in some clusters may make the projection technique extract a large number of rules to model the system. Figure 1.c shows the rules one should get if the problem was limited to identifying the clusters c1, c2, and c5 (see Figure 1.a). In this case, the projection into the variable domains leads to six rules. Including clusters c4 and c3 makes the problem more difficult and will require a larger number of rules to identify all the clusters. The complexity of the problem increases when dealing with high dimensional data.

In this work we propose to extract rules with multidimensional fuzzy sets since the full information about the data (clusters) may be in the entire space (see Figure 1). Indeed, a multidimensional fuzzy set with arbitrary shape (hyper-ellipsoidal) can capture the characteristics of the clusters with a better accuracy. The system can be modeled with a smaller set of rules (one per cluster). Another motivation for the use of multidimensional fuzzy sets in fuzzy rules is related to the knowledge that one expects to get from an automatic training in high dimensions. For a human expert, a rule with

---

[1] Hybrid (in contrast to combined) neuro-fuzzy models consist of homogeneous architectures that are usually neural network oriented (interpreting a FIS as NN), while a combined neuro-fuzzy model is a composed model of separate but cooperative NN and FIS.

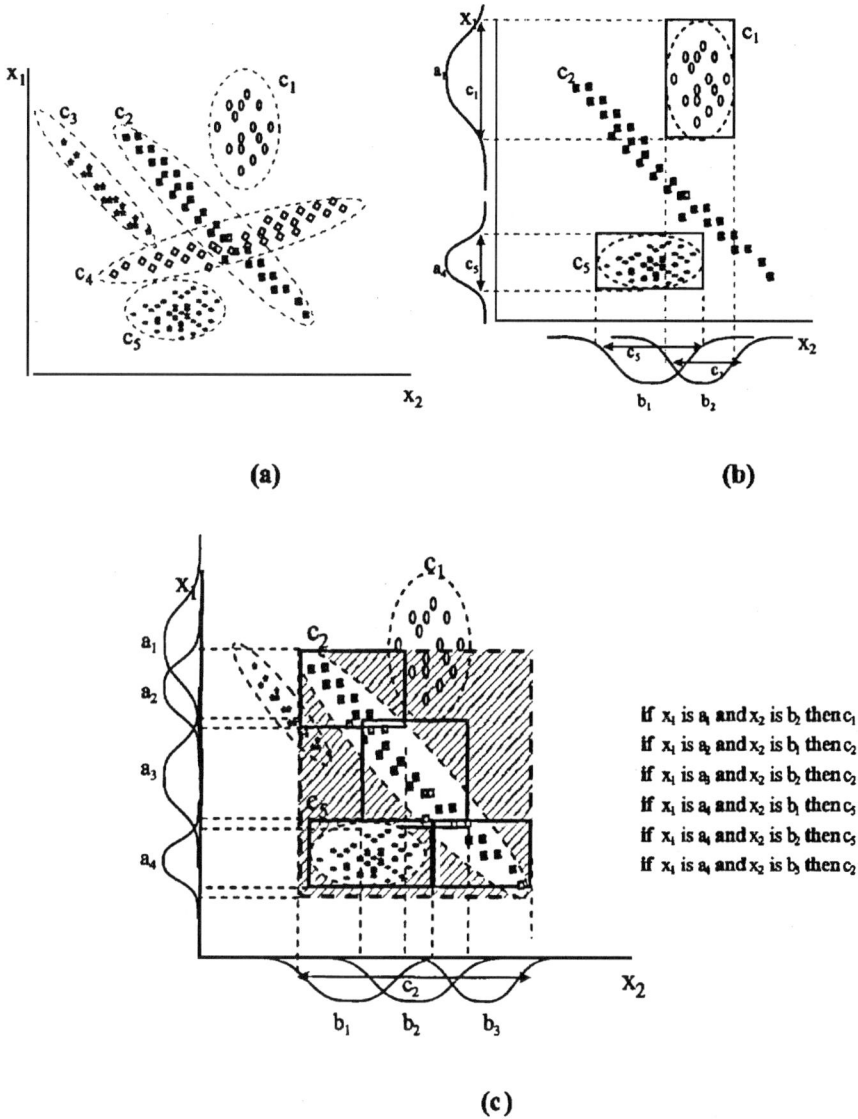

Figure 1. Fuzzy rule extraction using projection and grid partitioning. (a) Synthetic data presenting elongated and overlapping structures. (b) Projection of axes-parallel ellipsoids. (c) Projection of structures with correlated features.

a high number of input variables is very difficult to remember and thus, to learn. It is more intuitive to put a label on a multidimensional fuzzy set A and remember the rule "if x is A then y is B," than to put a label on each possible projection and learn several rules of type "if x_1 is A_1 and x_2 is A_2 and x_3 is A_3 and $\ldots x_n$ is A_n then y is B." When dealing with high dimensional data, feature selection methods are generally used to reduce the dimensionality and thus the complexity of the problem [10–11]. In some applications this approach may be fruitful. However, the accuracy of the system using less features may drop for other applications. Furthermore, the reduced number of features may still remain too high for rule extraction.

The idea of extracting rules using multidimensional fuzzy sets may sound as not new. Indeed, Delgado et al. proposed the characterization of fuzzy sets in the space dimension for a rapid prototyping for fuzzy rule-based modeling using fuzzy clustering [9]. However, because optimal characterization of multidimensional clusters is generally time-consuming and presents some practical difficulties, researchers neglected it and preferred the use of simple clustering techniques as the well-known Fuzzy-C-Means algorithm. In [9] the authors justified the use of a simple clustering algorithm by the fact that only a good initial set of rules (rapid prototyping) was the aim of the work. However, they suggested to tune the extracted set of rules by genetic algorithms, which are well known to be computationally demanding.

In this chapter, we present an efficient approach to fuzzy rule extraction in multidimensional problems based on optimal clustering and neuro-fuzzy modeling [42]. We present solutions to the practical problems that are generally encountered using such modeling procedures, and give a general methodology on how to design an optimal neuro-fuzzy model for fuzzy rule extraction in high dimensional data. The method integrates recent advances in optimal fuzzy clustering. The use of appropriate similarity measures to group data into clusters is addressed, and cluster validity indices to define an optimal set of clusters to capture the information from the data are discussed. We put the rule extraction issue in a neuro-fuzzy framework in order to take advantage of the supervised training ability of NNs (RBFN) in order to tune the rules extracted by the unsupervised clustering technique.

In order to make this chapter self explanatory, let us first recall some basic concepts.

1. FUZZY SET THEORY: BASIC DEFINITIONS AND TERMINOLOGY

The human brain interprets imprecise sensory information provided by the perceptive organs. Fuzzy set theory provides a systematic calculus to deal with such information linguistically and it performs numerical computations by using linguistic labels stipulated by membership functions [13,14,43,44].

In contrast to a classical set, a fuzzy set has no crisp boundary. That is, the transition from "belong to" and "not belong to" is gradual. This smooth transition is characterized by membership functions that give fuzzy sets flexibility in modeling commonly used linguistic expressions such as the "temperature is high" or "the value is small".

1.1. Fuzzy sets

Let X be a collection of objects denoted generally by x. A fuzzy set A in X is defined as a set of ordered pairs:

$A = \{(x, \mu_A(x)) / x \in X\}$. Where $\mu_A(x)$ is called the *Membership Function* (MF for short) for the fuzzy set A. The MF maps each element of X to a membership grade (or membership value) between 0 and 1.

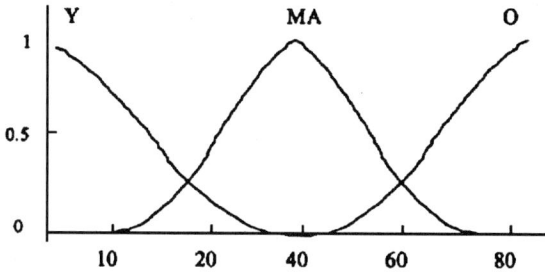

Figure 2. MFs of linguistic values "young" (Y), "middle aged" (MA) and "old" (O).

The definition of a fuzzy set is a simple extension of the definition of the classical set in which the characteristic function is permitted to have any values between 0 and 1 rather than to be restricted to either 0 or 1.

Usually X is referred to as the universe of discourse. X may consist of discrete (ordered or non ordered) objects or a continuous space. The construction of a fuzzy set depends on two things: the identification of a suitable universe of discourse and the specification of an appropriate membership function. The specification of membership functions is subjective; This means that the membership functions specified for the same concept by different persons may vary considerably. This subjectivity comes from individual differences in perceiving or expressing abstract concepts and has a little to do with randomness. *Therefore, the subjectivity and non-randomness of fuzzy sets is the primary difference between the fuzzy set theory and the probability theory, which deals with objective treatment and random phenomena.*

1.2. Linguistic variables and linguistic values

We can define fuzzy sets "young," "middle aged" and "old" that are characterized by MFs, $\mu_Y(x)$, $\mu_{MA}(x)$ and $\mu_O(x)$ respectively. Just as variable can have various values, a linguistic variable can assume different linguistic values (or linguistic labels), such as "young," "middle aged" or "old" in our example. If "age" assumes the value "young," then we say "age is young" and similarly for the other values. Linguistic labels are stipulated by MFs. Typical MFs for these linguistic values are given in Figure 2.

1.3. Membership function formulation and parametrization

A fuzzy set is completely characterized by its MF. Since most fuzzy sets in use have a universe of discourse X consisting of the real line R, it would be impractical to list all the pairs $(x, \mu_A(x))$ defining a membership function. A convenient and concise way to define a MF is to express it as a mathematical formula. Classes of parametrized functions are commonly used to define MFs of one dimension; MFs of higher dimensions can be defined similarly.

Triangular MFs:

A triangular MF is specified by three parameters $\{a, b, c\}$ as follows:

$$triangle\ (x; a, b, c) = \begin{cases} 0, & x \leq a \\ \frac{x-a}{b-a}, & a \leq x \leq b \\ \frac{c-x}{c-b}, & b \leq x \leq c \\ 0, & c \leq x \end{cases} \quad \text{with } a < b < c. \tag{1}$$

Trapezoidal MFs:

A trapezoidal MF is specified by four parameters $\{a, b, c, d\}$ as follows:

$$trapezoid\ (x; a, b, c, d) = \begin{cases} 0, & x \leq a \\ \frac{x-a}{b-a}, & a \leq x \leq b \\ 1, & b \leq x \leq c \\ \frac{d-x}{d-c}, & c \leq x \leq d \\ 0, & d \leq x \end{cases} \quad \text{with } a < b < c < d \tag{2}$$

Due to their simple formulas and computational efficiency, both triangular and trapezoidal MFs have been used extensively, especially in real-time implementations. However, these functions are not smooth at the corner points specified by the parameters.

Smooth membership function:

Gaussian MFs

A gaussian MF is specified by two parameters $\{c, \sigma\}$

$$gaussian\ (x; c, \sigma) = e^{-\frac{(x-c)^2}{2\sigma^2}} \tag{3}$$

Generalized bell MFs

A generalized bell MF is specified by three parameters $\{a, b, c\}$

$$Bell\ (x; a, b, c) = \frac{1}{1 + \left|\frac{x-c}{a}\right|^{2b}} \tag{4}$$

where b is usually positive. The Bell MF is also referred to as Cauchy MF.

Because of their smoothness and concise notation, Gaussian and Bell MFs are very popular for specifying fuzzy sets. Gaussian and Bell functions possess useful properties such as invariance under multiplication (the product of two Gaussian functions is a Gaussian with a scaling factor). The Bell MF has one more parameter than the

Gaussian; it has one more degree of freedom which allows to adjust the steepness at the crossover points.

It is important to note that Gaussian MFs and Bell MFs are unable to provide asymmetric MFs, which are important in certain applications. Sigmoidal MFs are either open left or open right. Closed asymmetric MFs can be generated using either the absolute difference or the product of two sigmoidal functions.

Sigmoidal MFs:

A sigmoidal MF is specified by two parameters $\{a, c\}$

$$sigmoid\,(x; a, c) = \frac{1}{1 + e^{-a(x-c)}} \tag{5}$$

where a controls the slope at the crossover point $x = c$. Depending on the sign of a, a sigmoidal MF is inherently open right or left. The sigmoidal MF is appropriate for representing concepts such as "very high".

MFs of two dimensions:

Two-Dimentional MFs (2D-MFs) refer to MFs with two inputs (variables), each in a different universe of discourse. Sometimes it is advantageous or necessary to use such MFs. One natural way to define 2D-MFs is to extend one dimensional MFs via cylindrical extension:

Let A be a fuzzy set in X. Its cylindrical extension in XxY is a fuzzy set c(A) defined by:

$$c(A) = \int_{X \times Y} \mu_A(x)/(x, y) \tag{6}$$

If a 2D-MF can be expressed as an analytic expression of two MFs of one dimension, then it is composite; otherwise it is non–composite.

Example:
Let A = "(x,y) state near (7,1)" defined by:

$$\mu_A(x, y) = e^{\left(-\left(\frac{x-7}{2}\right)^2 - (y-1)^2\right)} \tag{7}$$

This 2D-MF is composite since it can be decomposed into two Gaussian MFs:

$$\mu_A(x, y) = e^{-\left(\frac{x-7}{2}\right)^2} \cdot e^{-\left(\frac{y-1}{1}\right)^2} \tag{8}$$

If A is given by:

$$\mu_A(x, y) = \frac{1}{1 + |x - 7| |y - 1|^{2.5}} \tag{9}$$

then it is non–composite.

Table 1 Fuzzy complement functions

Function name	Function definition
Complement (classical)	$N(a) = 1 - a$
Sugeno's complement	$N_s(a) = \dfrac{1 - a}{1 + sa}$ where $s > -1$
Yager's complement	$N_w(a) = (1 - a^w)^{1/w}$

Note: When A is a product of two Gaussian functions it can be viewed as two statements joined by the connective AND. "x is near 7 AND y is near 1.

The product of two Gaussian MFs can thus express the AND operation. A composite MF could be defined using the OR connective operator as well. Classical AND and OR operations on fuzzy sets are min and max operators. The concept of defining 2D-MFs can be generalized to form the concept of n-dimensional MF.

1.4. Fuzzy set operations

Fuzzy Complement:

A fuzzy complement operator is a continuous function $N[0, 1] \rightarrow [0, 1]$ which meets the following axiomatic requirements.

$$N(0) = 1 \quad \text{and} \quad N(1) = 0 \quad \text{(boundary)}$$
$$N(a) \geq N(b) \quad \text{if } a \leq b \quad \text{(monotonicity)} \tag{10}$$

Another optional requirement imposes the involution property

$$N(N(a)) = a \quad \text{(involution)} \tag{11}$$

Fuzzy Intersection

The intersection of two fuzzy sets A and B is given by:

$$T : [0, 1] \times [0, 1] \rightarrow [0, 1]$$
$$\mu_{A \cap B}(x) = T(\mu_A(x), \mu_B(x)) = \mu_A(x) \tilde{*} \mu_B(x) \tag{12}$$

where $\tilde{*}$ is a binary operator for the function T. $\tilde{*}$ is usually referred to as a T-norm (Triangular norm) operator. A T-norm meets the following basic requirement:

$$T(a, 0) = 0 \quad T(a, 1) = a \quad \text{(boundary)}$$
$$T(a, b) \leq T(c, d) \quad \text{if } a \leq c \text{ and } b \leq d \quad \text{(monotonicity)}$$
$$T(a, b) = T(b, a) \quad \text{(commutativity)} \tag{13}$$
$$T(a, T(b, c)) = T(T(a, b), c) \quad \text{(associativity)}$$

The first requirement imposes the correct generalization to crisp sets. The second one implies that a decrease in the membership values in A or B cannot produce an increase in the membership value in A ∩ B. The third requirement indicates that

Table 2 Parameterized T-norms and the corresponding T-conorms

T-norm proposed by	Definition
Schweizer and Sklar	$T(a, b, p) = [\max(0, (a^{-p} + b^{-p} - 1))]^{-\frac{1}{p}}$
	$S_{ss}(a, b, p) = 1 - [\max(0, ((1 - a)^{-p} + (1 - b)^{-p} - 1))]^{-\frac{1}{p}}$
Yager	$T_y(a, b, q) = 1 - \min\left(1, ((1 - a)^q + (1 - b)^q)^{\frac{1}{q}}\right)$
	$S_y(a, b, q) = \min(1, (a^q + b^q)^{\frac{1}{q}})$ for $q > 0$
Dubois and Prade	$T_{DP}(a, b, \alpha) = ab/\max(a, b, \alpha)$ for $\alpha \in [0, 1]$
	$S_{DP}(a, b, \alpha) = [a = b - ab - \min(a, b, (1 - \alpha))]/\max((1 - a), (1 - b), \alpha)$
Sugeno	$T_S(a, b, \lambda) = \max(0, ((\lambda + 1)(a + b - 1) - \lambda ab))$ with $\lambda \geq -1$
	$S_S(a, b, \lambda) = \min(1, (a + b - \lambda ab))$ with $\lambda \geq -1$

the operator is indifferent to the order of the fuzzy sets to be combined. The final requirement allows the definition of the intersection of any number of sets in any order of pairwise grouping.

Fuzzy union operator:

The fuzzy union is specified by a function S given by:

$$S:[0, 1] \times [0, 1] \to [0, 1]$$

$$\mu_{A \cup B}(x) = S(\mu_A(x), \mu_B(x)) = \mu_A(x) \tilde{+} \mu_B(x) \tag{14}$$

where $\tilde{+}$ is a binary operator for the function S. $\tilde{+}$ is referred to as T-conorm or S-norm operator. A T-conorm satisfies the following basic requirements:

$$
\begin{aligned}
&S(1, 1) = 0 \quad S(a, 0) = a &&\text{(boundary)} \\
&S(a, b) \leq S(c, d) \quad \text{if } a \leq c \text{ and } b \leq d &&\text{(monotonicity)} \\
&S(a, b) = S(b, a) &&\text{(commutativity)} \\
&S(a, S(b, c)) = S(S(a, b), c) &&\text{(associativity)}
\end{aligned}
\tag{15}
$$

According to the generalized DeMorgan's law, for a given T-norm one can always find a corresponding S-norm, and vice versa.

The generalized DeMorgan's law is given by:

$$
\begin{aligned}
T(a, b) &= N(S(N(a), N(b))) \\
S(a, b) &= N(T(N(a), N(b)))
\end{aligned}
\tag{16}
$$

Several parametrized T-norms and dual T-conorms have been proposed in the literature; some of them are presented in table 2.

2. FUZZY REASONING AND FUZZY INFERENCE SYSTEMS

Fuzzy rules and fuzzy systems are the backbone of fuzzy inference systems, which are the most important modeling tools based on fuzzy logic.

2.1. Fuzzy if-then rules

A fuzzy if then rule assumes the form: "If x is A then y is B" where A and B are linguistic values defined by fuzzy sets on the universes of discourse X and Y, respectively. "x is A" is called the antecedent or premise, while "y is B" is called the consequence or conclusion. Examples of fuzzy if-then rules are widespread in our daily linguistic expressions such as:

If the weather is warm then give more water to the plants.

"If x is A then y is B" is sometimes abbreviated as A→B. This expression describes a relation between two variables x and y; this suggests that a fuzzy if-then rule be defined as a binary fuzzy relation R on the product space X×Y.

    Fuzzy reasoning (approximate reasoning) is an inference procedure that derives conclusions from a set of fuzzy if-then rules and known facts. The basic rule of inference in traditional two-valued logic is modus ponens, according to which one can infer the truth of a proposition B from the truth of A and the implication A→B. However, in human reasoning, modus ponens is employed in an approximate manner.

2.2. Approximate reasoning

Let A, A′ and B be fuzzy sets of X, X and Y respectively. The fuzzy implication A→B is expressed as a fuzzy relation R on X×Y. The fuzzy set B′ induced by "x is A′" and the fuzzy rule "if x is A then y is B" is defined by:

$$\mu_{B'}(y) = \max_x \left[\min \left[\mu_{A'}(x), \mu_R(x, y) \right] \right]$$
$$= \vee_x \left[\mu_{A'}(x) \wedge \mu_R(x, y) \right] \tag{17}$$

or equivalently $B' = A' \circ R = A' \circ (A \rightarrow B)$,

where "o" denotes the composition operator.

    The single rule with single antecedent is the simplest case. A fuzzy rule may have multiple antecedents. A fuzzy if-then rule with two antecedents is usually written as:

"if x is A and y is B than z is C"; a simpler form is $A \times B \rightarrow C$.

    Let A, A′ be the fuzzy sets corresponding to x, B and B′ those corresponding to y and C and C′ those corresponding to z. The fuzzy set C′ induced by "x is A′ and y is B′" and the fuzzy rule "if x is A and y is B then z is C" is defined by:

$$C' = (A' \times B') \circ (A \times B \rightarrow C) \tag{18}$$

A decomposition method for the calculation of C′ is:

$$C' = \left[A' \circ (A \rightarrow C) \right] \cap \left[B' \circ (B \rightarrow C) \right] \tag{19}$$

Thus C' can be expressed as the intersection of $C'_1 = A' \circ (A \rightarrow C)$ and $C_2' = B' \circ (B \rightarrow C)$, each of which corresponds to a single fuzzy rule with a single antecedent.

Multiple fuzzy rules with multiple antecedents can be involved in describing a system behavior. The interpretation of multiple rules is usually taken to be the union of the fuzzy relations corresponding to the fuzzy rules.

Fuzzy if-then rules and fuzzy reasoning constitute the base of fuzzy inference systems which are the most important modeling tool based on fuzzy set theory.

2.3. Fuzzy inference systems

Fuzzy Inference Systems (FIS) have been used successfully in a variety of fields (automatic control, data classification, decision analysis, expert systems, . . .) and thus are known by numerous other names , such as *fuzzy-rule-based systems, fuzzy expert systems, fuzzy models, fuzzy logic controllers* and simply *fuzzy systems*. The basic structure of FIS consists of three conceptual parts: a selection of fuzzy rules (rule base), definitions of the membership functions used in the fuzzy rules (dictionary), and a reasoning mechanism which performs the inference based on given facts to derive a conclusion (a fuzzy reasoning).

The basic FIS can accept either fuzzy inputs or crisp inputs (which are viewed as fuzzy singletons), but the outputs are always fuzzy sets. If a crisp output is desired, a method of defuzzification is required. Defuzzification consists of extracting a crisp value that best represents a fuzzy set. With crisp inputs and outputs, a FIS implements a nonlinear mapping from its input space to its output space. The mapping is accomplished by a set of if-then rules, each of which describes the local behavior of the mapping. The antecedent of a rule defines a fuzzy region in the input space, while the consequence specifies the output in the fuzzy region.

Two types of FIS have been widely used in various applications: the Mamdani model [11] and Sugeno model [8]. The difference between the two models lies in the consequent part of their rules. Figure 3 shows two Mamdani models using min-max as a choice of T-norm and T-conorm respectively.

Figure 4 shows the Mamdani model using product -max fuzzy reasoning. Other variations are possible if one uses a different T-norm and T-conorm.

The Mamdani FIS output is a fuzzy set and a defuzzification step is required if a crisp output is desired. In general there are five methods of defuzzification: the centroid of the fuzzy set area, its bisector, the mean of its maxima, the smallest of its maxima and the largest maximum. The calculation of most of the defuzzification operations is time-consuming (when arbitrary shaped MFs are used), so most of the studies are based on experimental results. This leads to the introduction of other FIS models that derive crisp values and thus do not need any defuzification computation.

The Sugeno fuzzy modeles do not need any defuzzification computation since it derives a crisp value. A typical fuzzy rule in the Sugeno model has the form:

"if x is A and y is B then z = f(x,y)".

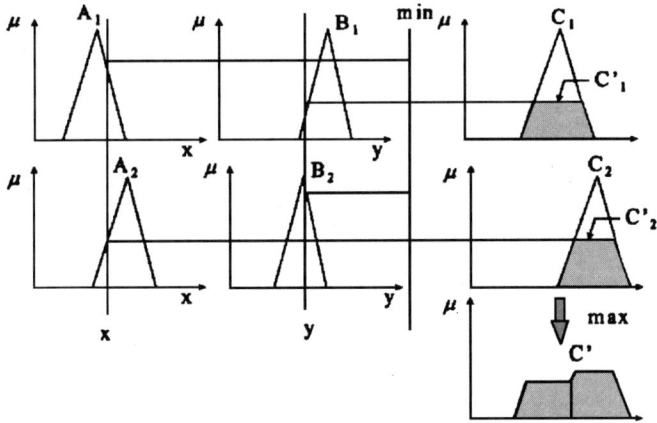

Figure 3. Mamdani FIS using min and max for T-norm and T-conorm. Two rules each with two antecedents.

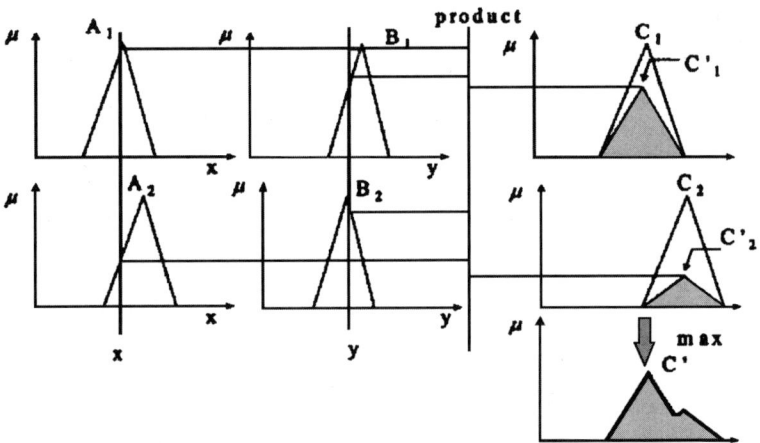

Figure 4. Mamdani FIS using product and max for T-norm and T-conorm. Two rules each with two antecedents.

where A and B are fuzzy sets in the antecedent, while z = f(x,y) is a crisp function in the consequent. In principle $f(x, y)$ can be any function, but normally it is a polynomial in the input variables x, y. When f(x,y) is a first-order polynomial, the FIS is called a first-order Sugeno FIS. The zero-order Sugeno FIS corresponds to a zero-order polynomial $f(x, y)$. Figure 5 shows the fuzzy reasoning procedure of a first-order Sugeno fuzzy model. Since each rule has a crisp output, the overall output of the system is obtained by weighted average. In practice the weighted average is

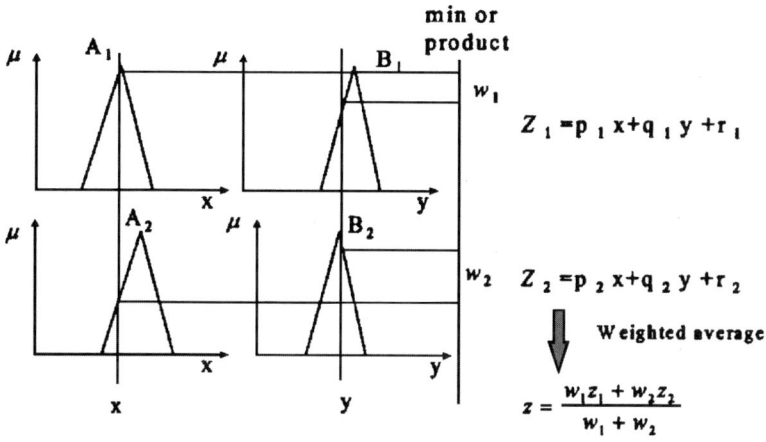

Figure 5. The Sugeno fuzzy model. Two rules with each two antecedents.

sometimes replaced by the weighted sum ($z = w_1 z_1 + w_2 z_2$). The zero–order Sugeno model can be viewed as a special case of the Mamdani model in which the consequent of each rule is a fuzzy singleton.

In general, one designs a fuzzy inference system based on the past known behavior of the target system. The FIS is expected to reproduce the behavior of the target system, for example a human decision in specific domain. Generally speaking, the standard method for constructing a fuzzy system, a process called fuzzy modeling, can be pursued in two stages. The first stage is called *surface structure determination* and includes the following tasks:

1. Select relevant input and output variables
2. Choose a specific type of FIS
3. Determine the number of linguistic terms associated with each input and output variable; if a Sugeno model is used determine the order of the FIS.
4. Design a collection of fuzzy if-then rules.

After the first stage, a rule base is obtained that can more or less describe the behavior of the target system by means of linguistic terms. The second stage consists of the determination of the MF of each linguistic term. This stage is referred to as *deep structure determination* and includes the following tasks:

1. Choose an appropriate family of parameterized MFs
2. Have a human expert help in the determination of the parameters of the MFs used in the rules.
3. Refine the parameters of the MFs using regression and optimization techniques.

Although the fuzzy inference system has a good structured knowledge representation in the form of fuzzy if-then rules, it lacks the adaptability to deal with a changing external environment. The FIS is used only to mime and not to learn and teach. If learning and automatic rule extraction abilities are required, then neural network concepts are incorporated in fuzzy inference systems, resulting in neuro-fuzzy modeling. J.-S. R. Jang proposed a class of adaptive network that is functionally equivalent to fuzzy inference systems [1]. The proposed architecture is referred to as the Adaptive Network-based Fuzzy Inference System (ANFIS) or adaptive neuro-fuzzy system. J.-S. R. Jang [45] demonstrated that under simple conditions, a radial basis function network (RBFN) is functionally equivalent to a FIS. Let us recall the concepts of RBFNs first and then present the functional equivalence.

3. RADIAL BASIS FUNCTION NEURAL NETWORKS

A Neural Network (NN) is a set of many simple processors (units), each possibly having a small amount of local memory. The units are connected by communication channels (connections) which usually carry numeric (as opposed to symbolic) data, encoded by any of various means. The units operate only on their local data and on the inputs they receive via the connections. The restriction to local operations is often relaxed during training.

Some NNs are models of biological neural networks and some are not, but historically, NNs originated in an attempt to build mathematical models of elementary processing units in the brain (neurons) and the inspiration came from the desire to produce artificial systems capable of sophisticated, may be "intelligent," computations similar to those that the human brain routinely performs.

Most NNs have some sort of training rule whereby the weights of connections are adjusted on the basis of data. In other words, NNs learn from examples and exhibit some capability for generalization beyond the training data.

There are many kinds of NNs by now. New ones (or at least variations of existing ones) are invented every month. The categorization of the NNs is related to their topology (the way the neurons are connected to one an other) and the distinction between supervised and unsupervised learning methods. In supervised learning, there is a "teacher" who in the learning phase "tells" the net how well it performs (reinforcement learning) or what the correct behavior would have been (fully supervised learning). It is what statisticians know as nonparametric regression and it corresponds to the problem of estimating a function, given only a training set of pairs of input-output points. However, in unsupervised learning the net is autonomous: it just looks at the data it is presented with, finds out about some properties of the data set and learns to reflect these properties in its output. What exactly these properties are, that the network can learn to recognize, depends on the particular network model and learning method. Usually, the net learns some compressed representation of the data.

The multilayer perceptron (MLP) architecture is the most popular one in practical applications that require supervised learning. It is a feedforward NN where the neurons are organized on layers: an input layer, one ore more hidden layers and an output layer. Neurons of the same layer are not connected to each others.

Although widely used, the MLP has drawbacks in three aspects : first, it tends to over generalize (in pattern classification). The network can be trained to have high accuracy in classifying patterns from a set of known categories, but will also classify any out-of-category pattern as one of the trained categories. In real life applications, this can have severe consequences. Second, the widely used backpropagation training method is often too slow, especially for large-scale problems (even with optimized algorithms). Third, the knowledge represented in a MLP is not easy to comprehend. They are considered as black-box decision systems.

Radial Basis Function Networks (RBFN) are being increasingly popular because they seem to solve the three MLP problems related above [12, 46]. First, the most popular RBFN with gaussian kernels, learns the pattern probability density functions instead of dividing the pattern space as the MPL do. Therefore, when an out-of-category pattern is presented to the network, it will be classified as an unknown category. Second, RBFN is generally easier to train than MLP. This is because the RBFN establishes the RBF parameters directly from the data, and training is mainly on the output layer. Third RBFN naturally introduces the notion of class membership which allows fuzzy partitioning of the input space and rule based interpretation of the represented knowledge.

3.1. Definition

The RBFN is a feedforward neural network which accomplishes an input–output non-linear mapping by linear combination of nonlinearly transformed inputs according to the following:

$$o_j = \sum_{i=1}^{m} w_i \phi_i(x) \tag{20}$$

where x is the input vector, o_j the output of the jth output node and w_i are the output linear combining weights. The $\phi_i(x)$ are Radial Basis Functions (RBF) and m is the number of RBFs. Figure 6 shows the network representation with RBF kernels represented as neurons of the hidden layer. An output of the network is a simple linear combination of the hidden neuron outputs. A more complicated method for calculating the overall output is to take the weighted average of the output associated with each receptive field:

$$o_j = \frac{\sum_{i=1}^{m} w_i \phi_i(x)}{\sum_{i=1}^{m} \phi_i(x)} \tag{21}$$

The weighted average is advantageous in that points in the area of overlap between two (or more) receptive fields will have a well-interpolated overall output between the outputs of the overlapping RBFs.

All the RBFN are not the same. They differ in type of RBFs used and in training method. Consequently, they differ in performances.

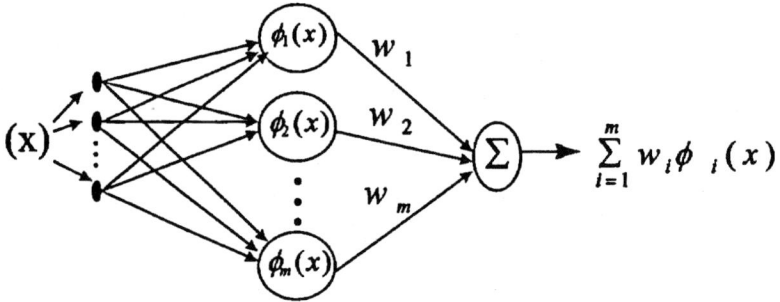

Figure 6. Radial Basis Function Network with one output node. Each component of the input vector x feeds forward to m radial basis function node whose output are linearly combined with weights $\{w_{i, i = 1...m}\}$ into the network output node.

The most distinguishing feature of RBFs is that they are local i.e. they give a significant response only in a neighbourhood near a central point. Their response decreases monotonically with distance from a central point. Strictly speaking, functions whose response increases monotonically away from a central point are also radial basis functions, but because they are not local, they are less interesting for classification applications. RBFs parameters are its centre , its shape, and its width.

A typical local RBF is the Gaussian function. Centered at c and of width (or radius) r, it has the form:

$$G(x, c, r) = \exp - \left(\frac{\|x - c\|_R^2}{2r^2} \right) \quad \text{where } \|x - c\|_R^2 = (x - c)^T R^{-1}(x - c) \tag{22}$$

where R is a positive definite matrix.

Other common choices of radial functions are the multiquadric function:

$$Mq(x, c, r) = \sqrt{\|x - c\|_R^2 + r^2} \tag{23}$$

the thin-pate-spline function

$$Tps(x, c) = \|x - c\|_R^2 \log(\|x - c\|_R) \tag{24}$$

and the inverse multiquadric function

$$Imq(x, c, r) = \frac{1}{\sqrt{\|x - c\|_R^2 + r^2}} \tag{25}$$

Gaussian–like functions (local) are more commonly used than multiquadric–like function (non local) which have a global response.

3.2. Training

Since Broomhead and Lowe's 1988 seminal paper [12], RBFNs have traditionally been associated with radial function networks in a single hidden layer. A RBFN is nonlinear if the basis functions can move or change size or if there is more than one hidden layer.

The hidden and the output layers are generally trained sequentially: the Radial Basis Function (RBF) parameters are first fixed and the optimal linear combining weights are then computed [14, 17].

3.2.1. Hidden layer definition:

The hidden layer definition is the most critical step in the design of an optimal RBFN. To determine its parameters, one has to decide the number of neurons of the layer and their Kernel functions (RBFs). A RBF is generally specified by its center and width. The simplest and most general method to decide the hidden layer number of neurons is to associate a neuron to each training pattern. However, for a large-scale data set this method is not convenient. Therefore, a process of selecting a subset of basis functions from large set of candidates is required. In linear regression theory subset selection is well known and one popular variant is *forward selection* in which the model starts empty (m = 0). Basis functions are selected one at a time and added to the network. The added RBF must reduce the sum of squared errors the most. The process will stop adding RBFs when the error riches a minimum and then starts to increase (heuristics are generally used). Orthogonal Least Squared Learning (OLS) speeds up the forward selection [13]. The OLS method involves the transformation of the set of input patterns into a set of orthogonal basis vectors, and thus makes it possible to calculate the individual contribution to the desired output energy from each basis vector.

An other way to define the hidden layer parameters is to first cluster the training patterns to a reasonable number of groups and then assign a neuron to each cluster. The prototype and standard deviation of each cluster are used to describe the corresponding RBF. Therefore unsupervised or partially supervised clustering algorithms can be used. Clustering algorithms will be addressed in section 5.1.

Once the number and parameters of the RBFs defined, the hidden layer performs a fixed nonlinear transformation; it maps the input space into a new space. The output layer then implements a linear combiner on this new space. The only output layer parameters to adjust are the weights of this linear combiner.

3.2.2. Output layer definition

When applied to supervised learning with linear models, the Least Square (LS) principle leads to a particularly easy optimization problem. Having a training set $\{(x_i, \hat{y}_i)\}_{i=1}^{P}$

the LS recipe is to minimize the sum-squared-error

$$S = \sum_{i=1}^{p} (\hat{y}_i - o(x_i))^2 \tag{26}$$

with respect to the weights of the model.

A potential problem when working with noisy training data, a large number of inputs and small training sets is the so called over-fitting. To counter its effect, a roughness penalty term can be added to the sum of squared errors to produce the cost function

$$S_G = \sum_{i=1}^{p} (\hat{y}_i - o(x_i))^2 + \lambda \sum_{j=1}^{m} w_j^2 \tag{27}$$

This is called *global ridge regression* and involves a single regulation parameter λ to control the trade-off between fitting the data and penalizing large weights.

Separate regularization parameter can be attached to each RBF which leads to local adaptation of the smoothing effect.

$$S_G = \sum_{i=1}^{p} (\hat{y}_i - o(x_i))^2 + \sum_{j=1}^{m} \lambda_j w_j^2 \tag{28}$$

This is called *local ridge regression* and can be viewed as a generalization of standard ridge regression.

3.2.3. Functional Equivalence to FIS

Although FIS and RBFN were developed on different bases, they seem to be rooted in the same soil [1]. While the RBFN consists of radial basis functions, the FIS comprises a certain number of membership functions. Both models have a mechanism whereby they can produce a center-weighted response to small receptive fields, localizing the primary input excitation. There are some conditions under which an RBFN and a FIS are functionally equivalent:

- Both the RBFN and the FIS use the same aggregation method (weighted average or weighted sum) to derive their overall output.
- The number of RBF units is equal to the number of fuzzy If-Then rules in the FIS.
- Each radial basis function of the RBFN is equal to a multidimensional composite MF of the premise part of the corresponding fuzzy rule.
- Corresponding RBF and fuzzy rule should have the same response function (a constant or a linear equation).

This functional equivalence provides a shortcut for better understanding of both FIS and RBFNs, in the sense that any development in the literature of one cross-fertilizes the other [3–6,47]. The analysis and learning algorithms for RBFNs are applicable to

Rule 1: If x is A1 and y is B1 then f1=p1x+q1y+r1

Rule 2: If x is A2 and y is B2 then f2=p2x+q2y+r2

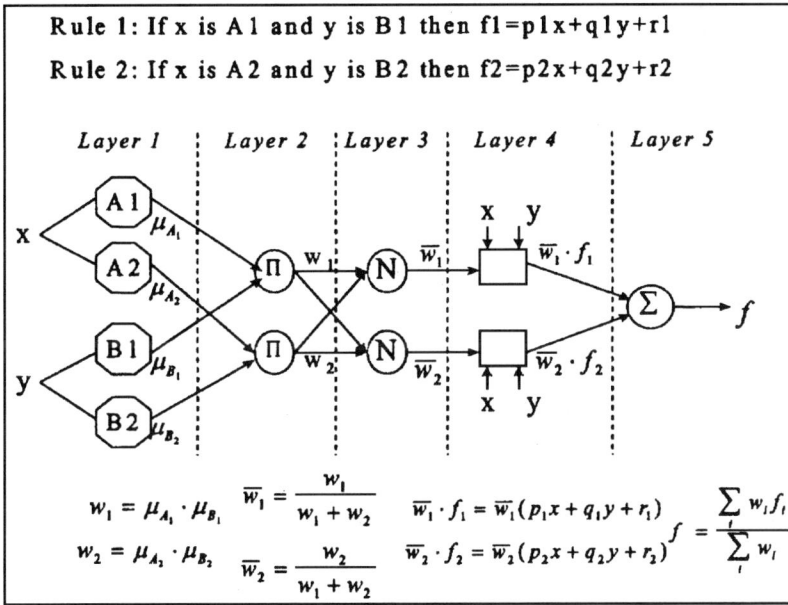

Figure 7. A two input one output ANFIS based on a first-order Sugeno model.

FIS and the fuzzy modeling procedure could be a good way of initializing a RBFN before training. This equivalence makes the FIS adaptive and prevents the RBFNs from being more black box networks, since fuzzy-if then rules can be extracted.

4. ANFIS ARCHITECTURE

Based on the RBFN/FIS functional equivalence, Jang proposed the Adaptive Neuro-fuzzy Inference System model. An ANFIS is a five layered network. Figure 7 shows an ANFIS with two inputs x and y, one output $z = f$ and two fuzzy if-then rules. The ANFIS of Figure 7 is based on the Sugeno model.

In Layer1 every node computes the membership degree of the input variable connected to the corresponding fuzzy membership function. Each node of this layer is an adaptive node. The nodes of Layer 2 are fixed nodes whose outputs are the product of all the incoming signals. The number of neurons in this layer is equal to the number of if-then rules in the system. Each node i of Layer 3 is a fixed node that calculates the ratio of the firing strength of rule i to the sum of the firing strengths of all rules. Every node in Layer 4 is an adaptive node whose parameter set is $\{p_i, q_i, r_i\}$. Layer 5 consists of a single node that computes the overall output as the summation of all incoming signals.

Training such a network consists of :

1. defining the optimal number of linguistic values (ie. the number of nodes in Layer 1 and their membership functions, corresponding with the input linguistic variables,

2. finding the optimal set of if-then rules (ie. the number of nodes in Layer 2.)
3. defining the parameter set $\{p_i, q_i, r_i\}$ of each node of Layer 4.

RBFNs and ANFIS have two distinct modifiable parts: the antecedent (hidden layer in RBFN) part and the consequent (output layer) part. These two parts are usually adapted by two different optimization methods. Beside using only a supervised learning scheme to update all modifiable parameters, a variety of two-phase training algorithms have been proposed. A typical scheme to define the receptive field functions is the use of unsupervised learning algorithms, also referred to as clustering algorithms.

Clustering algorithms are used extensively to organize and categorize data. Clustering partitions a data set into several groups such that the similarity within a group is greater than that among groups. Achieving such a partitioning requires a similarity metric which takes two input vectors and returns a value that reflects their similarity. "Hard clustering" assigns each data point (feature vector) to one and only one of the clusters with a degree of membership equal to one. Hard clustering assumes that the boundaries between the clusters are well defined. However, this model often does not reflect the nature of real data, where boundaries between clusters might be fuzzy. In this case, a more nuancial description between a feature and a specific cluster is required.

5. OPTIMAL DESIGN OF RBFN BASED ON FUZZY CLUSTERING

5.1. Fuzzy Clustering and similarity measures

Bezdek introduced several clustering algorithms based on fuzzy set theory and an extension of the least-squares error criterion [18]. Most analytical fuzzy clustering approaches are derived from Bezdek's fuzzy C-means (FCM) [19–21]. FCM has been proposed as an improvement over the earlier hard C-means clustering algorithm also known as the K-means algorithm.

FCM is a data clustering algorithm in which each data point belongs to a cluster to a degree specified by a membership degree. It partitions a collection of n data points $X_i (i = 1, \ldots, n)$ into c fuzzy groups and finds a cluster center in each group, such that a cost function of a dissimilarity measure is minimized. The algorithm employs fuzzy partitioning such that a given data point can belong to several groups with a degree specified by membership grades between 0 and 1. A fuzzy c-partition of X is represented by a matrix $U = [\mu_{ik}] \in \Re^{c \times n}$, the entries of which satisfy the following constraints:

(i) $\mu_{ik} \in [0, 1] \quad 1 \le i \le c; \quad 1 \le k \le n$

(ii) $\sum_{i=1}^{c} \mu_{ik} = 1, \quad 1 \le k \le n$ (29)

(iii) $0 < \sum_{k=1}^{n} \mu_{ik} < n, \quad 1 \le i \le c$

U can be used to describe the cluster structure of X by interpreting μ_{ik} as the degree of membership of x_k to the cluster i. Good partitions U of X may be defined by the minimization of the following objective function [18]

$$J_m(U, V) = \sum_{k=1}^{n} \sum_{i=1}^{c} (\mu_{ik})^m d_{ik}^2, \tag{30}$$

where $m \in [1, +\infty]$ is a weighting exponent called fuzzifier, $V = (v_1, v_2, \dots, v_c)$ is the vector of the cluster centers, and d_{ik} is the distance between x_k and the ith cluster.

FCM Theorem [18]: Assume $m \geq 1$ and $d_{ik}^2 > 0, 1 \leq i \leq c, 1 \leq k \leq n$. (U, V) may minimize J_m only if:

$$\mu_{ik}^* = \frac{1}{\sum_{j=1}^{c} \left(\frac{d_{ik}}{d_{jk}} \right)^{\frac{2}{m-1}}}, \tag{31}$$

$$v_i^* = \frac{\sum_{k=1}^{n} (\mu_{ik})^m x_k}{\sum_{k=1}^{n} (\mu_{ik})^m} \tag{32}$$

The FCM algorithm consists of iterations alternating between equations (31) and (32). This algorithm converges to either a local minimum or a saddle point of J_m [21].

FCM determines the cluster centers v_i and the membership matrix U for a given c value as follows:

Step 1: Initialize the membership matrix with random values between 0,1, such that the constraints (i), (ii) and (iii) in (29) are satisfied.

Step 2: Calculate c fuzzy clusters centers v_i, $i = 1, \dots, c$ using (32).

Step 3: Compute the cost function according to (30). Stop if either it is below a certain tolerance value or its improvement over the previous iteration is below a certain threshold.

Step 4: Compute a new U using (31). Go to Step 2.

One of the major factors that influences the determination of appropriate clusters of points is the "(dis)similarity measure" chosen for the problem at hand. Indeed, the computation of the membership degrees μ_{ik}^* depends on the definition of the distance measure d_{ik}, which is usually a norm. Recent advances in fuzzy clustering have shown a spectacular ability to detect not only hypervolume clusters of different shapes [22–27], but also clusters that are actually thin shells such as curves and surfaces [29], by using an appropriate distance measure.

The inner product norms (quadratic norms) on R^n are generally used. The squared quadratic norm (distance) between a pattern vector x_i and the center of the kth cluster v_k is defined as follows:

$$d_{ik}^2 = \|x_i - v_k\|_A = (x_i - v_k)^T A (x_i - v_k), \tag{33}$$

where A is any positive definite $(N \times N)$ matrix

Clusters found with inner product norms match smooth hyperellipsoidal shapes whose principal axes are determined by the eigenvectors of A. The identity matrix is the simplest and most popular choice of A. The corresponding d_{ik} is the standard Euclidean distance and the corresponding fuzzy clustering algorithm is the so called FCM. The major drawback of the FCM algorithm is that it searches for hyper-spherical shaped clusters of approximately the same size; it has the undesirable property of splitting large elongated clusters. A different choice of A leads to clusters with a more or less hyper-ellipsoidal shapes. When A is a diagonal matrix with positive elements on the diagonal, the extracted clusters are axes-parallel hyper-elliposoids. To extract clusters of arbitrary hyper-ellipsoidal shapes (not necessarily axis parallel), the covariance matrix is used [22][25][28]. Indeed, using the covariance matrix leads to a scaling distance in the principal component axes. Using the covariance matrix, one obtains the so-called Mahalanobis distance.

For a fuzzy cluster, the classical covariance matrix is substituted by its fuzzy version defined by:

$$F_k = \frac{\sum_{i=1}^{n} \mu_{ik} (x_i - v_k)(x_i - v_k)^T}{\sum_{i=1}^{n} \mu_{ik}} \tag{34}$$

According to our experience and to the literature [26], the use of the Mahanalobis distance makes the clustering algorithm tend to partition data into either very large or very small clusters. In order to avoid the extraction of very small clusters, Gustafson and Kessel [26] fixe the size of each cluster a priori and proposed the following distance:

$$d_{GK}^2(x_i, v_k) = \alpha_k \det(F_k)^{1/2} \times D_M(x_i, v_k) \tag{35}$$

where α_k is the predefined constant which constrains the size of cluster k, and $D_M(x_i, v_k)$ is the Mahanalobis distance using the fuzzy covariance matrix :

$$D_M(x_j, v_k) = (x_j - v_k)^T F_k^{-1} (x_j - v_k)$$

The fact that the cluster volumes have to be specified a priori constitutes a major limitation of the proposed algorithm when no prior knowledge is available. Later in the literature, methods based on the maximum likelihood criterion have been proposed [26–28] [30], which avoid the definition of constraints such as α_k. Gath and Geva proposed an elegant solution based on an "exponential" distance [22]:

$$d_{GG}^2(x_i, v_k) = \frac{\det(F_k)^{1/2}}{P_k} \times \exp\left(\frac{D_M(x_i, v_k)}{2}\right) \tag{36}$$

with

$$P_k = \frac{1}{n} \sum_{i=1}^{n} \mu_{ik} \tag{37}$$

where P_k is the *a priori* probability of selecting the kth cluster.

The major advantage of the corresponding fuzzy clustering algorithm is obtaining good partition results in cases of great variability of cluster shapes (still hyper-elliptical), number of points and densities. Its major drawback however, is its strong sensitivity to the initial values of U and V matrices. Because of the exponential distance, the clustering algorithm seeks an optimum in a very narrow region and might be unstable during the iterative process of the clustering algorithm. Therefore, the FCM (with Euclidean distance) is used to initialize the proposed algorithm [22]. Clustering using this distance is called Fuzzy Maximum Likelihood Estimation (FMLE).

All the algorithms tracking hyper-ellipsoidal shaped clusters require the computation of the cluster covariance matrices and their corresponding inverses. The computation of a (fuzzy) covariance matrix requires a large number of training samples. However, in practice the covariance matrix is estimated from a finite number of training samples. It is particularly important to note that, when the ratio between the training sample size and the number of features is significantly small[2], the covariance matrix becomes singular [30]. If the fuzzy covariance matrix is singular then the computation of the quadratic norm becomes theoretically impossible. In practice, one sets all the off-diagonal elements to zero so it becomes regular [14–15]. However, this is not always a good estimate of the covariance matrix and can lead to undesired partitions.

A second problem related to the use of the covariance matrices is related to the time consuming property of the corresponding clustering algorithms. Indeed, at each iteration, the covariance matrices and their corresponding inverses (and sometimes their determinant) have to be computed. This is computationally expensive in high dimensions with multiple clusters. This seems to be the reason why the Euclidean distance has been preferred in many applications.

In order to solve efficiently the problem of singularity of the covariance matrices and the time-consuming property of the computation of the inverse, we suggest to use a covariance matrix estimator.

5.2. Toeplitz covariance matrix estimator

Let F be a covariance matrix. The components f_{ij} of the matrix may be expressed by:

$$f_{ii} = \sigma_i^2, \quad f_{ij} = \rho_{ij} \sigma_i \sigma_j \quad 1 \le i \le N \text{ and } 1 \le j \le N \tag{38}$$

where σ_i^2 is the variance of x_i and ρ_{ij} is the correlation coefficient between x_i and x_j.

---

[2]According to the literature, a ratio smaller than three is considered significantly small.

Then $F = TRT$,

$$\text{where}\quad T = \begin{bmatrix} \sigma_1 & & & 0 \\ & \sigma_2 & & \\ & & \ddots & \\ 0 & & & \sigma_N \end{bmatrix} \quad (10) \quad \text{and}\quad R = \begin{bmatrix} 1 & \rho_{12} & \cdots & \rho_{1N} \\ \rho_{21} & 1 & & \\ \vdots & & \ddots & \\ \rho_{N1} & & & 1 \end{bmatrix} \quad (39)$$

Thus $\det(F) = \det(T)\det(R)\det(T)$ and $F^{-1} = T^{-1}R^{-1}T^{-1}$

$$\det(F) = \left(\prod_{i=1}^{N} \sigma_i \right)^2 \det(R)$$

$$T^{-1} = \begin{bmatrix} 1/\sigma_1 & & & 0 \\ & 1/\sigma_2 & & \\ & & \ddots & \\ 0 & & & 1/\sigma_N \end{bmatrix} \quad (40)$$

The matrix R can be approximated by a particular form of a Toepliz matrix given below:

$$R_T = \begin{bmatrix} 1 & \rho & \cdots & \rho^{N-1} \\ \rho & 1 & & \\ \vdots & & \ddots & \rho \\ \rho^{N-1} & & \rho & 1 \end{bmatrix} \quad (41)$$

$$R_T^{-1} = \frac{1}{1-\rho^2} \begin{bmatrix} 1 & -\rho & 0 & \cdots & & 0 \\ -\rho & 1+\rho^2 & & \ddots & & \vdots \\ 0 & & \ddots & & & 0 \\ \vdots & \ddots & & & 1+\rho^2 & -\rho \\ 0 & \cdots & & 0 & -\rho & 1 \end{bmatrix} \quad (42)$$

and $\det(R_T) = (1-\rho^2)^{N-1}$ \quad (43)

The estimation process of a covariance matrix is as follows:

(i) Estimate the sample variance σ_i^2.
(ii) Estimate the sample covariance f_{ij} and divide $f_{i,i+1}$ by $\sigma_i\sigma_{i+1}$ to estimate $\rho_{i,i+1}$
(iii) Average $\rho_{i,i+1}$ over $i = 1, \ldots, N-1$, to obtain an estimate of ρ.
(iv) Use ρ to form R_T.

Note that the Toeplitz matrix requires only $(N + 1)$ parameters, $\sigma_i (i = 1, \ldots, N)$ and ρ. Thus, its computational cost is not severe even if the dimension of the data is large.

The Toeplitz estimator has been used to estimate the covariance matrix in [31] for the design of a Parzen classifier. Two more kernel covariance estimators have been discussed: The Ness estimator and the orthogonal expansion estimator. The Toeplitz estimator has proven to be preferable to the others when the number of features is large or the number of training samples is small. Furthermore, it requires simple computations. The reader can refer to [32] and [33] for a presentation of Ness and orthogonal expansion estimator respectively, and to [34] for a detailed presentation of the Toeplitz estimator. The comparison of the performances using an estimated covariance matrix against the exact one is not in the scope of this chapter. Hamamoto *et al.* gave a comparison study in [31] in the case of Parzen classifier design, which is relatively close to the fuzzy clustering problem. They concluded that the performances were comparable.

In our approach, we use the Toeplitz estimator instead of the covariance matrix in (36) and refer to the distance as the *approximated exponential distance*.

5.3. Optimal number of clusters

Up to here the number of clusters was supposed to be known *a priori*. However, when this number can not be defined according to some a priori knowledge, a cluster validity criterion is required in order to determine the optimal number of clusters [35–37]. Automatic rule extraction issues are generally dealing with a given set of input-output pairs. In pattern recognition problems, the outputs are class labels. The true number of clusters is generally considered to be the number of labels present in the training data set. However, this number might not be optimal. Indeed, a class may be concave i.e. group a number of separated overlapping clusters (see Figure 8). When the visualization of the data is possible, that is, if the input space dimension is smaller than 4, one can identify these cases. However, in high dimensions this is not always possible. In this case, the use of cluster validity indices may solve the problem.

The criteria for the definition of an optimal partition of the data into subgroups are generally based on three requirements [37]:

1. Clear separation between the resulting clusters.
2. Minimal volume of the clusters.
3. Maximal number of relevant data points concerned in the vicinity of the cluster centroid.

There is a number of cluster validation indices available in the literature. An analysis of several indices was performed by Pal and Bezdek in [38–39]. Tracking the optimal partition consists of varying the number of clusters between fixed minimum and maximum values and for each given number, computing the cluster validity index. An optimal partition corresponds to a minimum or a maximum (depending on the used index) value.

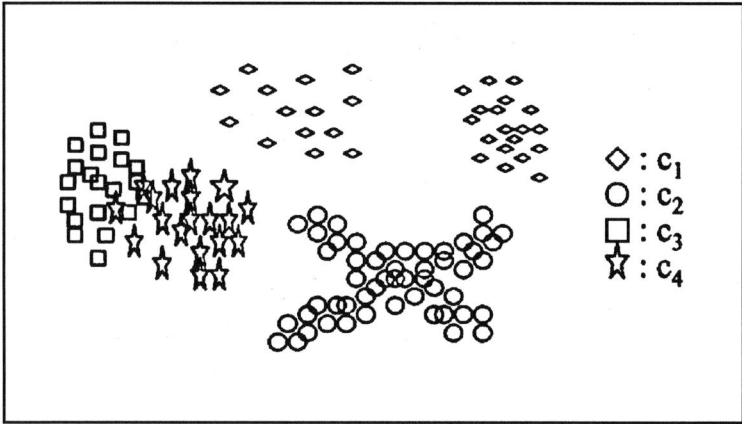

Figure 8. Concave and overlapping classes. Class c_1 is composed of two separate clusters and $c2$ is composed of two overlapping ellipsoidal clusters with different axis orientations. c1 and c2 are concave clusters and an optimal clustering procedure would suggest to split them into different clusters. Classes c3 and c4 are overlapping classes that may be merged by an unsupervised clustering process.

There is no superior cluster validity index for all possible applications (data sets) with all possible combinations of the parameters of a clustering algorithm (the fuzzifier coefficient m in fuzzy clustering for instance). We suggest to use some of the most reliable ones (according to some experiences and to the literature) simultaneously and retain the optimal value delivered by the majority. In this work, 6 validity indices, presented in Table 3, have been used in the experiments presented in section 6.

The minimal value of the optimal number of clusters is set to the number of labels (classes) present in the training data. A smaller number may cause the merging of different classes (especially overlapping ones) into the same cluster. Thus, the optimal value may be smaller than the "true" number of clusters. Cluster validity indices organize data in an optimal number of groups based on "blind" requirements, that is, they are used in unsupervised techniques that do not take advantage of the labels of the patterns provided in the training data set (supervised training). The three criteria presented above may lead to merging neighboring classes. In an unsupervised frame it its impossible to avoid this merging when the three criteria are satisfied. Therefore, we take advantage of the available labels: a penalty factor is added/subtracted to the validity index in case a cluster groups patterns belonging to different classes. The penalty factor reflects the variance of labels in the cluster. The higher the variance, the higher the penalty value. One can give different definitions for such a factor. The variance is added to the validity index when the minimum value represents the optimal number of clusters and it is subtracted to the index when a maximal value is desired.

5.4. Output layer supervised training and rule extraction

The remaining step in the optimal design of a RBFN is the determination of the weights of the output layer.

Table 3 Validity indices for optimal cluster-number identification

Validity index	Description	Optimal cluster nr.
Hyper Volume	$V_{HV} = \sum\limits_{i=1}^{c} [\det(F_i)]^{1/2}$	minimum
Partition Density	$V_D = \sum\limits_{i=1}^{c} \dfrac{S_i}{[\det(F_i)]^{1/2}}$ $S_i = \sum\limits_{j=1}^{N} u_{ij} \quad \forall x_j \in \left\{ x_j / (x_j - v_i) F_i^{-1} (x_j - v_i) < 1 \right\}$	maximum
Average Partition Density (using the determinant of Fi)	$V_{AD} = \dfrac{1}{c} \sum\limits_{i=1}^{c} \dfrac{S_i}{[\det(F_i)]^{1/2}}$	maximum
Average Partition Density (using the trace of Fi)	$D_{AD} = \dfrac{1}{c} \sum\limits_{i=1}^{c} \dfrac{S_i}{tr(F_i)}$	maximum
Trace of within cluster scatter matrix	$Vw = tr(Sw)$ $Sw = \sum\limits_{i=1}^{c} \left(F_i \sum\limits_{j=1}^{N} u_{ij} \right)$	maximum
Trace of Between cluster scatter matrix	$V_B = tr(S_B)$ $S_B = \sum\limits_{i=1}^{c} \left(\sum\limits_{j=1}^{N} u_{ij} \right) \cdot (v_i - v) \cdot (v_i - v)^T$ $v = \dfrac{1}{c} \sum\limits_{i=1}^{c} v_i$	minimum

The training of the output layer is considered as a labeling phase. Indeed, the optimal clustering phase determines the best set of clusters to model the structure of the data and outputlayer is actually used to put the adequate label on clusters grouping patterns of a same class. In terms of fuzzy rules this layer determines the consequence parts of the extracted rules. Each output node represents a class.

In general, the output weights of a RBFN can be determined by a pseudo-inverse matrix which can be computationally demanding when the training set is large. In this work we used the delta-rule type of learning algorithm (Back-propagation) which is a less demanding technique.

The weight between a hidden node j and a output node i can be interpreted as the certainty degree to assign a pattern belonging to cluster j, to class i. A value of 1 means that cluster j groups patterns belonging exclusively to class i. A zero value means that no patterns from class I are present in cluster j. An intermediate value means that the cluster is heterogeneous reflecting a possible class overlapping (or merging). The weight values are thus considered as certainty values that can be defined as the percentage of patterns belonging to class i that were grouped in cluster j by the clustering algorithm. These values can be computed after the optimal clustering phase and be considered as initial set of weights for a back-propagation algorithm or as the final weights of the output layer.

5.5. Algorithm: elliptical radial basis function network design

We have so far presented a general methodology for the optimal design of a RBFN for automatic fuzzy rule extraction; we refer to a RBFN designed by following this approach as Elliptical Radial Basis Function Network (ERBFN). In this section we recall the main steps in a concise algorithm for a practical usage.

Given a collection of n m-dimensional training data points $X_i (i = 1, \ldots, n)$ and their corresponding labels $l_i (i = 1, \ldots, n); l_i \in \{1, \ldots, c\}$ where c is the number of classes. The issue is to extract rules in order to label correctly the data points. Let n_c be the number of clusters (RBFs), and c_{max} be the maximum value n_c can have.

Step 1: Set n_c to c and set the centers of the RBFs $\varphi_i(x)$ to the mean values of the c classes. (one can choose to pick randomly a data point from each class to set the corresponding RBF).

Step 2: Unsupervised Fuzzy clustering: first cluster the data using the FCM algorithm for few iterations (as described in section 5.1), then apply the FMLE using the exponential distance. In relatively high dimensional problems one can use the Toeplitz estimator to compute the fuzzy covariance matrix and its inverse matrix and determinant, to reduce the computational time. The use of the Toeplitz estimator is required in case of singular covariance matrices.

Step 3: Compute the validity indexes as described in section 5.3. If n_c is equal to the c_{max} go to step 4 else increase n_c by 1. The new RBF center can be picked randomly. However, we suggest to pick it from the most heterogeneous cluster and move the actual center of that cluster (by adding small random values or picking another data point randomly). and go back to step 2.

Step 4: Set the optimal number of nodes/rules n_{opt} to the number delivered by the majority of the validity indexes.

Step 5: Design a RBFN with m input nodes, n_{opt} hidden nodes and c output nodes. The centers of the hidden nodes are set to the prototypes of the clusters of the optimal partition. The shape of each radial function is defined by the (estimated) fuzzy covariance matrix (used in the distance computation). For each cluster (in the optimal partition), compute the percentage of each class, as described in section 5.4. Set the weight of the connection between hidden node j and the output node i to the percentage of data points belonging to cluster j and labelled i. Test the obtained network. If further tuning is required, apply the well known backpropagation algorithm to train the network.

6. EXPERIMENTS

In order to evaluate the efficiency of the presented method, we performed experiments on synthetic and real world data. Cross validation technique is used to assess the performance of the classifiers. The results presented above are the average of 5 runs, where a random proportion of the data, 70% for synthetic data and 50% for the benchmark data (from each class), was used for training and the remaining data was used for testing.

Table 4 Data description of experiment 1

	Center (x,y)	Variance (x,y)	# Patterns
C1	(24, 10)	(24, 0.1)	123
C2	(24, 10)	(1, 2)	43
C3	(17, 7)	(1, 2)	102

6.1. Synthetic data experiments

The method was first tested on synthetic hyper-ellipsoidal clusters of varying size, axes orientation, position and density with normal distributions. By varying the distances between the cluster prototypes and controlling the variances of the features, cluster overlapping was controlled. Random fuzzy covariance matrices were generated in order to produce arbitrary oriented hyper-ellipsoids. The dimension, the number of clusters and the number of data points of each cluster were subjected to variation. Intuition about the system behavior was developed first on non-overlapping hyper elliptical clusters and then by increasing the overlap between clusters belonging to the same class and finally by overlapping clusters belonging to different classes. The number of clusters per class varied from 1 to 3, and the total number of clusters varied from 2 to 10. The dimensions tested were $\{2, 3, \dots, 10, 20, 40\}$.

In non-overlapping cases the system performed very well; the accuracy (acc) was 100% with the number of hidden nodes equal to the number of clusters. The overlapping of clusters belonging to the same class didn't affect the performance of the system. The number of hidden nodes was sometimes less than the number of clusters because overlapping clusters were merged. Since the merged clusters belong to the same class it didn't affect the performances when the neighboring clusters from different classes were relatively far. However, as expected, the system was sensitive to the overlapping of the clusters belonging to different classes. We varied the cluster overlap from 10% to 30%; the performances varied from 94.1% to 72.3% respectively. This behavior was predicted. In a totally overlapping area, the only way to distinguish the classes with acc = 100% is to assign a unit per pattern. However this guaranties the correct classification of the training patterns and not that of the test patterns.

In the following, we present two experiments to demonstrate the performances of our approach. For visualization convenience 2D-data sets are considered in the examples.

6.1.1. Experiment 1

Three elliptical classes with different variances and densities have been synthesized (see Figure 9). Table 4 gives the description of the clusters. Classes C1 and C2 cross each other and present an important overlapping (24% of C1 overlaps with C2). Moreover, the centers of the Classes are similar, what makes the Euclidean distance an inappropriate similarity measure. The performance of ERBFN is compared to that of the Gaussian RBFN (GRBFN). The parameters of the Gaussian functions are obtained after the FCM clustering step required for the initialization of the membership matrix

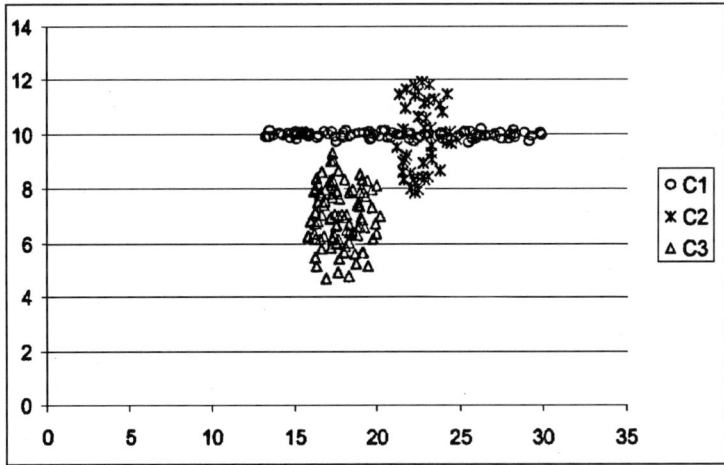

Figure 9. Overlapping elliptical 2D data set used in experiment 1. Cluster C1 crosses cluster C2 and presents 24% overlapping.

(U) for EFCM. The cluster prototypes and variances are used to define the center and width of the Gaussian kernels respectively.

Figure 10 shows the accuracy of the GRBFN versus that of ERBFN. As one may note, the ERBFN showed better accuracy than GRBFN. Furthermore, ERBFN showed a growing accuracy according to the number of hidden units, while GRBFN's accuracy was oscillating. GRBFN were not able to accurately separate class C1 and class C3 in spite of the fact that these classes do not overlap. Furthermore, the crossing of C1 and C2 was not modeled by GRBFN. In Figure 11, we show the optimal partition, according to the validity indices, for both FCM partitioning and FMLE partitioning. A number of seven clusters was a good compromise between the validity criteria and the homogeneity of the clusters. Figure 11.a shows that a part of C1 was merged with C2: cluster 5 groups the top half of class C2 with the middle part of class C1. This reduces considerably the ability of the network to separate Class C1 from Class C2. Figure 11.b shows that ERBFN provided a better modeling of the overlapping classes C1 and C2. In this case 3 clusters (cluster2, cluster3 and cluster 5) are used to model class C1 and two clusters (cluster1 and cluster4) for C2. Class C3 has been captured by 2 cluster6 and cluster7.

One can notice that the optimal number of clusters (7) didn't provide the best performance for ERBFN but for the GRBFN it did. One should keep in mind that cluster validity indices highly depend on the clustering algorithm. Different ways of partitioning lead to different optimal numbers of clusters. The optimal number of cluster is relative and not absolute. Since there are no best validity indices for all data sets and classifiers, it is difficult to define or choose appropriate ones. However, we

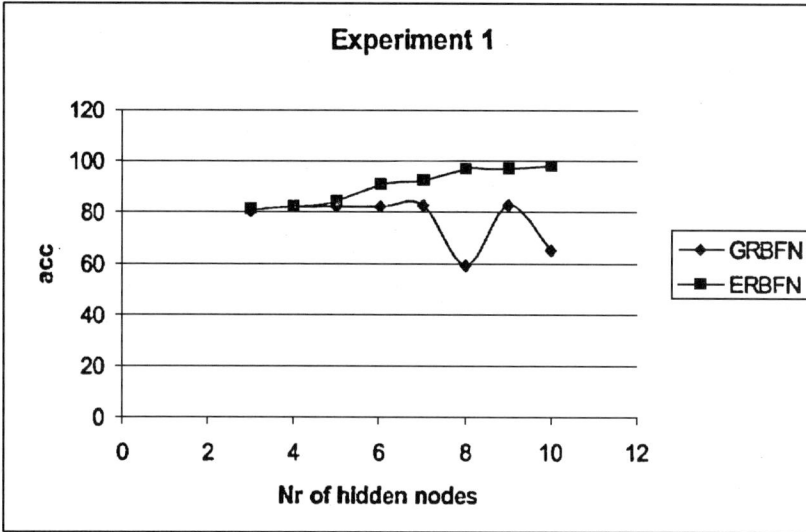

Figure 10. GRBFN versus ERBFN in experiment 1. The data presents elongated (highly elliptical) clusters with important overlapping. In such cases ERBFN outperforms GRBFN.

noticed that the best performance of the networks was generally obtained using a number superior or equal to the "optimal" number of clusters (7 in this experiment) and is generally close to the "optimal" one (10 in this case). Therfore, cluster validity indices should be used to determine a first guess of optimal number of hidden nodes.

Experiments in higher dimensions have been carried out and ERBFN showed better performances over GRBFN in presence of elongated and close elliptical clusters.

6.1.2. Experiment 2

In this second example two banana shaped classes B1(top) and B2 (bottom) were used to evaluate the method. Two data sets have been generated (see Figure 12). In the first data set (banana 1), B1 and B2 consisted of 100 patterns each while in the second case (banana2), B1 and B2 had 1000 patterns each. In both cases, a variance of 1 (around an arc) was used for each class. In the first set, B1 and B2 are adjacent but non–overlapping while in the second set they present an important overlap. Figure 13 gives the accuracy of the ERBFN and GRBFN. Very good accuracy was obtained using a small number of hidden nodes. Each class was split in several segments (clusters). In banana1, B1 was captured by 4 clusters (cluster2, cluster3, cluster5 and cluster7) and B2 was captured by 3 clusters (cluster1, cluster4 and cluster6). In banan2, B1 was captured by 4 clusters (cluster2, cluster4, cluster5 and cluster6) and B2 was captured by 3 clusters (cluster1, cluster3 and cluster7). Each cluster was modeled by a RBF node. The performances of GRBFN and ERBFN were comparable. The clusters automatically defined by fuzzy

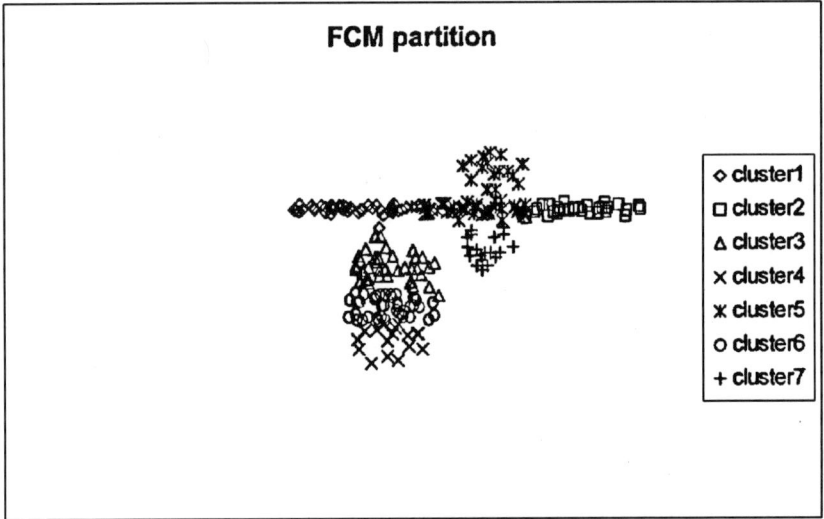

(a)

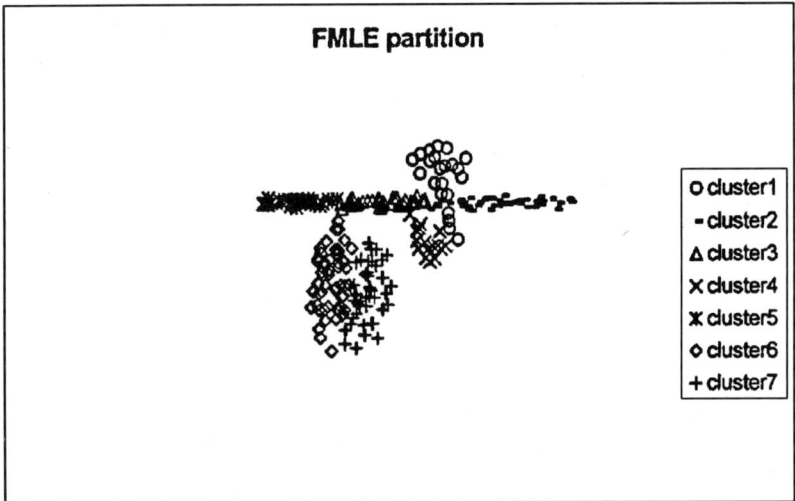

(b)

Figure 11. Optimal clustering output in experiment 1. (a) Partition delivered by the FCM algorithm (b) Partition delivered by the FMLE algorithm.

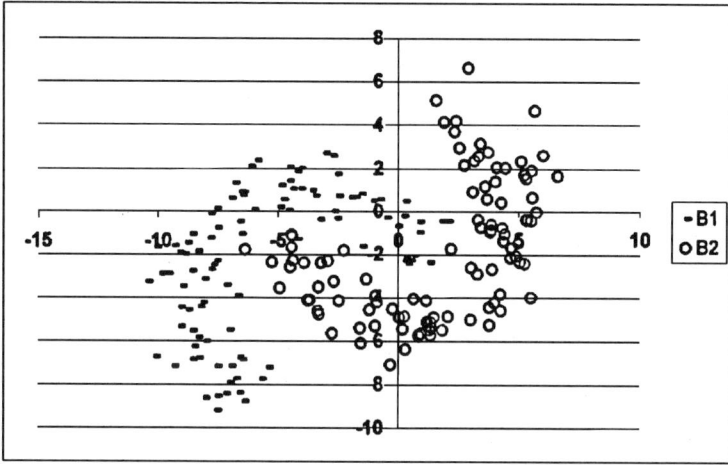

(a)

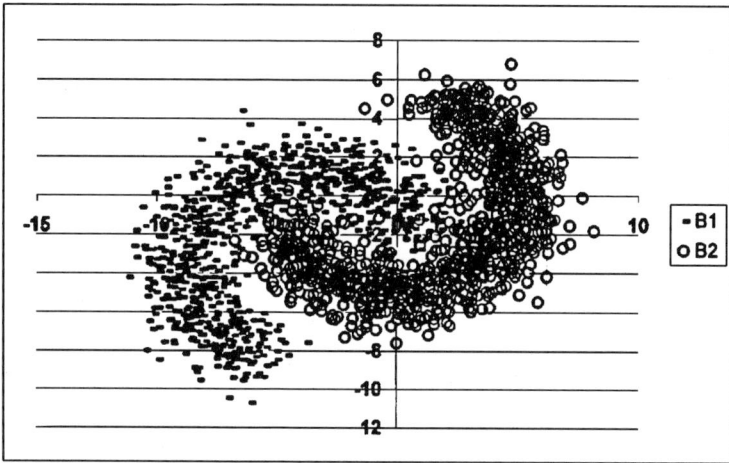

(b)

Figure 12. Experiment 2. (a) Banana1 data set: 100 patterns per class and no overlapping. (b) Banana2 1000 patterns per class and overlapping.

clustering are not highly elliptical and thus both kinds of RBFS can capture accurately the shape of the bananas using a set of circles or ellipses.

It is important to note that a small number of nodes (only 8 for banana1 and 10 for banana2) was sufficient to distinguish the two bananas with a very good accuracy (99% for Banana1 and 96.8 for Banana2). The optimal number of clusters was 7 for

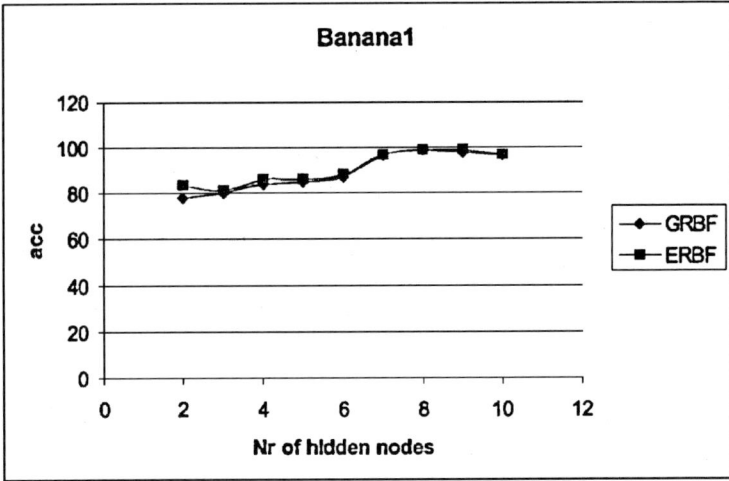

(a)

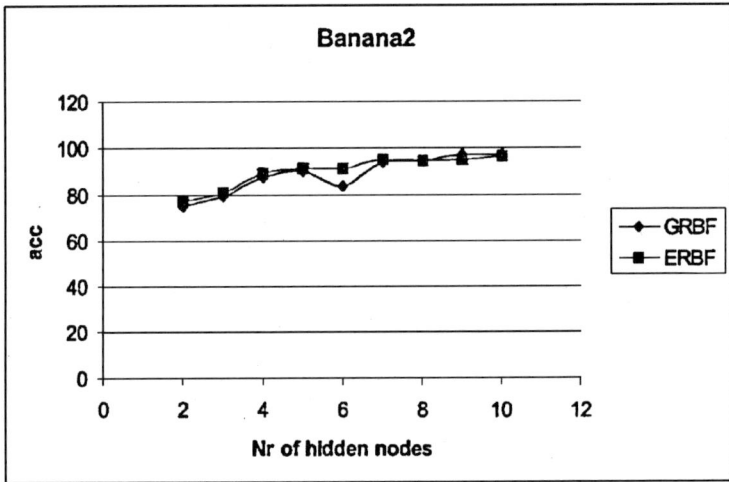

(b)

Figure 13. GRBFN versus ERBFN in experiment 2 when applied on the banana1 data set (a) and when applied to the banana2 data set (b). The performances are comparable.

banana1 and 8 for banana2. As in experiment 1, the best performances were obtained using a number of nodes which is higher but still close. Thus our set of validity criteria was still relatively good since it gives an indication of the number of hidden nodes that should be used. The optimal number is around the value delivered by the majority of indices.

Table 5 Benchmark data sets

	Dimension	# classes	# examples	majority
Bupa	6	2	345	58.0
Diabet	8	2	768	65.1
Glass	9	6	214	35.5
Vehicles	18	4	846	28.3

Extensive synthetic data experiments in higher dimensions have showed that in non-overlapping cases the performances were comparable and in hyper-spherically shaped clusters the GRBFN showed a slightly better generalization than the ERBFN. However, for highly elliptically shaped clusters the ERBFN showed superior performance over GRBFN and the number of hidden nodes was generally smaller in the ERBFN than in the GRBFN. In fact, ERBFN can be viewed as being the result of the tuning of a GRBFN. Indeed, since FCM is used to define a first partition as an initialization step for UOFC, a GRBFN parameters can be derived without extra computational efforts. In high dimensions it is worth training both RBFNs when one doesn't know a priori the shape of clusters. If ERBFN performs better that GRBFN it implies that the data present highly elliptical clusters (elongated classes). However, if GRBFN does better it means that the data present hyper-spherical clusters or sparse elliptical clusters that can be modeled by a number of hyper-spheres.

6.2. Benchmark data experiments

Our focus lies on domains of continuous data in relatively high dimensions. The selected benchmark data present non-linear decision surfaces (or oblique) and noisy/overlapping data. Recently, Miroslav Kubat [40] presented interesting results on benchmark data obtained using RBFN. He used decision trees to initialize the RBFs centers and widths and derived analytically the weights of the output layer by means of a pseudo inverse matrix to train the networks. His network is referred to as TB-RBFN (Tree Based Radial Basis Function Network). He compared the performances of a RBFN, initialized using decision trees, to the performances of the decision trees generated by Quinlan's C4.5. In this chapter, we compare the performances of the ERBFN to the performances given by Kubat in [40].

The public-domain benchmark data were selected from the University of California, Irvine, repository [41]: Liver disorder (bupa), diabetes (diab), glass and vehicles. Information about the data is given in Table 5. The rightmost column gives the percentage with which the majority concept is represented [40]. This number represents the performance that would be achieved if the system consistently labeled all testing examples with the label of the most frequently represented concept.

Table 6 presents the results obtained by Kubat in [40] using TB-RBF and C4.5 and the results we obtained for the same number of units. Table 7 presents the best results obtained by our approach. The number of rules per class is given in Table 8.

For the Bupa data set we obtained comparable results when using the same number of units (24). TB-TBF show a slightly better performance (2.53%). However, ERBFN

Table 6 Performances using the same number of hidden units as those derived for the TB-RBF and C4.5 approaches

Data set	GRBF # units	acc	ERBF # unit	acc	TB-RBF # unit	acc	C4.5 acc
Bupa	24	66.2	24	62.2	24.0	68.8	65.3
Diabet	42	74.7	42	77.34	42.6	74.8	71.8
Glass	16	64.7	16	68,57	16.4	62.8	61.7
Vehicles	57	74.2	57	63.27	57.2	74.6	64.9

Table 7 Optimal number of hidden nodes

Data set	GRBF # units	acc	ERBF # unit	acc
Bupa	53.0	66.86	54	73.2
Diabet	39.0	75.78	55	79.4
Glass	21.0	75.3	21	73.3
Vehicles	57.0	74.29	57	63.2

Table 8 Number of rules (clusters) per class for each data set

	# nodes	C1	C2	C3	C4	C5	C6
Bupa	54	36	18	—	—	—	—
Diabet	55	36	19	—	—	—	—
Glass	21	5	6	0	4	2	4
Vehicles	57	19	15	8	15	—	—

showed a better accuracy when increasing the number of units. A significant improvement was obtained with 54 rules. GRBFN had the same performances and increasing the number of clusters (node) didn't show any significant improvement. Thus, this data must present elongated structures.

In Diabet, ERBFN showed the best performances while GRBFN showed comparable performances with those of TB-RBFN when using the same number of hidden units. ERBFN showed significant improvements (4.62%) using 55 units instead of 42. This data presents concave classes and hyper-elliptical (elongated) structures, since ERBFN did better than GRBFN and the accuracy increased when the number of nodes was increased. With 55 nodes (rules) the ERBFN presented the best accuracy reported in the literature for the Diabet dataset.

The glass data set presented the most spectacular results. ERBF showed a significant improvement (5.77%) over TB-RBFN while using the same number of hidden units. GRBFN presented comparable accuracy. Significant improvement is obtained with

21 hidden units by both RBFNs (12.5% for GRBFN and 10.53 for ERBFN). The data doesn't seem to present elongated structures since GRBFN and ERBFN performances are nearly identical. However, both RBFNs didn't succeed to distinguish class c3 (see Table 8). No node (rule) is dedicated to this class. This is because few patterns (17) represent this class and it seems that it has an important overlap with other class C1 and C2. Class C4 groups less patterns (13) and so does class C5 (9). These two classes are still distinguishable, thus, they do not present overlap with other classes.

In the vehicle data set, GRBFN presented comparable results to TB-RBFN however ERBFN didn't show any improvement compared to C4.5. This brings back in mind the known drawback of FMLE algorithm: It can seek an optimum in a narrow local region and may show some time instability.

Our approach was successful in most of the experiments we carried out. Besides the design of a good classifier one can derive some information about structure of the data in high dimensions (presence of convex or concave classes, presence of overlapping, the shape of the classes or their segments).

7. SUMMARY

In this chapter an efficient method to design RBFNs in high dimensional data sets for rule extraction is presented. Rules are extracted in the entire feature space in order to model the eventual correlation between the feature (arbitrary shaped and oriented classes). The method takes advantage of the functional equivalence between RBFNs and FISs pointed out by Jang. Advanced fuzzy clustering is used to design an optimal RBFN. Optimality concerns the smaller number of hidden nodes possible with adequate shapes of kernel functions with high accuracy. Moreover, there is a straightforward mapping of fuzzy clustering output to RBF nodes: one node per cluster, RBF centers correspond to the cluster prototypes and the shape and width of the kernels are determined by the fuzzy covariance matrix of the corresponding cluster.

Optimal fuzzy clustering allows optimal RBFN design, although it is well known that clustering may be sensitive to the type of similarity measure used to group the patterns. In this chapter we suggested the use of the estimated exponential distance, which is an approximation of the distance proposed by Gath and Geva [22]. Our distance is based on the Toeplitz covariance matrix estimator. This makes the distance insensitive to matrix singularity and does not involve inversion of the covariance matrix. Indeed the inverse and determinant of the Toeplitz estimator are analytically known. Hyper-elliptical radial basis functions are then used to model the extracted elliptical clusters.

Since there is no best validity index, the optimal number of neurons (= clusters or rules) is defined using several validity indices. The optimal number is the one suggested by the majority in a voting procedure. Furthermore, in order to avoid blind clustering, a penalty factor is added to the validity index, reflecting the heterogeneity of labels in clusters. The computation of such a factor is possible a supervised training application.

The higher the variance of labels, the higher the penalty values. The "true" number of cluster may be higher than the number of classes in case of concave classes. The optimal fuzzy clustering can identify concave structures. A concave class may be split in several convex clusters and thus be modeled by several convex hyper-spherical or hyper-elliptical kernels. Since each cluster corresponds to a RBF node and thus to a fuzzy rule, optimal set of rules describing the structure of the data in the entire space is extracted.

In this chapter, efficient and practical solutions to known problems encountered while designing RBFN networks are proposed and a general methodology is presented. The performances of the method are demonstrated on challenging synthetic and real world data sets. The focus lied on domains of continuous data presenting non-linear decision surfaces and noisy and/or overlapping areas. For each example small networks were derived to model the data with good accuracy. The structure of the data can be identified and described by few fuzzy rules defined in the entire space, which is more practical for high dimensional data sets.

REFERENCES

[1] J. S. Roger Jang, and C. T. Sun, Functional Equivalence Between Radial Basis Function Networks and Fuzzy Inference Systems, IEEE Transactions on Neural Networks, 4 (1) (1993) 156–158.

[2] R. T. Yager, and D. P. Filev, Unified Structure and Parameter Identification of Fuzzy Models, IEEE Transactions on System Man and Cybernetics, 23 (1993) 1198–1205.

[3] J. Nie, and D. A. Linkens, Learning Control Using Fuzzified Self-Organizing Radial Basis Function Network, IEEE Transactions on Fuzzy Systems, 1(4) (1993) 280–287.

[4] C. F. Juang, and C. T. Lin, An On-Line Self-Constructing Neural Fuzzy Inference Network and its Applications, IEEE Transactions on Fuzzy Systems, 6(1) (1998) 12–32.

[5] F. Klaw, and R. Kruse, Constructing a Fuzzy Controller from Data, Fuzzy Sets and Systems, 85 (1997) 177–193.

[6] K. M. Lee, D. H. Kwak, and H. Leekwang, Tuning of Fuzzy Models by Fuzzy Neural Networks, Fuzzy Sets and Systems, 76 (1) (1995) 47–63.

[7] Z. Q. Liu, and F. Yan, Fuzzy Neural Network in Case-Based Diagnostic System, IEEE Transactions on Fuzzy Systems, 5 (2) (1997) 209–222.

[8] T. Takagi and M. Sugeno, Fuzzy Identification of Systems and its Applications to Modeling and Control, IEEE Transactions on System Man and Cybernetics, (15) (1985) 116–132.

[9] M. Delgado, A. F. Gomez-Skarmeta, and F. Martin, A Fuzzy Clustering-Based Rapid Prototyping for Fuzzy Rule-Based Modeling, IEEE Transactions on Fuzzy Systems, 5(2) (1997) 223–233.

[10] S. J. Raudys, and A. K. Jain, Small Sample Size Effects in Statistical Pattern Recognition: Recommendations for Practitioners, IEEE Transactions on Pattern Analysis and Machine Intelligence, 13 (3) (1991) 252–264.

[11] M. Ramze Rezaee, B. Goedhart, B. P. F. Lelieveldt, and J. H. C. Reiber, Fuzzy Feature Selection, Pattern Recognition 32 (1999) 2011–2019.

[12] D. S. Broomhead, and D. Lowe, Multivariable Function Interpolation and Adaptive Networks, Complex Systems, 2 (1988) 321–355.

[13] S. Chen, C. F. N. Cowan, and P. M. Grant, Orthogonal Least Square Learning Algorithm for Radial Basis Function Networks, IEEE Transaction on Neural Networks, 2(2) (1991) 302–309.

[14] Y. S. Hwang and S. Y. Bang, An Efficient Method to Construct a Radial Basis Function Neural Network Classifier, Neural Networks, 10(8) (1997) 1495–1503.

[15] M. J. D. Powell, Radial Basis Functions Approximations to Polynomials, Proceeding of 12th Biennial Numerical Analysis Conference, Dundee, 1987, pp. 223–241.

[16] B. Mulgrew, Applying Radial Basis Functions, IEEE Signal Processing Magazine, (1996) 50–64.

[17] M. Musavi, W. Ahmed, K. Chan, K. Faris and D. Hummels, On the Training of Radial Basis Function Classifiers, Neural Networks, 5(4) (1992), 595–603.

[18] J. C. Bezdek, Pattern Recognition with Fuzzy Objective Function Algorithms, New York: Plenum, (1981).

[19] S. Abe, and R. Thawonmas, A Fuzzy Classifier with Elliptical Regions, IEEE Transactions on Fuzzy Systems, 5 (1997) 358–368.

[20] S. Abe, R. Thawnmas, and M. Kayama, A fuzzy Classifier with Ellipsoidal Regions for Diagnosis Problems, IEEE Transactions on System Man and Cybernetics, part C: Application and Reviews, 29(1) (1999) 140–149.

[21] M. S. Yang, Convergence Properties of the Generalised Fuzzy-C-Means Clustering Algorithms, Computers & Mathematics with Applications, 25(12) (1993) 3–11.

[22] I. Gath, and A. B. Geva, Unsupervised Optimal Fuzzy Clustering, IEEE Transactions on Pattern Analysis and Machine Intelligence, 11(7) (1989) 773–781.

[23] R. N. Davé, and R. Krishnapuram, Robust Clustering Methods: A Unified View, IEEE Transactions on Fuzzy Systems, 5(2) (1997) 270–293.

[24] L. Bobrowski, and J. C. Bezedek, C-Means Clustering with the L1 and L∞ Norms, IEEE Transactons on System Man and Cybernetics, 21(3) (1991) 545–554.

[25] P. J. Rousseeuw, L. Kaufma, and E. Trauwaert, Fuzzy Clustering Using Scatter Matrices, Computational Statistics & Data Analysis, 23 (1996) 135–151.

[26] D. E. Gustafson, and W. C. Kessel, Fuzzy Clustering with a Fuzzy Covariance Matrix, IEEE CDC, San Diego, (1979) 761–766.

[27] P. J. Rousseeuw, E. Trauwaert, and L. Kaufma, Fuzzy Clustering with High Contrast, Journal of Computational and Applied Mathematics 64 (1995) 81–90.

[28] I. Gath, and A. B. Geva, Fuzzy Clustering for the Estimation of the Parameters of the Components of Mixtures of Normal Distributions, Pattern Recognition Letters, 9 (1989) 77–86.

[29] R. N. Davé, and R. Krishnapuram, Robust Clustering Methods: a Unified View, IEEE Transactions on Fuzzy Systems, 5(2) (1997) 270–293.

[30] E. Trauwaert, L. Kaufman, and P. Rousseeuw, Fuzzy Clustering Algorithms based on the Maximum Likelihood Principle, Fuzzy Sets and Systems 42 (1991) 213–227.

[31] Y. Hamamoto, Y. Fujimoto, and S. Tomita, On the Estimation of a Covariance Matrix in Designing Parzen Classifiers, Pattern Recognition, 29 (10) (1996) 1751–1759.

[32] J. V. Ness, On the Dominance of Non-Parametric Bayes Rule Discriminant Algorithms in High Dimensions, Pattern Recognition 12 (1988) 355–368.

[33] F. Kimura, K. Takashima, S. Tsuruoka, and Y. Miyake, Modified Quadratic Discriminant Functions and the Application to Character Recognition, IEEE Transaction on Pattern Analysis and Machine Intelligence, 9(1) (1987) 149–153.

[34] K. Fukunaga, Introduction to Statistical Pattern Recognition, 2nd edn. Academic Press, New York, 1990.

[35] X. L. Xie, and G. A. Beni, Validity Measure for Fuzzy Clustering, IEEE Transactions on Pattern Analysis and Machine Intelligence, 13(8) (1991), 841–846.

[36] R. P. Nikhil, and J. C. Bezdek, On Cluster Validity for the Fuzzy C-Means Model, IEEE Transactions on Fuzzy Systems 3(3) (1995) 370–379.

[37] M. Ramze Rezaee, B. P. F. Lelieveldt, and J. H. C. Reiber, A New Cluster Validity Index for the Fuzzy C-Mean, Pattern Recognition Letters 19 (1998) 237–246.

[38] N. R. Pal, and J. C. Bezdek, On Cluster Validity for Fuzzy c-Means Model, IEEE Transactions on Fuzzy Systems 3(3) (1995) 370–379.

[39] N. R. Pal, and J. C. Bezdek, Correction to on Cluster Validity for the Fuzzy-C-Means Model, IEEE Transactions on Fuzzy Systems, 5(1) (1997) 152–153.

[40] M. Kubat, Decision Trees can Initialize Radial Basis Function Networks, IEEE Transactions on Neural Networks 9(5) (1998) 813–821.

[41] P. Murphy, and D. Aha, "UCI Repository of Machine Learning Databases [machine-readable data respository]," Tech. Rep., Univ. Calif., Ivrine, CA. http:www.ics.uci.edu/AL/ML/Machine-Learning.html.

[42] F. Behloul, B. P. F. Lelieveldt, A. Boudraa, and J. H. C. Reiber, "Optimal design of radial basis function neural networks fo fuzzy rule extraction in high dimensional data," Pattern recognition, vol. 35, pp. 659–675, 2002.

[43] D. Dubois and H. Padre. *Fuzzy Sets and Systems: Theory and Applications.* Academic Press, Inc, 1980.

[44] L. A. Zadeh, "Fuzzy sets," Information and Control, 1965, vol. 8, pp. 333–353.

[45] J. S. R. Jang, "ANFIS: Adaptive-Network-based Fuzzy Inference Systems," IEEE Transactions on Systems, Man and Cybernetics, 1993, vol. 23, no. 3, pp. 665–685.
[46] J. Moody and C. Darken, "Fast learning in networks of locally-tuned processing units," Neural Computations, 1989, vol. 1, pp. 281–294.
[47] Z.-Q. Liu and F. Yan, "Fuzzy neural network in case-based diagnostic system," IEEE Transactions on Fuzzy Systems, 1997, vol. 5, no. 2, pp. 209–222.

FUZZY DECISION MODELING OF PRODUCT DEVELOPMENT PROCESSES

JUITE WANG AND ANDREW KUSIAK

1. INTRODUCTION

Product development has become a focus of competition in many industries. Due to decreasing product life cycle, it is important to reduce the time and cost of product development. The product development process includes six main phases: product planning, concept development, system-level design, detailed design, testing and refinement, and production ramp-up [34]. Concept development process consists of four stages: identifying customer needs, establishing product specifications, and generating and selecting product concepts. Recent efforts have been made to improve the product development decisions [20], especially at the early stages of product development, since it has been recognized that nearly 75% of product life-cycle cost is committed by the end of concept development [26]. However, it is difficult to make product design decisions at the early development stages, because decision makers have to consider all life cycle issues [21, 22] with vague project information available.

Since the decisions made at the early development stages significantly impacts downstream decisions and the product life cycle cost, it is important to develop decision models to assist decision makers in analyzing tradeoffs among life cycle issues and improve decision making. Most research attempts to address decision support in the domain of well-defined variables and specifications where all values are assumed to be known. A few methodologies and tools have been developed to support development decisions for early development stages. Some researchers modeled design uncertainties with probability distributions [30]. However, since new product development, especially for innovative products, is usually unique in nature and there may be no historical data available to estimate the probability distributions for certain variables, the stochastic models may not be the best choice to improve design decisions at the early development stages. Fuzzy set theory [18] may provide an alternative to a convenient framework of modelling the imprecise project or product information. Wood et al. [47] concluded that fuzzy set theory is more appropriate for representing and manipulating imprecise design parameters, whereas probability theory is more appropriate for dealing with stochastic uncertainty of design parameters. The literature of applying fuzzy set theory to product development decisions is reviewed next.

At the product specification stage, fuzzy set approach was used to assist development teams in setting engineering requirements that will be considered in developing a product. Most of the published frameworks are based on the Quality Function Deployment (QFD) approach [12]. Wang [38] developed a fuzzy ranking model to prioritize engineering requirements and applied sensitivity analysis to examine the quality of the selected requirements. Temponi et al. [33] developed a fuzzy logic-based requirements analysis tool to identify imprecise relationships between engineering requirements. Kim et al. [17] combined multi-attribute value theory with fuzzy regression and fuzzy optimization for making trade-off among various engineering requirements and to choose target values for engineering requirements. Karsak et al. [14] integrated the analytical network and goal programming approaches to determine design requirements. For other related research in QFD, refer to the review paper by Chan and Wu [4].

Most research in concept development is based on fuzzy set theory to evaluate and select design concepts for developing a product. Knosala and Pedrycz [16] utilized the Analytical Hierarchical Process methodology [29] to construct membership functions for performance and weight of each criterion, and then used the fuzzy weighted mean of the overall evaluation for ranking alternatives. Carnahan et al. [3] represented evaluation results and weights regarding to all evaluation criteria with linguistic terms and ranked alternatives based on the fuzzy weighted mean of distance from a fuzzy goal. Wang [37, 40] proposed fuzzy ranking decision models for selecting "best" design concepts that have the least possibility to be worse than other alternative concepts. Jiao and Tseng [13] adapted Wang's approach [37] and introduced customer satisfaction to concept evaluation using the concept of information content proposed by Suh [32]. Vanegas and Labib [36] proposed a new fuzzy-weighted average approach to select design concepts. Wang [41] develop a fuzzy set extension of Pugh's concept selection method and proposed three indices to examine the quality of the selected design concepts.

A frequently used goal at the product planning stage is to identify a portfolio of products to be developed by the organization and the timing of their introduction to the market. Fuzzy set theory can be applied to improve decisions at this stage. The CPM and PERT networks have been extended with fuzzy durations of activities [23, 25]. In project scheduling, Hapke and Slowinski [11] applied twelve fuzzy dispatching rules to generate a number of schedules and selected the schedule with the minimum fuzzy makespan. Wang [39, 42] proposed the measure of "schedule risk" and its dual measure "schedule robustness" [44] to evaluate schedule performance for the product development project and developed an efficient fuzzy beam search algorithm to determine the schedule that minimizes the possibility of being late. For portfolio management, Wang and Hwang [46] evaluated the value of a product development project using a fuzzy real options approach [1, 2] and developed a fuzzy optimization model to select the set of projects that maximizes the total project values and balances R&D strategic goals under limited resources.

This chapter presents fuzzy decision models for robust decision-making in an imprecise and uncertain product development environment. Section 2 presents basic concepts of fuzzy set theory and possibility theory that are used in the developed decision models. Section 3 describes a fuzzy QFD technique for prioritizing design requirements. A fuzzy concept selection model is introduced in Section 4 to determine the best concepts for further development. The two decision models select the "best" design requirements or concepts with the least possibility to be worse than other alternatives. Section 5 presents a fuzzy project scheduling approach for determining a schedule that minimizes the risk of late project. Finally, Section 6 concludes the chapter.

2. MODELLING PRODUCT DEVELOPMENT INFORMATION WITH FUZZY SETS

2.1. Introduction to fuzzy set theory

In this section, basic elements of fuzzy set theory [18] related to the approach proposed in this paper are presented. If X is a collection of objects denoted by x, then a fuzzy set $\tilde{F}$ in X is a set of ordered pairs $\tilde{F} = \{(x, \mu_{\tilde{F}}(x) | x \in X\}$, where $0 \leq \mu_{\tilde{F}}(x) \leq 1$, which is called the membership function or grade of membership of x in $\tilde{F}$.

A fuzzy set $\tilde{F}$ is convex, if and only if $\forall x, \gamma \in R$,

$$\mu_{\tilde{F}}(\lambda x + (1 - \lambda)\gamma) \leq \min\{\mu_{\tilde{F}}(x), \mu_{\tilde{F}}(\gamma)\}, \quad \forall \lambda \in [0, 1] \tag{1}$$

A fuzzy set $\tilde{F}$ is normal, if and only if

$$\sup_x \mu_{\tilde{F}}(x) = 1, \quad \forall x \in R \tag{2}$$

This means that the highest value of $\mu_{\tilde{F}}(x)$ is equal to 1. A fuzzy number $\tilde{F}$ is defined as a fuzzy set which is convex and normal and its membership function can be described as follows:

$$\mu_{\tilde{F}}(x) = \begin{cases} L_{\tilde{F}}(x), & a \leq x \leq b \\ 1, & b \leq x \leq c \\ R_{\tilde{F}}(x), & c \leq x \leq d \\ 0, & \text{otherwise} \end{cases} \tag{3}$$

where: $L_{\tilde{F}} : [a, b] \to [0, 1]$ and $R_{\tilde{F}} : [c, d] \to [0, 1]$.

Many different membership functions can be defined based on the definition in (3). Two types of special fuzzy numbers are introduced as they are frequently used in the literature to reduce the amount of computational effort. A trapezoidal fuzzy number $\tilde{F} = (a, b, c, d)$ is defined as:

$$
\mu_{\tilde{F}}(x) = \begin{cases}
(x - a)/(b - a), & a \leq x \leq b \\
1, & b \leq x \leq c \\
(d - x)/(d - c), & c \leq x \leq d \\
0, & \text{otherwise}
\end{cases}
\tag{4}
$$

with the $[b, c]$ interval containing the most likely values for $\tilde{F}$ and values less than a and greater than d being impossible. A triangular fuzzy number is a specialized trapezoidal fuzzy number with $b = c$ and is usually denoted as $\tilde{F} = (a, b, b, d)$ or (a, b, d).

Fuzzy arithmetic operations, addition ($\oplus$), subtraction ($\ominus$), multiplication ($\otimes$), and maximum ($\tilde{Max}$) used later in this chapter are defined next. Let $*$ denote three basic arithmetic operations $\oplus, \ominus, \otimes$ and let $\tilde{A}, \tilde{B}$ denote fuzzy numbers. Then we define a fuzzy set on $\Re$, $\tilde{A} * \tilde{B}$, by the equation:

$$
\mu_{\tilde{A} * \tilde{B}}(z) = \sup_{z = x^* y} \min[\mu_{\tilde{A}}(x), \mu_{\tilde{B}}(y)]
\tag{5}
$$

for all $z \in \Re$. Similarly, the membership function of $\tilde{Max}\{\tilde{A}, \tilde{B}\}$ is denoted:

$$
\mu_{\tilde{Max}\{\tilde{A}, \tilde{B}\}}(z) = \sup_{z = Max\{x, y\}} \min[\mu_{\tilde{A}}(x), \mu_{\tilde{B}}(y)]
\tag{6}
$$

Please refer to Klir and Yuan [18] for details.

2.2. Representing imprecision and preference information with fuzzy sets

Fuzzy sets theory allows to model imprecision or preference information in a product development project. As fuzzy set is used to interpret imprecision information, $\mu_{\tilde{F}}(x)$ is the degree of possibility that a parameter D has value x, given that "D is $\tilde{F}$." For example, a design engineer wants to represent the maintenance cost of a product with "about \$190." Sh/e may not know the exact maintenance cost but can specify a possible range [160, 230]. Therefore, the maintenance cost of the design can be described with a triangular fuzzy number (160, 190, 230). The value 190 has the possibility of one in the fuzzy set: "about \$190," and values away from 190 have lower possibility (see Figure 1).

As fuzzy set is used to interpret preference information, $\mu_{\tilde{F}}(x)$ represents the degree of preference in favor of value x. For example, a project manager may prefer that a project should be completed before e_1, but no later than e_2; otherwise, it may delay the product to enter the market. In this case, the preferred project deadline can be represented as a triangular fuzzy number $\tilde{e} = (e_1, e_1, e_2)$ (see Figure 2). In the same

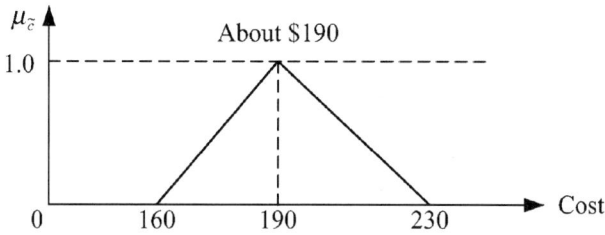

Figure 1. Uncertain maintenance cost.

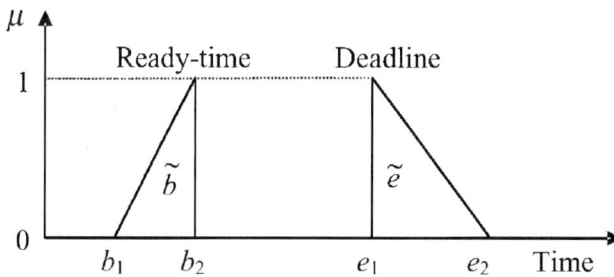

Figure 2. Preferred project ready-time and deadline.

way, the preferred ready-time of a project can also be represented as a triangular fuzzy number $\tilde{b} = (b_1, b_2, b_2)$ (see Figure 2).

2.3. Measures of possibility and necessity

Dubois and Prade [6] developed a set of four ranking indices in the framework of Zadeh's [49] possibility theory. The four indices, based on possibility measure Π and necessity measure N, can be used to compare two fuzzy numbers.

Definition: Possibility measure
Given the possibility distribution $\tilde{F}$, the possibility of realizing fuzzy event $\tilde{A}$ is:

$$\Pi_{\tilde{F}}(\tilde{A}) = \sup_{x} \min(\mu_{\tilde{F}}(x), \mu_{\tilde{A}}(x)) \tag{7}$$

Definition: Necessity measure
Given the possibility distribution $\tilde{F}$, the necessity of realizing fuzzy event $\tilde{A}$ is:

$$N_{\tilde{F}}(\tilde{A}) = \inf_{x} \min(1 - \mu_{\tilde{F}}(x), \mu_{\tilde{A}}(x)) \tag{8}$$

Two sets of numbers having a fuzzy number $\tilde{A}$ as a fuzzy bound should be defined (Dubois and Prade 1988). The set of numbers possibly greater than or equal to $\tilde{A}$ is denoted as $[\tilde{A}, +\infty)$ with membership function:

$$\mu_{[\tilde{A},+\infty)}(\gamma) = \sup_{x \leq \gamma} \mu_{\tilde{A}}(x) \tag{9}$$

The set of numbers necessarily greater than $\tilde{A}$ is denoted as $]\tilde{A}, +\infty)$ with membership function:

$$\mu_{]\tilde{A},+\infty)}(\gamma) = \inf_{x \geq \gamma} (1 - \mu_{\tilde{A}}(x)) \tag{10}$$

Given two fuzzy numbers $\tilde{A}$ and $\tilde{B}$, four indices are defined to assess the possible relationships between them:

$$PG(\tilde{A}, \tilde{B}) = \prod_{\tilde{A}} ([\tilde{B}, +\infty)) = \sup_{u; u \geq v} \min (\mu_{\tilde{A}}(u), \mu_{\tilde{B}}(v)) \tag{11}$$

$$PSG(\tilde{A}, \tilde{B}) = \prod_{\tilde{A}} (]\tilde{B}, +\infty)) = \sup_{u} \inf_{v; v \geq u} \min (\mu_{\tilde{A}}(u), 1 - \mu_{\tilde{B}}(v)) \tag{12}$$

$$NG(\tilde{A}, \tilde{B}) = N_{\tilde{A}} ([\tilde{B}, +\infty)) = \inf_{u} \sup_{v; v \leq u} \max (1 - \mu_{\tilde{A}}(u), \mu_{\tilde{B}}(v)) \tag{13}$$

$$NSG(\tilde{A}, \tilde{B}) = N_{\tilde{A}} (]\tilde{B}, +\infty)) = 1 - \sup_{u \leq v} \min (\mu_{\tilde{A}}(u), \mu_{\tilde{B}}(v)) \tag{14}$$

The four indices take values in $[0, 1]$. $PG(\tilde{A}, \tilde{B})$ (respectively, $PSG(\tilde{A}, \tilde{B})$) implies that the grade of possibility of the proposition "$\tilde{A}$ is greater than or equal to $\tilde{B}$" (respectively, "$\tilde{A}$ is strictly greater than $\tilde{B}$"). It estimates the maximum chance that an event "$\tilde{A} \geq \tilde{B}$" (respectively, "$\tilde{A} > \tilde{B}$") will occur. Similarly, $NG(\tilde{A}, \tilde{B})$ (respectively, $NSG(\tilde{A}, \tilde{B})$) implies that the grade of necessity of the proposition "$\tilde{A}$ is greater than or equal to $\tilde{B}$" (respectively, "$\tilde{A}$ is strictly greater than $\tilde{B}$"). It provides an index to estimate the minimum chance that an event "$\tilde{A} \geq \tilde{B}$" (respectively, "$\tilde{A} > \tilde{B}$") will occur.

3. A FUZZY SET APPROACH FOR PRIORITIZATION OF DESIGN REQUIREMENTS

3.1. Problem formulation

To remain successful, companies strive to develop products that satisfy customer needs. Poor product definition commonly leads to either failure of that product in the marketplace or extended product development time. Good understanding of customers' needs, when done early, leads to successful products and shortens the development time.

Design requirements are generally established by a product development team at the early product development stage, according to the customer needs, company's strategic goals, government regulations, or specification practice standards. The development team needs to create or improve a product design in the downstream design process, based on the identified design requirements. The quality function deployment (QFD)

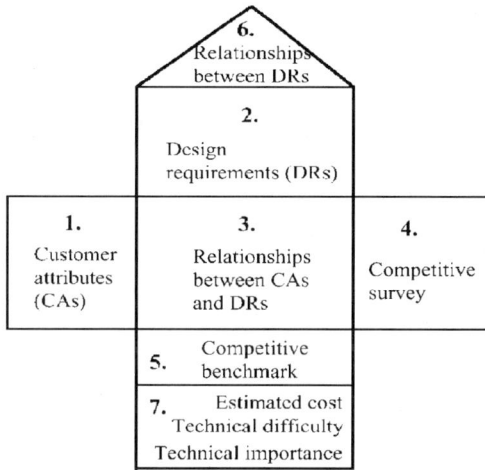

Figure 3. The components of a QFD.

[12] is a tool to systematically relate attributes that represent the overall customer concerns to the design requirements that represent technical performance specifications of a product to be developed. It has been used successfully by industries in both Japan and USA. The elements of QFD are displayed in Figure 3. The QFD planning process is summarized into the following seven steps:

1. Obtaining the customer attributes and their relative importance.
2. Developing design requirements responsive to the customer attributes.
3. Relating design requirements to the customer attributes.
4. Completing the customer competitive survey.
5. Performing the competitive technical benchmarking.
6. Determining the relationships among design requirements.
7. Calculating the technical importance ratings of design requirements and evaluating their technical difficulties and estimated costs.

A product development team creates or improves a product based on the design requirements represented by the QFD matrix. However, it is not possible to consider all design requirements, because a perfect product may require a longer time and higher development costs. Product designers need to know how to make tradeoffs in the selection of the design requirements that result in higher level of customer satisfaction and the balanced design of a product.

A fuzzy ranking preference model [38] based on possibility theory [6] is presented next. The model establishes a preference structure of design requirements and identifies critical requirements that are the focus at the later development stages. The purpose of the proposed model is not only to satisfy the customer requirements but also accomplish a balanced design.

Table 1 The linguistic scales for input data of QFD

Linguistic scale for relative importance	Linguistic scale for relationships between CAs and ERs	Linguistic scale for estimated cost	Linguistic scale for technical difficulty	Fuzzy scale
Very unimportant	Weakest	Very expensive	Very difficult	L1
unimportant	Weak	Expensive	Difficult	L2
Fairly unimportant	Fairly weak	Fairly expensive	Fairly difficult	L3
Medium	Medium	Medium	Medium	L4
Fairly important	Fairly strong	Fairly reasonable	Fairly easy	L5
Important	Strong	Reasonable	Easy	L6
Very important	Strongest	Very reasonable	Very easy	L7

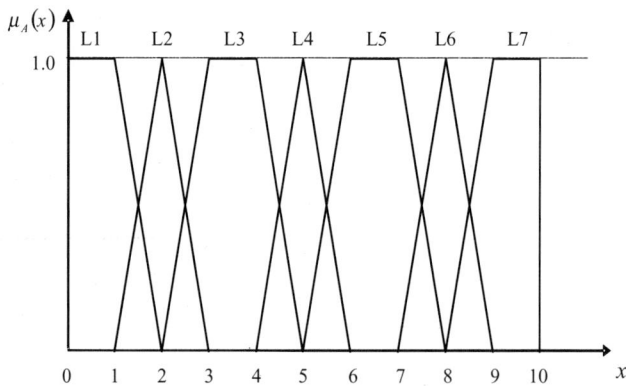

Figure 4. Membership functions of the linguistic terms defined in Table 1.

3.2. A fuzzy outranking preference model to prioritize design requirements

3.2.1. Representing imprecise information in QFD

Due to the imprecise and incomplete design information at the early product development stages, most approaches use the subjective numerical values to represent the inputs required by QFD [4]. For example, a 1-5-9 numerical scale is used to denote weak, medium, and strong relationships between customer attributes and design requirements. However, it is more natural to allow team members to describe the performance of each criterion with some linguistic terms, such as "Important," "Unimportant," "Very important," etc. Those linguistic terms can be interpreted as specific membership functions or fuzzy numbers for performing tradeoff analysis among various criteria.

Table 1 illustrates four linguistic scales used to assess the required input data for a QFD. The membership functions corresponding to the linguistic terms defined in Table 1 are shown in Figure 4. For simplicity, we assume that the same membership functions are used to characterize each linguistic scale. Based on the linguistic scales provided, each team member evaluates each criterion and provides the result of his/her evaluation. For example, the strongest (weakest) strength of relationship between a customer attribute and design requirement is given the highest (lowest) linguistic value "Very important" ("Very unimportant") in the scale.

In QFD, the technical importance of each design requirement is computed as the weighted sum of the relationships with customer attributes. As the relative importance of customer attributes and the relationship between customer attributes and design requirements are represented by linguistic terms, the technical importance for design requirement j is computed from (15):

$$\tilde{s}_j = (\tilde{y}_1 \otimes \tilde{d}_{1j}) \oplus (\tilde{y}_2 \otimes \tilde{d}_{1j}) \oplus \cdots \oplus (\tilde{y}_m \otimes \tilde{d}_{mj}) \tag{15}$$

where:

$\tilde{s}_j$: technical importance of design requirement j, $j = 1, \ldots, n$.
$\tilde{y}_i$: relative importance of customer attribute i, $i = 1, \ldots, m$
$\tilde{d}_{ij}$: relationship between customer attribute i and design requirement j; $i = 1, \ldots,$
   m, $j = 1, \ldots, n$

3.2.2. A fuzzy outranking preference model for prioritizing design requirements

The design information collected at the QFD planning stage may be vague or incomplete, and therefore it may be difficult to compare and/or distinguish various design requirements. The proposition "requirement a is better than b" may not be determined precisely. There may be some degrees of agreement and disagreement about this proposition. To tackle this problem, the fuzzy outranking relation proposed by Roy [28] is used to model the imprecise preference relations between design requirements. Alternative a outranks b ($a\,\mathbf{S}\,b$) if and only if there is a sufficient evidence to believe that a is better than b or at least a is as good as b.

Definition: Fuzzy outranking relation
Given two alternatives a and b, the statement "a outranks b" signifies that the decision-maker has enough reasons to admit that a is at least as good as b. A fuzzy outranking relation indicates the degree of outranking, denoted by $S(a, b)$, associated with each pair of alternatives a and b, where $S(a, b) \in [0, 1]$.

$S(a, b) = 1$ implies that a outranks b with certainty. On the contrary, $S(a, b) = 0$ implies that there is no evidence that b is outranked by a. $S(a, b) \in (0, 1)$ indicates a credibility of an existing preference of a over b. Therefore, applying the concept of outranking relation to model the imprecise preference relations between design requirements prevents some important requirements that have enough evidence to support their criticality from ignorance.

Based on the fuzzy outranking relation defined above, the problem of prioritizing design requirements is described. Let A be a finite set of design requirements evaluated in QFD according to a set C of criteria. The set of criteria may include the technical importance, estimated cost, technical difficulty, and so on. The evaluation result of a design requirement for each criterion can be defined as a vector $g(a) = [g_1(a), g_2(a), \ldots, g_n(a)]$, where the function $g_k(a)$ represents the evaluation result of requirement $a \in A$ for criterion $c_k \in C$. The objective of prioritizing design requirements is to determine the fuzzy outranking relations between individual requirements and to build a preference structure $(L_1, L_2, \ldots, L_n)$ of design requirements, such that:

$$\forall b \in L_q, \exists a \in L_p \Rightarrow a\mathbf{S}b, \quad \text{where } p < q.$$

The preference structure indicates the preferences among design requirements, where the requirements in set L_p dominate the requirements in set L_q for $p < q$.

The degree of outranking can be obtained from two types of relation: concordance relation and discordance relation, namely degrees of agreement and disagreement. For two design requirements a and b, the concordance relation expresses the credibility of the hypothesis that a is at least as good as b with respect to a certain criterion. The discordance relation is used to express some doubt towards the hypothesis that "a is not at least as good as b" with respect to some criterion.

Definition: Concordance relation
Concordance relation that a is at least as good as b with respect to criterion c_k is defined:

$$CI_k(a, b) = \theta \, PG(g_k(a), g_k(b)) + (1 - \theta) NG(g_k(a), g_k(b)), \tag{16}$$

where $g_k(a)$ and $g_k(b)$ are the fuzzy rating regarding criteria c_k for requirements a and b, respectively, and θ is the preference ratio, $0 \le \theta \le 1$.

Both possibility and necessity measures are used to define the concordance relation. The necessity measure $NG(g_k(a), g_k(b))$ calculates the least chance that a is at least as good as b with respect to criterion c_k from the conservative viewpoint. On the contrary, the possibility measure $PG(g_k(a), g_k(b))$ computes the best opportunity from the aggressive viewpoint. Therefore the concordance index that a is at least as good as b with respect to criterion c_k should be located between $NG(g_k(a), g_k(b))$ and $PG(g_k(a), g_k(b))$. We use the Hurwicz criterion [9] to take a middle course and a preference ratio θ is defined to incorporate the attitude of decision maker into the decision model. If the attitude of decision maker is toward to the optimistic, then the value of θ should be greater than 0.5. On the other hand, the value of θ should be less than 0.5, if the attitude is toward to pessimistic.

The global concordance relation, $GCI(a, b)$, that a is greater than or equal to b is defined as the aggregation of all single-criterion concordance relations:

$$GCI(a, b) = \sum_k w_k CI_k(a, b), \tag{17}$$

where w_k is the weight used to express the relative importance of criterion c_k.

Definition: Discordance relation
Discordance relation that a is at least as good as b with respect to criterion c_k is defined as follows:

$$DI_k(a, b) = NG(g_k(b), g_k(a)). \tag{18}$$

The least chance that requirement b is better than or equal to a is used to define the degree of doubt that a is better than or equal to b with respect to criterion c_k.

Next, the concordance relation and discordance relation between a and b for each criterion are aggregated to establish the outranking relation between them. The aggregation function developed by Sisko et al. [31] is used to obtain the degree of outranking:

$$
S(a, b) = \begin{cases} GCI(a, b), & \text{if } GCI(a, b) \geq DI_k(a, b), \forall c_k \in C \\ \prod_{k^*} [1 - DI_{k^*}(a, b)] \dfrac{GCI(a, b)}{1 - GCI(a, b)}, & \text{for } \{k^* \mid GCI(a, b) < DI_{k^*}(a, b)\} \end{cases}
$$

(19)

If there is no single-criterion discordance relation greater than the obtained global concordance relation, then the degree of outranking between requirements a and b is set to the global concordance relation between them. Otherwise, the single-criterion discordance relations that are greater than the global concordance relation for certain criteria will take effect to weaken the belief that a outranks b. If there is a single-criterion discordance relation $DI_{k^*}(a, b) = 1$ with respect to criterion c_{k^*}, then $S(a, b) = 0$, i.e. b is not outranked by a absolutely.

To prioritize a set A of design requirements, the outranking relation used to establish the preference structure of design requirements is defined as follows:

$\forall a, b \in A$:

(Outranking) $a \, \mathbf{S} \, b$,   if $S(a, b) \geq \delta$

where δ is the outranking threshold, $0 \leq \delta < 1$.

(20)

The outranking threshold δ is used to determine the existence of outranking relation between a and b. If the degree of outranking between a and b does not exceed outranking threshold, then it is not considered significant and requirement b is not outranked by a. The value of outranking threshold may range from the smallest value that allows to distinguish between two alternatives to the largest value that does not distinguish between them.

The decision model presented does not force to distinguish the preference between two design requirements. Requirements a and b may be incomparable to each other, because the available design information is usually incomplete at the early design stage. Based on the outranking relation defined in (20), two other relations are defined:

$\forall a, b \in A$:

(Indifference) $a \, \mathbf{I} \, b$,   if $a \, \mathbf{S} \, b$ and $b \, \mathbf{S} \, a$ (21)

(Incomparability) $a \, \mathbf{R} \, b$,   otherwise   (22)

Customer attribute	Attribute Importance	Misfeed rate 1	Multifeed rate 2	Jam rate 3	Copy rate 4	Jam clearance rate 5	Paper damage rate 6	Umc 7
1 Always get a copy	L7	L7		L7				
2 No blank sheets	L4							
3 No jams to clear	L6		L4	L7				
4 Medium speed	L5				L7			
5 Copies on cheap paper	L5	L5	L5	L5				
6 Copies on heavy paper	L2	L5		L5				
7 Copies on light paper	L3		L5	L5				
8 Easy to clear jams	L6					L7		
9 No paper damage	L4						L7	
10 Low cost	L6							L7
11 Estimated cost		L3	L5	L6	L2	L4	L4	L3
12 Technical difficulty		L4	L6	L5	L3	L3	L4	L2

Figure 5. The linguistic QFD input data for the copier design.

According to (21) and (22), the requirements that are indifferent or incomparable to each other will be identified in the preference structure of design requirements.

3.3. Illustrative example

An example of a copier design adapted from [5] is used to illustrate the approach developed. Assume that the low–cost market segment is the development focus. The set of customer attributes includes "always get a copy," "no blank sheet," "no jams to clear," "medium speed," "copies on cheap paper," "copies on light paper," "copies on heavy paper," "easy to clear jams," "no paper damage," and "low cost" and the corresponding design requirements consist of "misfeed rate (r_1)", "multifeed rate (r_2)," "jam rate (r_3)," "copy rate (r_4)," "jam clearance rate (r_5)," "paper damage rate (r_6)," and "unit manufacturing cost (r_7)." The criteria involved in the prioritizing process include technical importance (c_1), estimated cost (c_2), and technical difficulty (c_3). Figure 5 lists the required input data for prioritization using the linguistic scales defined in Table 1.

Assume that the preference ratio (θ) is set to 0.5 and the weighting factors for technical importance (w_1), estimated cost (w_2), and technical difficulty (w_3) are equal to 0.3, 0.2, and 0.5, respectively. The individual concordance relations between design requirements for criteria of technical importance, cost, and technical difficulty can be computed according to Eq. (16) and the global concordance matrix can be obtained in Table 2, where element (i, j) aggregates the corresponding concordance

Table 2 Global concordance relations between design requirements

		r_j					
(i, j)	1	2	3	4	5	6	7
1	—	0.29	0.34	1.00	0.70	0.65	0.90
2	0.91	—	0.60	1.00	1.00	1.00	1.00
3	0.91	0.75	—	1.00	1.00	1.00	1.00
r_i 4	0.15	0.00	0.00	—	0.33	0.41	0.42
5	0.45	0.10	0.00	0.95	—	0.75	0.84
6	0.55	0.10	0.05	0.80	0.53	—	0.60
7	0.33	0.02	0.02	0.85	0.50	0.50	—

Table 3 Fuzzy outranking relations between design requirements

		r_j					
(i, j)	1	2	3	4	5	6	7
1	—	0.00	0.00	1.00	0.00	0.00	0.90
2	0.91	—	0.00	1.00	1.00	1.00	1.00
3	0.91	0.00	—	1.00	1.00	1.00	1.00
r_i 4	0.00	0.00	0.00	—	0.00	0.00	0.00
5	0.00	0.00	0.00	0.95	—	0.00	0.84
6	0.00	0.00	0.00	0.76	0.00	—	0.00
7	0.00	0.00	0.00	0.00	0.00	0.00	—

relations between requirements r_i and r_j regarding three criteria according to Eq. (17). Next, the discordance relations between design requirements can be computed using Eq. (18) and the outranking relations between requirements can be constructed in Table 3 according to Eq. (19).

A preference graph is used to represent the preference structure of design require-ments. A node of a preference graph denotes a design requirement and a directed arc from node a to b denotes a relationship of a outranking b. An example of the preference graph with respect to $\theta = 0.5$ and $\delta = 0.5$ is shown in Figure 6 and the preference structure of design requirements are as follows:

$$L_1 = \{r_2, r_3\}, \quad L_2 = \{r_1, r_5, r_6\}, \quad \text{and} \quad L_3 = \{r_4, r_7\}.$$

It is observed that design requirements r_2 and r_3 (i.e., "multifeed rate" and "jam rate") dominate other requirements and should be chosen for designing the copier. If the budget is allowed to incorporate additional requirements for the copier design, then the requirements in L_2 have higher priority than L_3 for further consideration.

The value of preference ratio θ may influence the degree of outranking between design requirements and change the preference structure. Figure 7 shows the rela-tionship between the preference ratio to the degree of outranking for certain design requirements. It indicates that the requirements that are sensitive to the preference ratio

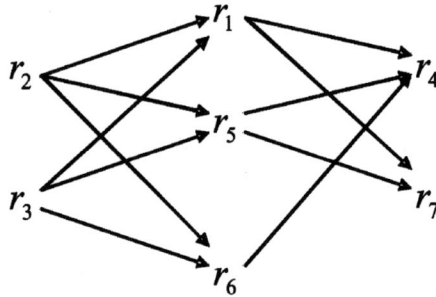

Figure 6. The preference graph ($(\theta = 0.5$ and $(\delta = 0.5)$.

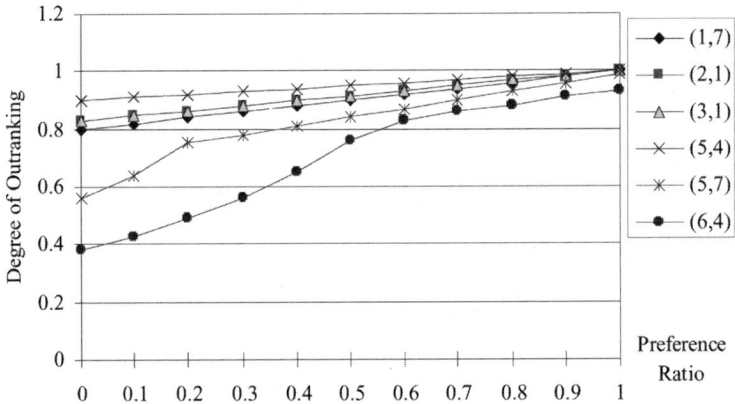

Figure 7. Relationship between the preference ratio to the degree of outranking for certain design requirements.

need to consider more carefully, since it may not be easy to determine the proper value of θ for decision makers. For example, the outranking relation between requirements r_6 and r_4 is most sensitive to the preference ratio and both of them should be examined carefully.

4. A FUZZY SET APPROACH FOR SELECTION OF DESIGN CONCEPTS

4.1. Problem formulation

The major task of concept development phase is to generate design concepts, evaluate them, and select one or more "best" concepts for further refinement in the latter development stages. Concept development is usually an iterative process. A set of design concepts is generated and evaluated, according to the design requirements determined in the stage of product specifications. The design concepts that are superior to others become the candidates for further improvement. Some new concepts may be improved based on old concepts, or be combined from other concepts with one or more new feature. Poor concepts will be eliminated from further consideration. The process continues until the design is well understandable and one or more "best" design concepts can be determined for further development for the next design stage.

The concept selection problem is important, because selecting a poor design concept can rarely be compensated at later development stages and may lead to high redesign costs. The selection of the "best" design concepts from a set of concept variants can be expressed as a multi-criteria decision making (MCDM) model [8, 15]. A product development team needs to consider not only the required product functionality, but also other life-cycle issues (e.g., manufacturability, assembability, reliability, maintainability, etc). Some design criteria may contradict each other. The development team should analyze the trade-offs among various criteria and select the best alternative. However, it is difficult to assess the performance of each concept variant that is just a rough idea or sketch at this stage. Fuzzy set theory can be applied to assist decision makers in evaluating design concepts and selecting the "best" design concepts among them.

There have been many studies that apply the fuzzy set analysis for design evaluation at different design stages [3, 13, 16, 36]. Most often it is assumed that a trade-off among various criteria can be made. Therefore, the original multi-criteria problem can be transformed into a single-criterion problem by aggregating the individual criteria. However, at the concept development stage, it may be difficult to distinguish between any two concepts as the design information is subjective or incomplete to make a judgment. The incomparable design concepts may be required to remain in the design process until sufficient information is collected. Some researchers used non-compensatory operator, such as the minimum operator, for evaluating a design alternative based on its worst aspects [27]. In both cases, a complete order of all alternatives is built. The incomparability, which exists in practice, between alternatives is completely ignored. In addition, it is preferred to classify the set of concepts into different subsets from the "best" to "worst," rather than ranking the concepts into a complete order at the concept development stage.

Using the above description, the concept selection problem is defined next. Let A be a finite set of design concepts evaluated, according to a set C of criteria. Let $g(a) = [g_1(a), g_2(a), \ldots, g_n(a)]$ be the performance of design concept $a \in A$, where the function $g_k(a)$ represents its performance rating for criterion $c_k \in C$. The objective of the concept selection problem is to determine the set S_{ND} of non-dominated design concepts from A for continuous improvement in concept development or further development in the following design stages.

A fuzzy outranking preference model developed in [40] is presented next to represent the imprecise preference structure among a set of design concepts and to determine a non-dominated set of design concepts for continuous improvement or further development at later development stages.

4.2. Fuzzy outranking preference model for concept selection

4.2.1. Construction of fuzzy outranking relations

Since product life cycle information is incomplete it may be difficult to compare design concepts. It is undesirable to ignore any potentially "good" concepts. The incomparable design concepts may be required to remain in the design process until sufficient design information is collected.

To tackle this problem, the fuzzy outranking relation presented in Section 3 is used to model the imprecise preference relations between design concepts. Concept a outranks b ($a \textbf{ S } b$) if and only if there is a sufficient evidence to believe that concept a is better than b or at least a is as good as b. The fuzzy outranking preference model presented in this section applies the measures of possibility and necessity to model the imprecise preference structure of design concepts.

The four indices PG, PSG, NG, and NSG defined in Eqs. (11)–(14) characterize different comparison situations from worst to best between two fuzzy numbers. However, four indices may not lead to the same ordering, and decision makers still have to make the final choice. This somewhat defeats the purpose of the ranking method that is supposed to derive a conclusion for decision makers. In this section, an aggregation function, called the ordered weighted averaging (OWA) operator [48], is applied to combine these four indices to assist the decision making in the concept selection process.

Definition: OWA Operator

An OWA operator of dimension n is a mapping $\Psi: I^n \rightarrow I$ (where $I = [0, 1]$) that has an associated weighting vector $V = (v_1, v_2, \ldots, v_n)^T$ such as (1) $v_i \in [0, 1]$, $1 \leq i \leq n$, and (2) $\sum_{i=1}^{n} v_i = 1$. Furthermore,

$$\Psi(a_1, a_2, \ldots, a_n) = v_1 b_1 + v_2 b_2 + \cdots + v_n b_n, \tag{23}$$

where b_j is the j-th largest element in the collection $a_1, a_2, \ldots, a_n$.

The OWA operator provides a continuous transition from the "*pure-and*" to the "*pure-or*." The following illustrate three important special cases of OWA aggregation:

(1) The "Max" case: $V^* = (1, 0, 0, \ldots, 0)$
   $\Psi^*(a_1, a_2, \ldots, a_n) = \text{Max} \{a_1, a_2, \ldots, a_n\}$
(2) The "Min" case: $V_* = (0, 0, 0, \ldots, 1)$
   $\Psi_*(a_1, a_2, \ldots, a_n) = \text{Min} \{a_1, a_2, \ldots, a_n\}$
(3) The "Average" case: $V^* = (1/n, 1/n, 1/n, \ldots, 1/n)$
   $\Psi_{Avg}(a_1, a_2, \ldots, a_n) = (a_1 + a_2 + \cdots + a_n)/n$

To avoid the cumbersome assignment of weights to the weighting vector V, the quantified guided aggregation function $Q(r) = r^\alpha$ is used to guide V for the aggregation of PG, PSG, NG, and NSG [48]. The weights associated with V are obtained as follows:

$$v_i = Q(i/n) - Q((i-1)/n), \quad i = 1, \ldots, n \tag{24}$$

The OWA operator allows decision makers to decide about the pair-wise comparison strategy. As mentioned above, four ranking indices characterize different situations from best to worst between two evaluation ratings represented by fuzzy numbers. For two fuzzy performance ratings, if the best situation is to be considered, then we can increase "*orness*" by decreasing the value of α towards zero (i.e., aggressive attitude). On the contrary, if the worst situation is to be considered, then we can increase α towards a large number greater than one (i.e., conservative attitude). Otherwise, we set α to one for the average situation.

The degree of outranking between two concepts is determined by the concordance and discordance relations. In this section, the concordance relation is redefined by aggregating four indices PG, PSG, NG, and NSG with the OWA operator:

$$CI_k(a, b) = F_Q(PG(g_k(a), g_k(b)), PSG(g_k(a), g_k(b)), NG(g_k(a), g_k(b)), NSG(g_k(a), g_k(b))), \tag{25}$$

where F_Q is the OWA operator and the weighting vector $V_Q = (v_1, v_2, v_3, v_4)$ is determined by linguistic quantifier $Q(r) = r^\alpha$, according on Eq. (24). Parameter α allows team members to specify the comparison strategy from conservative to aggressive viewpoint. In the same way, the global concordance relation, the discordance relation, the degree of outranking between design concepts are computed from Eqs. (17), (18), and (19), respectively.

4.2.2. Determination of non-dominated design concepts

After degrees of outranking between pairs of design concepts have been computed, the preference indices, indifference indices, and incomparability indices are defined to determine the non-dominated design concepts [8].

Definition: Preference index
Given two alternatives a and b, the statement "a is preferred to b" reflects the presence of arguments strong enough to support the statements "a outranks b" but not "b outranks a." The credibility that a is preferred to b is defined:

$$P(a, b) = \text{Max}\{S(a, b) - S(b, a), 0\}. \tag{26}$$

Definition: Indifference index
Given two alternatives a and b, the statement "a and b are indifferent" reflects the presence of arguments strong enough to support both the statements "a outranks b"

and "b outranks a." The credibility that a and b are indifferent is defined:

$$I(a, b) = \text{Min}\{S(a, b), S(b, a)\}. \tag{27}$$

Definition: Incomparability index

Given two alternatives a and b, the statement "a and b are incomparable" reflects the absence of arguments strong enough to support the statements "a outranks b" and "b outranks a." The credibility that a and b are incomparable is defined:

$$J(a, b) = \text{Min}\{1 - S(a, b), 1 - S(b, a)\}. \tag{28}$$

Concept a is preferred to b if and only if $P(a, b) > I(a, b)$ and $P(a, b) > J(a, b)$; otherwise, a is indifferent or incomparable to b.

$$a\mathbf{P}b \Leftrightarrow P(a, b) > I(a, b) \quad \text{and} \quad P(a, b) > J(a, b) \tag{29}$$

$$a\,\mathbf{I}\,b \text{ or } a\,\mathbf{J}\,b \Leftrightarrow \text{otherwise.} \tag{30}$$

Therefore, the non-dominated set S_{ND} can be identified, such that:

$$\forall b \notin S_{ND}, \exists a \in S_{ND} \Rightarrow a\mathbf{P}b \tag{31}$$

The non-domination degree of concept $a \in A$ can also be determined [8]:

$$\mu_{ND}(a) = \min_{b \in A} \{1 - P(b, a)\} \tag{32}$$

4.3. Illustrated example

Consider a preliminary selection of the splashguard design for the mountain bikes that can be used for both sports and street transportation [35]. The mountain bikes have no fenders, since mud would be easily trapped between tire and fender. When riding on trails, the rider generally does not care whether he or she gets muddy. However, as riding on the street, there is a need for an easily removable device to protect bike rider and baggage from road water.

Assume that seven types of concepts are generated by the splashguard development team. The linguistic scale and the corresponding fuzzy numbers used to evaluate seven splashguard design concepts is shown in Figure 8. The performance ratings for the seven concepts corresponding to eight criteria are listed in Table 4.

The outranking preference model is applied to rank these seven design concepts. The relative importance of eight criteria is evaluated with the linguistic scale listed in Table 5. The weight of each criterion can be obtained by transforming the assigned linguistic term to the corresponding quantitative value. The obtained normalized weights for all criteria are listed in Table 6.

Assume that parameter α of the quantifier-guided aggregation function is set to 1.0; i.e., $V_{\alpha=1.0} = (0.25, 0.25, 0.25, 0.25)$. The degrees of outranking for pairs of concepts

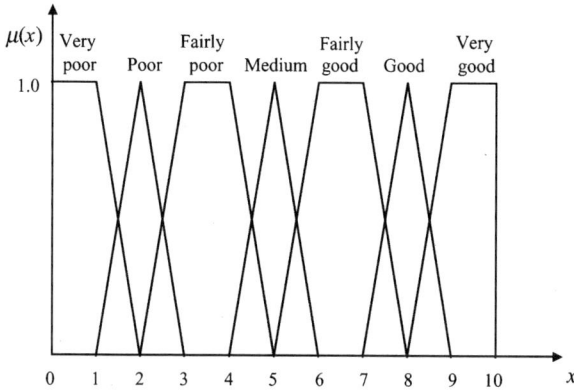

Figure 8. Seven levels of a linguistic scale used to design a splashguard.

Table 4 Performance ratings for seven splashguard design concepts corresponding to eight criteria

				Criterion				
Concept	Easy attach	Not mar	Not catch water	Not rattle	Long life	Light-weight	Fits Most bikes	stream-lined
I	fgood	vpoor	poor	poor	vpoor	good	good	vpoor
II	vgood	good	good	medium	poor	fgood	fgood	vgood
III	good	fgood	poor	fpoor	poor	fgood	fpoor	poor
IV	good	fgood	fgood	fgood	fgood	fpoor	fgood	poor
V	fgood	fgood	medium	good	fgood	fpoor	medium	good
VI	vpoor	medium	medium	fpoor	medium	medium	medium	medium
VII	poor	medium	medium	medium	medium	medium	medium	medium

Table 5 Linguistic scale of relative importance

Linguistic weight	Quantitative scale
Very important	7
Fairly important	6
Important	5
Medium	4
Unimportant	3
Fairly unimportant	2
Very unimportant	1

are determined in Table 7 from Eqs. (17), (18), (19), and (25) and then the corresponding preference indices, indifference indices and incomparability indices are computed from Eqs. (26)–(28) and shown in Tables 8-10.

Figure 9(a) shows the preference graph, where the concepts in L_p dominate the concepts in L_q for $p < q$. It is observed that the preference structure of seven concepts with

Table 6 Relative importance for eight criteria

Criterion	Qualitative scale	Normalized weight
Easy attach/detach	3	0.097
Not mar	6	0.194
Not catch water	3	0.097
Not rattle	4	0.129
Long life	7	0.226
Lightweight	3	0.097
Fit most bikes	3	0.097
Streamlined	2	0.065

Table 7 Degrees of outranking for pairs of concepts (as $\alpha = 1.0$)

		Concept a_j						
		1	*2*	*3*	*4*	*5*	*6*	*7*
	1	—	0.00	0.00	0.00	0.00	0.00	0.00
	2	0.80	—	0.79	0.00	0.00	0.00	0.00
	3	0.00	0.00	—	0.00	0.00	0.00	0.00
Concept a_i	*4*	0.00	0.00	0.00	—	0.00	0.00	0.00
	5	0.00	0.00	0.00	0.11	—	0.77	0.77
	6	0.00	0.00	0.00	0.00	0.00	—	0.18
	7	0.00	0.00	0.00	0.00	0.00	0.59	—

Table 8 Preference indices for pairs of concepts (as $\alpha = 1.0$)

		Concept a_j						
		1	*2*	*3*	*4*	*5*	*6*	*7*
	1	—	0.00	0.00	0.00	0.00	0.00	0.00
	2	0.80	—	0.79	0.00	0.00	0.00	0.00
	3	0.00	0.00	—	0.00	0.00	0.00	0.00
Concept a_i	*4*	0.00	0.00	0.00	—	0.00	0.00	0.00
	5	0.00	0.00	0.00	0.11	—	0.77	0.77
	6	0.00	0.00	0.00	0.00	0.00	—	0.18
	7	0.00	0.00	0.00	0.00	0.00	0.59	—

Table 9 Incomparability indices for pairs of concepts (as $\alpha = 1.0$)

		Concept a_j						
		1	*2*	*3*	*4*	*5*	*6*	*7*
	1	—	0.20	1.00	1.00	1.00	1.00	1.00
	2	0.20	—	0.21	1.00	1.00	1.00	1.00
	3	1.00	0.21	—	1.00	1.00	1.00	1.00
Concept a_i	*4*	1.00	1.00	1.00	—	0.89	1.00	1.00
	5	1.00	1.00	1.00	0.89	—	0.23	0.23
	6	1.00	1.00	1.00	1.00	0.23	–	0.41
	7	1.00	1.00	1.00	1.00	0.23	0.4-1	—

Table 10 Indifference indices for pairs of concepts (as $\alpha = 1.0$)

		Concept a_j						
		1	2	3	4	5	6	7
	1	—	0.00	0.00	0.00	0.00	0.00	0.00
	2	0.00	—	0.00	0.00	0.00	0.00	0.00
	3	0.00	0.00	—	0.00	0.00	0.00	0.00
Concept a_i	4	0.00	0.00	0.00	—	0.00	0.00	0.00
	5	0.00	0.00	0.00	0.00	—	0.00	0.00
	6	0.00	0.00	0.00	0.00	0.00	—	0.18
	7	0.00	0.00	0.00	0.00	0.00	0.18	—

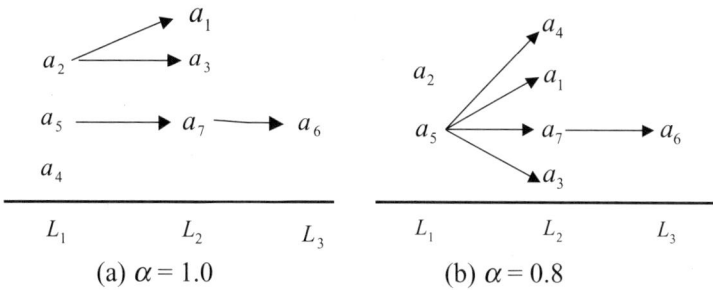

Figure 9. Preference structure of seven design concepts.

the credibility greater than 0.5 is: $L_1 = \{a_2, a_4, a_5\}$, $L_2 = \{a_1, a_3, a_7\}$, and $L_3 = \{a_6\}$. Concepts a_2, a_4 and a_5 are included in the non-dominated set and they may be considered for further improvement. According to Eq. (32), the non-domination degrees of concepts a_i, $i = 1$ to 7, are obtained: 0.37, 0.51, 0.49, 0.23, 1.0, 0.36, and, 1.0. This result is consistent with the obtained ranking order of design concepts.

Figure 9 indicates that parameter α influences the preference structure of design concepts. The influence of parameter α on the ranking order of design concepts is shown in Table 11. The development team can select the concepts which are less sensitive to the changes of parameter α. In this example, concepts a_2 and a_5 may be the better choice for continuous improvement or further development at the later development stage, because they keep in the non-dominated set as the value of parameter α varies. If the budget allows, concept a_4 may be included for further improvement.

Figure 10 shows the non-dominance degree of seven design concepts. It indicates that concepts a_2 and a_5 are the most robust and are insensible to the value of α. The concepts a_2, a_4, and a_5 strictly dominate other design concepts for any value of α.

Table 11 The influence of parameter α on the ranking order of seven valve types

Parameter α	Orness	Ranking order
$\alpha = 0.20$	0.83	$L_1 = \{a_2, a_5\}, L_2 = \{a_1, a_3, a_4, a_6, a_7\}$
$\alpha = 0.40$	0.71	$L_1 = \{a_2, a_5\}, L_2 = \{a_1, a_3, a_4, a_6, a_7\}$
$\alpha = 0.60$	0.63	$L_1 = \{a_2, a_5\}, L_2 = \{a_1, a_3, a_4, a_6, a_7\}$
$\alpha = 0.80$	0.56	$L_1 = \{a_2, a_5\}, L_2 = \{a_1, a_3, a_4, a_7\}, L_3 = \{a_6\}$
$\alpha = 1.00$	0.50	$L_1 = \{a_2, a_4, a_5\}, L_2 = \{a_1, a_3, a_7\}, L_3 = \{a_6\}$
$\alpha = 1.20$	0.45	$L_1 = \{a_2, a_4, a_5\}, L_2 = \{a_1, a_3, a_7\}, L_3 = \{a_6\}$
$\alpha = 1.40$	0.42	$L_1 = \{a_2, a_4, a_5\}, L_2 = \{a_1, a_3, a_6, a_7\}$
$\alpha = 1.60$	0.38	$L_1 = \{a_2, a_4, a_5\}, L_2 = \{a_1, a_3, a_6, a_7\}$

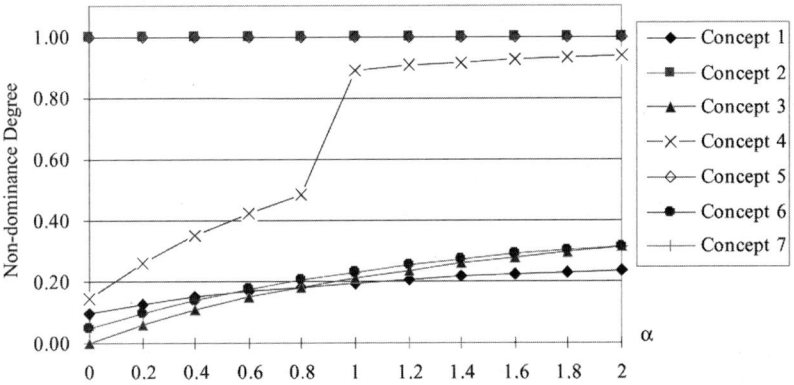

Figure 10. The non-dominance degrees of seven concepts.

5. A FUZZY SET APPROACH FOR SCHEDULING OF PRODUCT DEVELOPMENT PROJECTS

5.1. Problem formulation

A product development project may involve hundreds or even thousands of activities. Unlike the manufacturing process, a product development project is usually unique and "open-ended," especially for innovative designs. A major problem in managing a product development project is that the duration of an activity involved in the project is difficult to predict [39]. This is due to insufficient information available at the early stage of product development. Uncertainty concerning what or how much work must be performed to complete an activity seriously complicates the task of accurately estimating the distribution of activity duration.

In addition, there are several ways to realization of a selected project schedule, due to uncertainties in product development. For example, an activity cannot be finished on time, because the activity duration may be underestimated or some engineering changes occur during its execution. The delay of an activity impacts succeeding activities and may lead to the delay of the entire project. Under this uncertain scheduling environment, risk-averse project managers intend to consider the worst situation of a schedule under various realizations, i.e., the schedule robustness, especially when the scheduling problem is unique [44].

The fuzzy product development project scheduling problem is formulated next. A product development project p has a preferred fuzzy ready-time $\tilde{b}$ and a fuzzy deadline $\tilde{e}$ between which all its activities i $(1 \leq i \leq n)$ have to be performed. There may exist some precedence relationships among activities. The preceding activity produces information required by the succeeding activities. In order to be successfully executed, activity i has specific fuzzy duration $\tilde{d}_i$ and its execution requires the exclusive use of a number of resources (e.g., engineers, teams, computer-aided design tools, simulation software, laboratory, etc.) defined by a vector $N_i = (n_{i1}, n_{i2}, \ldots, n_{iq})$, whose elements determine the usage of resource types 1, 2, ..., q. The resource availability for the project is also defined by a vector $R = (m_1, m_2, \ldots, m_q)$, where m_k indicates the availability of resource type k, $k = 1, \ldots, q$. The objective is to determine a project schedule with the least possibility of violating the predefined fuzzy ready-time and fuzzy deadline.

Note that we use fuzzy sets to model uncertain and preference information involved in a product development project. Although the duration of an activity is difficult to predict accurately, it can be approximately estimated by project managers based on the past experience. Experienced managers are able to specify most and least possible values rather than to provide exact values. In addition, the ready-time and deadline associated with a project may be flexible, because they are often determined by the project managers. Both uncertain and preference temporal information can be represented by possibility distributions [18] that can be further characterized by fuzzy numbers.

5.2. A fuzzy scheduling model to minimize schedule risk

5.2.1. Comparison of two fuzzy temporal parameters

It is required to compare fuzzy temporal parameters to generate a feasible schedule. For example, the start time assignment for an activity should satisfy the precedence constraints; i.e., the value that can be assigned to the start time of an activity should be greater than or equal to the finish time of each predecessor. Possibility theory is used to compare fuzzy temporal parameters in the proposed scheduling algorithm. Given two fuzzy temporal parameters $\tilde{M}$ and $\tilde{N}$, the degree that $\tilde{M}$ is greater than or equal to $\tilde{N}$ is defined as the weighted sum of $PG(\tilde{M}, \tilde{N})$ and $NG(\tilde{M}, \tilde{N})$:

$$g(\tilde{M} \geq \tilde{N}) = \beta \times PG(\tilde{M}, \tilde{N}) + (1 - \beta) \times NG(\tilde{M}, \tilde{N}), \tag{33}$$

where β is the optimism-pessimism index, $0 \leq \beta \leq 1$.

$NG(\tilde{M}, \tilde{N})$ represents the least chance that $\tilde{M}$ is greater than or equal to $\tilde{N}$ from the pessimistic viewpoint. On the contrary, $PG(\tilde{M}, \tilde{N})$ computes the best opportunity from the optimistic viewpoint. Parameter β is the optimism-pessimism index that is applied to determine the degree that $\tilde{M}$ is greater than or equal to $\tilde{N}$, according to the weighted average of the security and optimism levels. If the attitude of project manager is optimistic, then β is greater than 0.5. On the other hand, β is less than 0.5, if his/her attitude is towards pessimism.

After $g(\tilde{M} \geq \tilde{N})$ is determined, the relationship between $\tilde{M}$ and $\tilde{N}$ is identified by the following decision rule:

If $g(\tilde{M} \geq \tilde{N}) > g(\tilde{N} \geq \tilde{M})$ then $\tilde{M} \geq \tilde{N}$

else if $g(\tilde{M} \geq \tilde{N}) < g(\tilde{N} \geq \tilde{M})$ then $\tilde{N} \geq \tilde{M}$

else $\tilde{M} = \tilde{N}$

5.2.2. Performance measure of fuzzy project scheduling

As the duration of each activity is represented with a fuzzy number, the computed project completion time is also a fuzzy number. A new performance measure is defined to evaluate the effectiveness of a schedule in an uncertain product development environment.

Given schedule s, its performance measure, called the schedule risk, is defined in terms of the weighted sum of PSG and NSG:

$$SR(s) = \beta \times PSG(\tilde{D}(s), \tilde{e} \ominus \tilde{b}) + (1 - \beta) \times NSG(\tilde{D}(s), \tilde{e} \ominus \tilde{b})$$

$$= \beta \times \sup_{u} \min \left(\mu_{\tilde{D}(s)}(u), \mu_{]\tilde{e}\ominus\tilde{b},+\infty)}(u) \right) + (1 - \beta)$$

$$\times \inf_{u} \max \left(1 - \mu_{\tilde{D}(s)}(u), \mu_{]\tilde{e}\ominus\tilde{b},+\infty)}(u) \right) \tag{34}$$

where:

$\tilde{D}(s)$ is the fuzzy project duration with respect to s,

$\tilde{e}$ is the predefined fuzzy project deadline,

$\tilde{b}$ is the predefined fuzzy project ready-time, and

β is the optimism–pessimism index, $0 \leq \beta \leq 1$.

$SR(s)$ determines the chance of the project duration greater than the difference between the project deadline and ready-time regarding schedule s. PSG and NSG estimate the maximum and minimum chance that $\tilde{D}(s)$ is strictly greater than $\tilde{e} \ominus \tilde{b}$, respectively. The Hurwicz criterion is used to take a middle course, because few project managers would wish to be extremely pessimistic or optimistic. Wang [42] showed that a project manager with the risk-averse attitude will prefer a schedule with more precise project duration. On the contrary, a risk-seeking project manager will take the risk to select a schedule that produces more uncertain project duration, but may have chance to finish the project earlier. In addition, the proposed schedule risk can be interpreted by the qualitative decision theory developed by Dubois and Prade [7].

5.2.3. Fuzzy scheduling with a genetic algorithm

A genetic algorithm (GA) is developed to produce a minimum risk schedule. Genetic algorithms are general search strategies and optimization methods based on some concepts from natural evolution [10]. The main components of a genetic algorithm consist of a finite population of solutions, a chromosomal representation, a fitness function, and genetic operators. The chromosomal representation is an encoding that specifies a member of the population of solutions. Each solution in the population is encoded as a string of symbols called a chromosome. The fitness function is used to evaluate a member in the population of solutions. The members with the higher fitness values are assigned higher probability of selection for survival and reproduction. In each generation, the algorithm creates a new population by applying genetic operators selected individuals from previous population. This process continues until the stopping criterion is met. Reproduction is achieved by genetic operators: crossover and mutation. The procedure of genetic algorithm is summarized as follows:

Procedure: Genetic Algorithm
1. **begin**
2. $t \leftarrow 0$
3.   initiate $P(t)$ // $P(t)$: population at generation t
4.   evaluate $P(t)$ according to a fitness function
5.   **while** (not termination condition) **do**
6.   **begin**
7. $t \leftarrow t + 1$
8.   select $P(t)$ from $P(t-1)$
9.   reproduce $P(t)$ by crossover and mutation operations
10.   evaluate $P(t)$ according to a fitness function
11.   **end**
12. **end**

In contrast to other local search algorithms that are based on manipulating one feasible solution, a genetic algorithm considers a set of random solutions called a population. Working with the population permits exploration and exploitation of the search space. It is especially helpful to examine multiple solutions when the scheduling evaluation function is fuzzy.

Encoding of a solution is of importance in genetic algorithms. There are two basic types of encoding in the GA-based project scheduling literature. The priority value representation encodes a solution as a string of numbers representing priorities of activities. The other type of encoding is the priority rule representation that encodes a solution as a series of priority rules for generating a schedule. The priority value representation is used in this research as it characterizes all feasible solutions and is easy to implement comparing to the priority rule representation. An example of priority value representation is described next. Consider a hypothetical project with eight activities numbered from 1 to 8. An example of a chromosome using this representation can be written as (3, 1, 7, 2, 8, 5, 6, 4). The number in the position i of the list represented the priority of activity i. For example, the priority of activity 3 is 7.

According to a chromosome representing the priority list, the fuzzy parallel scheduling procedure [11] is used to generate a schedule. The procedure is described as follows.

Denote:
$\tilde{t}$:   current time
CS: completed set containing the activities that have been scheduled and completed.
DS: decision set containing the unscheduled activities which are available for scheduling with respect to precedence constraints and resource capacity constraints.
AS: active set containing the activities in progress.
RA: a vector $(r_1, r_2, \ldots, r_q)$ indicating the availability of resource types $k = 1, \ldots, q$.
S: scheduled set that stores the sequence of activities being processed.
$\tilde{s}_i$:   the fuzzy start time of activity i.
$\tilde{f}_i$:   the fuzzy finish time of activity i.
$p(j)$: priority of activity j
Input: p, a priority list (chromosome)
Output: a schedule including schedule sequence and fuzzy start time for each activity
Procedure: Fuzzy Parallel Scheduling Procedure
1. **begin**
2. $\tilde{t} \leftarrow 0, DS \leftarrow \{1\}$, $CS \leftarrow \phi$, $AS \leftarrow \phi$, $RA \leftarrow R$;
3. **while** (number of activities in $CS \leq n$) **do**
4. **begin**
5. **while** $(DS \neq \phi)$ **do**
6. **begin**
7. $i^* \leftarrow \min_{i \in D}\{p(i)\}$;
8. $\tilde{s}_{i^*} \leftarrow \tilde{t}$;
9. $\tilde{f}_{i^*} \leftarrow \tilde{t} \oplus \tilde{d}_{i^*}$;
10. $r_k \leftarrow r_k - n_{i*k}$, for all k;
11. $AS \leftarrow AS \cup \{i^*\}$;
12. $S \leftarrow S \cup \{i^*\}$;
13.   determineDS;
14. **end**
15. $j^* \leftarrow \min_{j \in AS} \{j | \tilde{f}_j = \min\{\tilde{f}_i | i \in AS\}\}$;
16. $\tilde{t} \leftarrow \tilde{f}_{j^*}$;
17. $r_k \leftarrow r_k + n_{j*k}$, for all k;
18. $AS \leftarrow AS \{j^*\}$;
19. $CS \leftarrow CS \cup \{j^*\}$;
20.   determine DS;
21. **end**

Given a priority list, the fuzzy parallel scheduling procedure is started by identifying the decision set DS that contains the unscheduled activities with their predecessors that have been completed and the resource capacity constraints are satisfied. At line 7, the activity i^* in DS with the highest priority is selected for processing. From line 8 to 10, the start time and finish time of activity i^* are assigned and resource availability is updated. At lines 11 and 12, the activity is inserted into the active set AS and the scheduled set S. The process is repeated until the set DS is empty. Then go to lines 15 and 16 to replace the current time with the earliest finish time of the activities in AS. Activity j^* is the identified earliest finish activity in AS.

Note that because the finish times of activities in AS are all fuzzy numbers, the fuzzy ranking method described in Section 5.2.1 is used to select the smallest activity finish time (line 15). If more than two activities have the same smallest finish time, then the activity with the smallest activity number is chosen. From line 17 to 19, the resource availability, active set, and completed set are updated, as activity j^* is completed. The entire procedure continues, until all activities are completed.

The genetic algorithm for solving the research problem is initialized with the initial population of chromosomes generated randomly. For each chromosome in the population, the fuzzy parallel scheduling procedure is applied and a schedule is generated correspondingly. As mentioned, three operations are performed to produce a next generation with fitter chromosomes. The chromosomes with higher fitness values have more chance to copy into the next generation. This can be done by randomly selecting and duplicating a chromosome with a probability that is proportional to the fitness value of the chromosomes.

Since our objective is to produce a minimum risk schedule defined in section 5.2, the fitness function is defined next:

$$f(s) = 1.0 - SR(s) \tag{35}$$

The linear scaling mechanism [10] is used to avoid the problem of premature convergence to a local minimum.

After the reproduction operation is performed, the crossover operator is applied to introduce new chromosomes by combining individuals in the new population with a probability called crossover rate. In this paper, the order crossover operator [24] is used to maintain the permutation representation of the chromosomes. For the order crossover operation, two chromosomes are randomly selected from the new population. Two crossing sites are selected randomly along the chromosomes. These two points define a matching section that is used to effect a crossover. For example, consider two parents p_1 and p_2 with the two cut points marked by '|':

$p_1 = (5\,3\,4\,|\,2\,6\,8\,|\,7\,1)$

$p_2 = (1\,8\,2\,|\,5\,7\,3\,|\,4\,6)$

When p_1 maps to p_2, p_2 will leave holes in the chromosome:

$p_2 = (1\,X\,X\,|\,5\,7\,3\,|\,4\,X)$

These holes are filled with a sliding motion that starts following the second crossing site:

$p_2 = (5\,7\,3\,|\,X\,X\,X\,|\,4\,1)$.

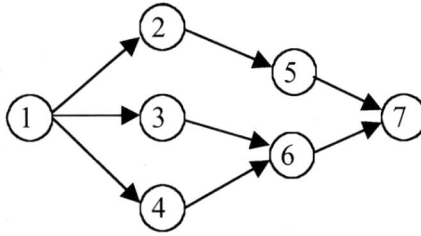

Figure 11. Precedence graph with seven design activities. (Reprinted from FUZZY SETS AND SYSTEMS, 127, J. Wang "A fuzzy project scheduling approach to minimize schedule risk for product development," pp. 99–116, with permission from Elsevier.)

Then the holes are then filled with the matching section from p_1:

$$p_2' = (5\,7\,3\,|\,2\,6\,8\,|\,4\,1).$$

Similarly, p_1 can also be obtained:

$$p_1' = (2\,6\,8\,|\,5\,7\,3\,|\,1\,4).$$

After the crossover operator is performed, the mutation operator is applied to each chromosome with a probability called mutation rate to introduce more variation in the current population. The swap mutation [24] that swaps the values of two randomly selected positions for each chromosome. For example, a new chromosome p_1'' can be produced from p_1 by interchange the values of positions 2 and 7:

$$p_1'' = (5\,1\,4\,2\,6\,8\,7\,3).$$

5.3. Illustrative example

Assume that a project consists of seven activities and is represented with the precedence graph shown in Figure 11. The corresponding activity information is listed in Table 12. The fuzzy project ready-time and deadline are set to (0, 1, 1, 1) and (57, 57, 57, 63), respectively. Only one type of resource is required for the project and its resource availability is 2. Assume that the optimistic-pessimistic index is set to 0.5 for both the fuzzy comparison method and the schedule risk.

Applying the proposed GA, the best solution found is $\tilde{C} = (45, 59, 75, 91)$ and $\tilde{D} = (45, 58, 74, 90)$ with the schedule risk 0.55. Table 13 lists start times for the schedule produced.

As shown in Table 13, the start time of each activity is a fuzzy number. Project managers need to select a crisp start time for each activity to execute the project. The crisp start time of an activity can be assigned by the smallest value of the α-level set of its fuzzy start time. For example, activity 3 can be started at time 8, if the value of α is set to 0.8 (see Figure 12). This is because a risk-averse project manager usually wants to

Table 12 Activity information corresponding to the activities in Figure 11

Activity	Duration	Resource usage
a_1	(5, 7, 8, 10)	1
a_2	(8, 10, 15, 18)	1
a_3	(14, 17, 20, 24)	1
a_4	(9, 12, 16, 20)	1
a_5	(3, 5, 7, 9)	1
a_6	(5, 9, 12, 15)	1
a_7	(20, 24, 28, 33)	1

(Reprinted from FUZZY SETS AND SYSTEMS, 127, J. Wang "A fuzzy project scheduling approach to minimize schedule risk for product development," pp. 99–116, with permission from Elsevier.)

Table 13 Schedule generated by the GA for the illustrative example

Activity ($i = 1 \sim 7$)	$\tilde{st}_i$
1	(0, 1, 1, 1)
2	(14, 20, 25, 31)
3	(5, 9, 10, 11)
4	(5, 8, 9, 11)
5	(22, 30, 40, 49)
6	(19 , 25, 29, 35)
7	(25, 35, 47, 58)

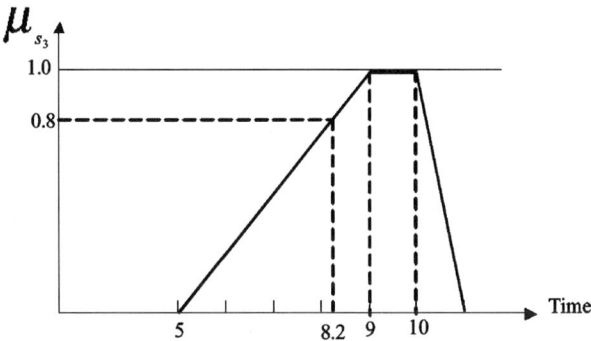

Figure 12. Start time of activity 3 in the illustrative example.

initiate the activities as early as possible to avoid project delays, even though its preceding activities may not be fully completed. This is called in concurrent engineering an overlapping approach [19]. The preceding activities release partial design information to the succeeding activities before they have been completed. This allows downstream activities to provide early feedbacks to the upstream activities to improve the design quality and reduce the product development cycle. Wang [42] proposed an approach to select the activity start times that maximize the satisfaction degrees of all temporal constraints.

Table 14 Fuzzy project makespan and schedule risk for variable resource level

No.	Additional resources	Resource avail.	Project makespan	Schedule risk
1	0	(5, 4, 5, 4)	(180,239,294)	0.63
2	1 unit of r_1	(6, 4, 5, 4)	(178, 235, 289)	0.60
3	1 unit of r_2	(5, 5, 5, 4)	(180, 239, 294)	0.63
4	1 unit of r_3	(5, 4, 6, 4)	(172, 227, 280)	0.49
5	1 unit of r_4	(5, 4, 5, 5)	(175, 232, 284)	0.56
6	2 unit of r_1	(7, 4, 5, 4)	(177, 233, 286)	0.58
7	2 unit of r_2	(5, 6, 5, 4)	(180, 239, 294)	0.63
8	2 unit of r_3	(5, 4, 7, 4)	(168, 223, 275)	0.43
9	2 unit of r_4	(5, 4, 5, 6)	(174, 229, 280)	0.52
10	1 unit of r_1 and r_2	(6, 5, 5, 4)	(178, 235, 289)	0.60
11	1 unit of r_2 and r_3	(5, 5, 6, 4)	(172, 227, 280)	0.49
12	1 unit of r_3 and r_4	(5, 4, 6, 5)	(178, 235, 289)	0.60
13	1 unit of r_1 and r_4	(6, 4, 5, 5)	(163, 214, 264)	0.34

(Reprinted from FUZZY SETS AND SYSTEMS, 127, J. Wang "A fuzzy project scheduling approach to minimize schedule risk for product development," pp. 99–116, with permission from Elsevier.)

The proposed fuzzy scheduling approach evaluates resource allocation to avoid the risk of a project delay. Table 14 shows the fuzzy project makespans and the corresponding schedule risks under distinct resource availability for an electronics product development project. Assume that four resource types ($r_1 - r_4$) are required in this project and the resource availability, the obtained project makespan, and the schedule risk for the original schedule are (5, 4, 5, 4), (180, 239, 294), 0.63, respectively. If a project manager feels that there is a great chance that the project will be late, s/he may consider allocating more resources to the project. For example, assigning one more hardware engineer (r_3) to the project can reduce fuzzy project duration to (172, 227, 280) with the schedule risk 0.49.

6. CONCLUSION

Since decisions made at early product development stages significantly impacts on downstream decisions and the product life cycle cost, it is important to develop methods to improve decision-making at these stages. This chapter showed that fuzzy set theory may provide a framework to cope with imprecise and subjective information existing at the early product development. Three decision models based on possibility theory were presented to improve decision-making and performing sensitivity analysis to examine quality of the obtained solutions. Fuzzy set theory can be used to improve other product development decisions, such as configuration of product supply chains [43], configuration management [45], and portfolio management [46].

REFERENCES

[1] F. Black and M. Scholes, "The pricing of options and corporate liabilities," *Journal of Political Economy*, vol. 81, pp. 637–659, 1973.

[2] C. Carlsson and R. Fuller, "Real option evaluation in fuzzy environment," in *Proceedings of the International Symposium of Hungarian Researchers on Computational Intelligence*, 2000, pp. 69–77.

[3] J. V. Carnahan, D. L. Thurston, and T. Liu, "Fuzzing ratings for multiattribute design decision-making," *ASME Journal of Mechanical Design*, vol. 116, pp. 511–521, 1994.

[4] L. K. Chan and M. L. Wu, "Quality functionality deployment: A literature review," *European Journal of Operational Research*, vol. 143, pp. 463–497, 2002.

[5] D. Clausing, *Total Quality Management: A Step-By-Step Guide to World-Class Concurrent Engineering*. New York: ASME Press, 1994.

[6] D. Dubois and H. Prade, *Possibility Theory: An Approach to Computerized Processing of Uncertainty*. New York: Plenum Press, 1988.

[7] D. Dubois and H. Prade, "Qualitative possibility theory and its applications to constraint satisfaction and decision under uncertainty," *International Journal of Intelligent Systems*, vol. 14, pp. 45–61, 1999.

[8] J. Fodor and M. Roubens, *Fuzzy Preference Modelling and Multicriteria Decision Support*. Dordrecht: Kluwer, 1994.

[9] S. French, *Decision Theory: An Introduction to the Mathematics of Rationality*. New York: Ellis Horwood, 1993.

[10] D. E. Goldberg, *Genetic Algorithms in Search, Optimization, and Machine Learning*. Massachusetts: Addison-Wesley, 1989.

[11] M. Hapke and R. Slowinski, "Fuzzy project scheduling system for software development," *Fuzzy Sets and Systems*, vol. 67, pp. 101–117, 1994.

[12] J. R. Hauser and D. Clausing, "The house of quality," *Harvard Business Review*, vol. 66, no. 3, pp. 63–73, 1988.

[13] J. X. Jiao and M. M. Tseng, "Fuzzy ranking for concept evaluation in configuration design for mass customization," *Concurrent Engineering: Research and Applications*, vol. 6, no. 3, pp. 189–206, 1998.

[14] E. E., Karsak, S. Sozer, and S. E. Alptekin, "Product planning in quality function deployment using a combined analytic network process and goal programming approach," *Computers and industrial Engineering*, vol. 44, pp. 171–190, 2002.

[15] R. L. Keeney and H. Raiffa, *Decisions with Multiple Objectives: Preferences and Value Tradeoffs*, New York: John Wiley, 1976.

[16] R. Knosala and W. Pedrycz, "Evaluation of design alternatives in mechanical engineering," *Fuzzy Sets and Systems*, vol. 47, pp. 269–280, 1992.

[17] K. J. Kim, H. Moskowitz, A. Dhingra, and G. Evans, "Fuzzy multicriteria models for quality function deployment," *European Journal of Operational Research*, vol. 121, no. 3, pp. 504–518, 2000.

[18] G. J. Klir and B. Yuan, *Fuzzy Sets and Fuzzy Logic: Theory and Applications*, New Jersey: Prentice Hall, 1995.

[19] V. Krishnan, "Managing the simultaneous execution of coupled phases in concurrent product development," *IEEE Transactions on Engineering Management*, vol. 43, no. 2, pp. 210–217, 1996.

[20] V. Krishnan and K. T. Ulrich, "Product development decisions: A review of the literature," *Management Science*, vol. 47, no. 1, pp. 1–21.

[21] A. Kusiak, ed., *Concurrent Engineering: Automation, Tools, and Techniques*, New York: John Wiley & Sons, 1994.

[22] A. Kusiak, *Engineering Design: Products, Processes, and Systems*, New York: Academic Press, 1999.

[23] F. A. Lootsma, "Stochastic and fuzzy PERT," *European Journal of Operational Research*, vol. 43, pp. 174–183, 1989.

[24] Z. Michalewicz, *Genetic Algorithms + Data Structures = Evolution Programs*, Berlin: Springer-Verlag, 1992.

[25] S. H. Nasution, "Fuzzy critical path method," *IEEE Transactions on Systems, Man, and Cybernetics*, vol. 24, pp. 48–57, 1994.

[26] J. L. Nevins and D. E. Whitney, *Concurrent Design of Products and Processes*, New York: McGraw-Hill, 1989.

[27] K. N. Otto and E. K. Antonsson, "Trade-off strategies in engineering design," *Research in Engineering Design*, vol. 3, pp. 87–103, 1991.

[28] B. Roy, "Partial preference analysis and decision aid: the fuzzy outranking relation concept," in Conflicting Objectives in Decisions, O. E. Bell, R. L. Keeney and H. Raiffa, Eds. New York: Chichester, 1977.

[29] T. L. Satty, *The Analytic Process*, New York: HcGraw-Hill, 1980.

[30] J. Siddall, *Probabilistic Engineering Design: Principle and Applications*, New York: Marcel Dekker, 1983.

[31] J. L. Siskos, J. Lochard, and J. Lombard, "A multicriteria decision making methodology under fuzziness: application to the evaluation of radiological protection in nuclear power plants," in *TIMS/Studies in the Management Sciences*, H. J. Zimmermann, Ed. Amsterdam: North-Holland, 1984, pp. 261–283.

[32] N. P. Suh, *The Principle of Design*, New York: Oxford University Press, 1990.

[33] C. Temponi, J. Yen, and W. A. Tiao, "House of quality: A fuzzy logic-based requirements analysis," *European Journal of Operational Research*, vol. 117, no. 2, pp. 340–354, 1999.

[34] K. T. Ulrich and S. D. Eppinger, Product Design and Development, 2nd Edition, New York: McGraw-Hill, 2000.

[35] D. G. Ullman, The Mechanical Design Process, New York: McGraw-Hill, 1992.

[36] L. V. Vanegas and A. W. Labib, "Application of new fuzzy-weighted average (NFWA) method to engineering design evaluation," *International Journal of Production Research*, vol. 39, no. 6, pp. 1147–1162, 2001.

[37] J. Wang, "A fuzzy outranking method for conceptual design evaluation," *International Journal of Production Research*, vol. 35, no. 4, pp. 995–1010, 1997.

[38] J. Wang, "A fuzzy outranking approach to prioritize design requirements in quality function deployment," *International Journal of Production Research*, vol. 37, no. 4, pp. 899–916, 1999.

[39] J. Wang, "A fuzzy set approach to activity scheduling for product development," *Journal of the Operational Research Society*, vol. 50, no. 12, pp. 1217–1228, 1999.

[40] J. Wang, "Ranking engineering design concepts using a fuzzy outranking preference model," *Fuzzy Sets and Systems*, vol. 119, no. 1, pp. 161–170, 2001.

[41] J. Wang, "Improved engineering design concept selection using fuzzy sets," *International Journal of Computer Integrated Manufacturing*, vol. 15, no. 1, pp. 18–27, 2002.

[42] J. Wang, "A fuzzy project scheduling approach to minimize schedule risk for product development," *Fuzzy Sets and Systems*, vol. 127, pp. 99–116, 2002.

[43] J. Wang, "Developing robust inventory strategy for new product supply chain," *Proceedings of the Fourth Asia-Pacific Conference on Industrial Engineering and Management Systems*, Taipei, Taiwan, ROC, 2002.

[44] J. Wang, "A fuzzy robust scheduling approach for product development projects," *European Journal of Operational Research*, vol. 152, no. 1, pp. 180–194, 2004.

[45] J. Wang and Y. I. Lin, "A fuzzy multicriteria group decision making approach to select configuration items for software development," *Fuzzy Sets and Systems*, vol. 134, no. 3, pp. 343–363, 2003.

[46] J. Wang and W. L. Hwang, "A compound-options-based approach to determine robust R&D project portfolio," Dept. of Industrial Engineering, Feng Chia Univ., Taichung, Taiwan, ROC, Tech. Rep. TR-2003-04, June, 2003.

[47] K. L. Wood, E. K. Antonsson, and J. L. Beck, "Representing imprecision in engineering: Comparing fuzzy and probabilistic calculus," *Research in Engineering Design*, vol. 1, no. 3/4, pp. 187–203, 1990.

[48] R. R. Yager, "On ordered weighted averaging aggregation operators in multicriteria decisionmaking," *IEEE Transactions on Systems, Man, and Cybernetics*, vol. 18, pp. 183–190, 1988.

[49] L. A. Zadeh, "Fuzzy sets as a basis for a theory of possibility," *Fuzzy Sets and Systems*, vol. 1, no. 1, pp. 3–28, 1978.

EVALUATION AND SELECTION IN PRODUCT DESIGN
FOR MASS CUSTOMIZATION

XUAN F. ZHA, RAM D. SRIRAM, WEN F. LU, AND FU J. WANG

1. INTRODUCTION

Today's highly competitive, global marketplace is redefining the way companies do business. Mass customization (Pine, 1993) provides a new paradigm for manufacturing industries, whereby variety and customization supplant standardized products, heterogeneous and fragmented markets spring from once homogeneous markets, and product life cycles and development cycles spiral downward (Tseng and Jiao 1996, 1998). It has recently received much attention and popularity from both industry and academia, and has been considered as a new battlefield for manufacturing enterprises (Wortmann et al. 1997). Mass customization aims at delivering an increasing product variety to satisfy diverse customer needs while maintaining near mass production efficiency (Tseng and Jiao 1996). Essentially, it is an oxymoron of variety to cater for customization and the low costs of variety fulfillment. To adopt the mass customization paradigm, many companies are being faced with the challenge of providing as much variety as possible in the marketplace with as little variety as possible between products in order to maintain economies of scale, while satisfying a wide range of customer requirements.

A product family (line) refers to a collection of product variants that have the same or similar functions but with different combinations of attribute levels. In a market characterized by a large variety of customer preferences and with competitions, companies introduce a product family to satisfy as best as possible the preferences of different customers and also achieve their business goals (Li and Azarm 2002). Family-based product design has been recognized as an efficient and effective means to realize

183

sufficient product variety to satisfy a range of customer demands in support for mass customization (Tseng and Jiao 1996). Customized product development is resembled as configuration design, in which a family of products can widely variegate the selection and assembly of modules or pre-defined building blocks at different levels of abstraction so as to satisfy diverse customization requirements. The essence of configuration design is to synthesize product structures by determining what modules or building blocks are in the product and how they are configured to satisfy a set of requirements and constraints. Thus, product/family design evaluation plays an important role in this process, as a poor selection of either a building block or module or a configuration structure is difficult to be compensated for at later design stages and can give rise to expensive redesign costs (Pahl and Beitz 1996). Because of its paramount importance in configuration design, the alternative evaluation and selection problem has received enormous attention both in the academia and in the industry. Although a number of methods have been investigated, there is still much to be desired due to the hindrance inherent in the conceptual evaluation and selection process. Difficulties associated with such a task lie in problem solving complexity, various decision criteria, and product performance assessment (Jiao and Tseng 1998; Zha and Lu 2002a,b).

Contemporary design has become increasingly knowledge-intensive (Tong and Sriram 1991a,b; Sriram 2002). Knowledge-intensive support becomes more critical in the design process and has been recognized as a key solution towards future competitive advantages in product development. To improve the product family design for mass customization process, it is imperative to provide knowledge support and share design knowledge among distributed designers. The aim of this chapter is to develop methodologies and technologies of knowledge support for modular product family evaluation and selection in customer-driven design for mass customization. The focus of this chapter is on the development of a comprehensive systematic fuzzy clustering and ranking methodology for product family evaluation and selection in the context of design for mass customization.

The organization of this chapter is as follows. Section 2 reviews the previous research related to product family design evaluation and selection. Section 3 addresses issues and technologies for customer-driven modular product family design for mass customization and its knowledge support framework. Section 4 discusses a knowledge support scheme for product family evaluation in design for mass customization. A fuzzy clustering and ranking methodology is proposed and discussed in detail. Section 5 provides a case study and a scenario of knowledge support for product customization in power supply family design. Section 6 presents the research results and discusses the benefits or advantages of the proposed approach. Section 7 summarizes and concludes the chapter.

2. CURRENT STATUS OF RESEARCH

In this section, previous research work related to knowledge supported product family design for mass customization and design alternative evaluation and selection, is briefly reviewed. We first review the literature on design alternative evaluation and selection. Next we review the application of design alternative evaluation and selection to product family design evaluation and selection.

2.1. Design alternatives evaluation and selection

The literature on design alternative evaluation and selection can be generally classified into five categories (Jiao and Tseng 1998a): 1) multi-criteria utility analysis, 2) fuzzy set analysis, 3) design analytic methodology, 4) hybrid approach, and 5) information content approach. The first three approaches are generally used. The following review focuses mainly on these first three approaches.

Multi-criteria utility analysis, originally developed by von Neumann and Morgenstern (1947), is an analytical method for evaluating a set of alternatives, given a set of multiple criteria. It has been widely applied in the areas of engineering and business for decision-making (Hwang and Yoon, 1981). Thurston (1991) has applied this technique to the material selection problem that evaluates alternatives based on utility functions that reflect the designer's preferences for multiple criteria. Mistree et al. (1992, 1995) modeled design evaluation as a compromise decision support problem (DSP) and employed goal-programming techniques to make optimal selection decisions. While mathematical programming and utility analysis enhance algorithm-rigorous optimization modeling, such methods require the expected performance with respect to each criterion to be represented in a quantitative form. They are not appropriate for use in the early design stages, where some qualitative design criteria, i.e., intangible criteria, are involved and difficult to quantify (Thurston and Carnahan, 1992).

Fuzzy analysis, based on fuzzy set theory (Zadeh 1965), is capable of dealing with qualitative or imprecise inputs from designers by describing the performance of each criterion with some linguistic terms, such as "good," "poor," "medium," *etc.* Fuzzy analysis has proven to be quite useful in decision-making problems with multiple goals or criteria (Zimmermann 1987, 1996). Wood and Antonsson (1989) have demonstrated its viability in performing computations with imprecise design parameters in mechanical design. Wood et al. (1990) compared fuzzy sets with probability methods and concluded that fuzzy set analysis is most appropriate when there are imprecise design descriptions, while probability analysis is most appropriate for dealing with stochastic uncertainty. Thurston and Carnahan (1992) revealed that fuzzy set analysis is more useful and appropriate at very early stages of the preliminary design process. Knosala and Pedrycz (1992) utilized the analytic hierarchical process method (Satty 1991) to construct membership functions for the performance and weight of each criterion, and then applied the fuzzy weighted mean of the overall evaluation to ranking alternatives. Carnahan et al. (1994) represented evaluation results and weights regarding each criterion with linguistic terms and ranked alternatives based on the fuzzy weighted mean of distance from a fuzzy goal. While fuzzy analysis excels in capturing semantic uncertainty with linguistic terms, it requires discreet deliberation in dealing with crisp information. A domain-specific method is needed to fuzzify each tangible criterion whose evaluation is naturally estimated as an ordinary real variable (Carnahan et al. 1994). Another challenge is the incomparability between various criteria (Wang 1997, Siskos et al. 1984). This necessitates mechanisms to be capable of converting various types of performance evaluation with respect to different criteria to a common metric so as to specify suitable membership functions for them.

To reflect customer preferences in multi-criteria design evaluation, the relative importance or weighting factor for each criterion has been considered by numerous evaluation procedures (Jiao and Tseng 1998). Frazell (1985) assigned weights to criteria on a 0–100 scale. Sullivan (1986) presented a similar method called the linear additive model, in which ranking is included. Huang and Ghandforoush (1984) presented another procedure for quantifying subjective criteria. They computed intangible criteria measures as the multiplication of the intangible criterion weights by the subjective customer rating. Dixon et al. (1986) measured the performance by degree of satisfaction, ranging from excellent to unacceptable. They combined this measure with priority categories of high, moderate, or low to evaluate a design. Nielsen et al. (1986) used factor-criteria to establish the level of importance of attributes. A priority level, i.e., absolutely necessary, important, or desirable, is indicated for each factor-criterion and is used to guide decision-making. The main drawback of these evaluation methods is that they ignore the inconsistency issue on the part of the decision maker (Saaty 1991), which occurs when the solution does not match the decision maker's preference and results from the randomness of the decision maker's judgments. The analytical hierarchy process (AHP) was developed to deal with the decision-maker's inconsistency and to mimic the human decision-making process (Saaty 1991). The AHP determines weights by means of pair-wise comparisons between hierarchical decision levels. It has been proven to be a more rigorous procedure for determining customer preferences, and has been approached from the fuzzy point of view by Boender et al. (1989). Carnahan et al. (1994) proposed an approach to fuzzify the weights after they have been obtained by the AHP.

There are also many other product feasibility and quality assessment tools that are useful for planning the design of products, such as quality function deployment (QFD) (Clausing 1994), concurrent function deployment (Prasad 1996), conceptual selection matrix (Pugh 1991), and Taguchi robust design method (Taguchi 1986). Quality function deployment (QFD) provides a set of matrix-based techniques to quantify the organizational characteristics and identify quality characteristics that would meet customer expectations and needs (Clausing 1994). While QFD addresses only the quality aspect, CFD deals with total life-cycle concerns from a concurrent engineering perspective. The concept selection matrix initially proposed by Pugh (1991) is another matrix-based approach to quantify and measure product quality characteristics. It is based on a list of product and customer requirements. The purpose of Taguchi's robust design method is to reduce or control variations in a product or process (Taguchi 1986). Depending upon the complexity and stage of a design, there could be a large number of iterations required. While these methodologies provide high-level guidelines for design evaluation, detailed supporting techniques are essential. As Prasad (1996) pointed out, 4Ms (models, methods, metrics and measures) are the core in integrated product development.

2.2. Product family design evaluation and selection

In the literature, the problem on product family design evaluation and selection has received much attention of researchers from both engineering design (for designer) and management and marketing (for customer). From an engineering design perspective, multi-objective optimization models have been used to obtain a performance optimal product family (line) in order to satisfy a range of customer requirements, and to quantify the influence of a product platform (Nelson et al. 1999, Li and Azarm 2000, 2002; Simpson et al. 1998, 2001). In addition, the engineering design literature reports on models that account for cost, expected profit, risks, and benefits of delayed decisions in producing a product family (line) (Fujita et al. 1998, Gonzale-Zugasti 2000). From the management and marketing perspectives, research efforts have been made mainly on product line positioning (Green and Krieger 1985; Kohli and Sukumar 1990; Dobson and Kalish 1993). In the product line-positioning problem, a line of products is selected from a set of already available design alternatives, considering cost, customers' preferences and market competition to optimize a business goal such as profit or market share. Li and Azarm (2002) proposed an integrated approach for a product line design selection based upon marketing potential of candidate product lines, those that have the best possible variants from an engineering design point of view. The integrated approach accounts for a large variety of customers' preferences, market competitions, and commonality (i.e., multi-component variants that share one or more components across the product line). However, the previous work did not sufficiently account for uncertainties of parameters such as customer preferences, product's life cycle, market size, and discount rate, etc.

The literature review indicates that several quantitative frameworks have been proposed for product family design evaluation and selection. They provide valuable managerial guidelines in implementing the overall platform-based product family development. However, there are very few systematic qualitative or integrated intelligent methodologies to support the product development team members to adopt the platform product development practice, despite the progress made in several research projects (Zha and Lu 2002a,b; Simpson et al. 2003).

3. CUSTOMER-DRIVEN PRODUCT FAMILY DESIGN FOR MASS CUSTOMIZATION

The approach advocated in this work is for companies to realize a family of products that can be easily modified and quickly adapted to satisfy a variety of customer requirements or target specific market niches. Details about the knowledge supported product family design for mass customization are discussed below.

3.1. Strategies and technical challenges for mass customization

The paradigm of mass customization is variety and customization through flexibility and quick responsiveness. The essence of mass customization is to satisfy customers' requirements precisely without increasing costs, regardless of how unique these requirements may be. That is, a manufacturer or company has to perceive and capture latent market niches and correspondingly develop its technical capabilities to meet diverse customer needs. Perceiving latent customization requires the exploration of market niches. The capture of target customer groups means emulating or outclassing competitors in either quality or cost or quick response or a combination of one or more. Therefore, the requirements of mass customization lie in the following aspects: 1) time to market (quick responsiveness), 2) variety (customization), 3) flexibility, and 4) economies of scale (mass efficiency). The oxymoron of mass customization depends on the leverage of these requirements. There are eight identified strategies that have worked in many circumstances (Baudin 2001):

(1) *Analysis of the structure of customer demands.* The premise is that it is only necessary to make what customers do order, not everything they might. Most of the actual customer demands tend to cluster around a few configurations, and production must be organized to take advantage of this structure.

(2) *Standardization of components.* Customized products do not always have to be made from scratch. Instead, they can be made from a small number of standard components.

(3) *Use of products catalogs with a discrete set of sizes.* Products made in size increments meet the needs of almost all consumers.

(4) *Postponement of customization.* Customization is best employed at or near the end of the manufacturing process. Postponing customization, however, may require substantial process engineering efforts.

(5) *Identification of a common process.* Treat customized products like options on standard products.

(6) *Maintenance of a design repository.* A database of previous designs should help in rapidly determining an appropriate starting point for a new design. The challenge is finding ways to organize this data for easy retrieval of similar designs rather than exact matches.

(7) *Design a customized manufacturing process.*

(8) *Setup of a simple production control system.*

Considering the above requirements, the main technical challenge in developing a coherent framework for mass customization is in the ability to simultaneously satisfy the following requirements within a single approach (Tseng and Jiao 1996):

(1) *Reusability and commonality.* Optimizing reusability and commonality to achieve low cost and high efficiency, i.e. the economy of scale, an advantage characterized by mass production.

(2) *Product platform.* Providing a technical foundation for realizing customization, managing varieties and leveraging core capabilities to optimize flexibility and foster a customer-focused and product driven business.

(3) *Integrated product development.* Facilitating meta-level integration throughout the product development process and over the product life cycle to achieve quality and increased responsiveness.

3.2. Customer-driven design for mass customization

With regards to the challenges and strategies presented in the previous section, this research investigates mass customization from a product development perspective, namely

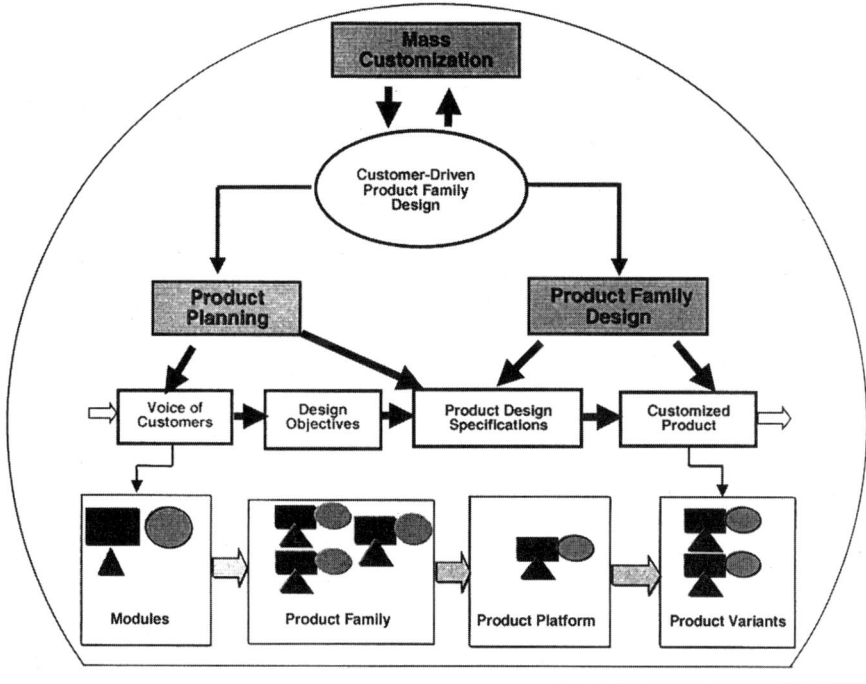

Figure 1. Framework for CDFMC based on the module-based product family design.

customer-driven design for mass customization (CDFMC). Our approach is based on the belief that mass customization can be effectively approached from a design perspective (Tseng and Jiao 1996, 1998). Essentially, we attempt to include customers into the product development life cycle through proactively connecting customer needs to the capabilities of a company. The main emphasis of CDFMC is to elevate the current practice from designing individual products to designing product families. In addition, CDFMC advocates extending the traditional boundaries of product design to encompass a larger scope, spanning from sales and marketing to distribution and services (Tseng and Jiao 1998). To support customized product differentiation, a product family platform is required to characterize customer needs and subsequently to fulfill these needs by configuring and modifying well-established building blocks.

Figure 1 outlines the concept for CDFMC used in this research (this is an adaptation of the process model presented in (Barkmeyer et al. 1997)). Recognizing the rationale of family-based product design with respect to mass customization, the whole process of CDFMC ranges from capturing voices of customers and market trends for generating product design specifications, designing product platform for generating product variety or family, to deriving and customizing products (variant) by evaluating and selecting product family for customers' satisfaction. CDFMC can be divided into two major stages: 1) product planning, and 2) family design. The product planning stage

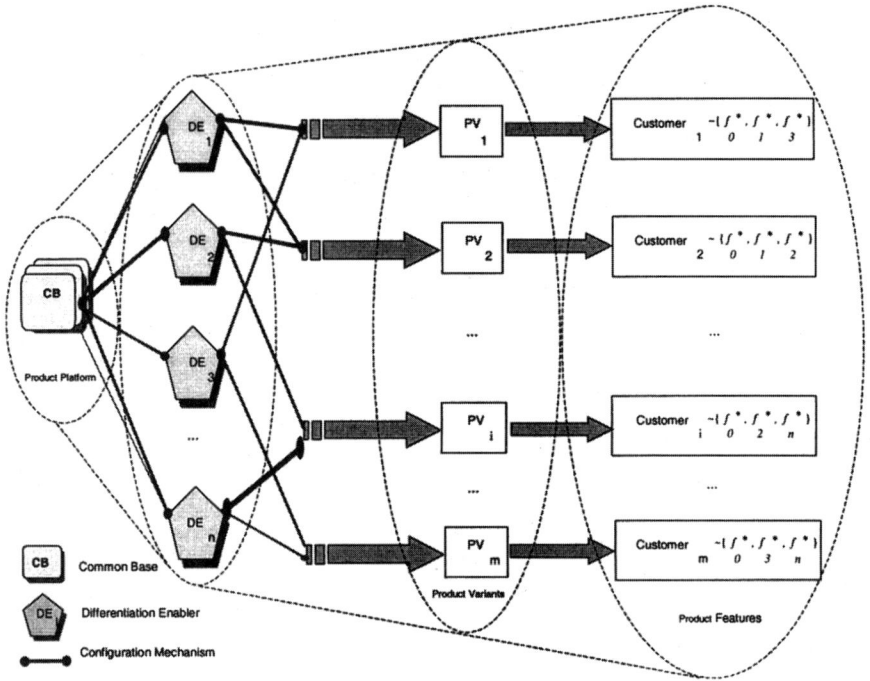

Figure 2. Architecture of product family for mass customization.

embeds the voices of customers into the design objective and generates product design specifications. The product family design stage realizes sufficient product variety- a family of products to satisfy a range of customer demands. Figure 2 illustrates a product family architecture (PFA) to support mass customization (Du et al. 2000). From customers' point of view, products are functional features and the related feature values. A product family is designed to address the requirements of a market segment wherein the customers share some similar requirements and have their special requirements in the mean time. Customer requirements characterized by the different combinations of functional features can be satisfied by the product variants derived by the common bases and differentiation enablers of the product family. It is the configuration mechanisms that determine the generative aspect of a product family, which guarantee that the technically feasible and market-wanted product variants are derived.

3.3. Module-based product family design

Modular systems provide the ability to achieve product variety through the combination and standardization of components (Kusiak and Huang 1996). Fujita and Ishii (1997) decompose product families into systems, modules, and attributes. Under this

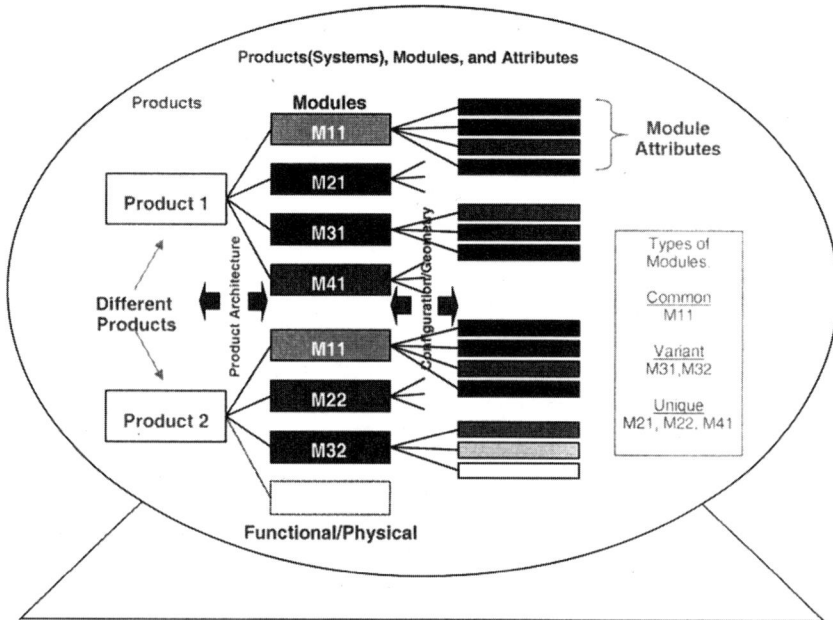

Figure 3. Products, modules, and attributes.

hierarchical representation scheme, as shown in Figure 3, product variety can be implemented at different levels within the product architecture. The steps for creating a module-based product family are as follows (Zha and Sriram 2004):

(1) Decompose products into their representative functions;
(2) Develop modules with one-to-one (or many-to-one) correspondence with functions;
(3) Group common functional modules into a common product platform; and
(4) Standardize interfaces to facilitate addition, removal, and substitution of modules.

The module-based product family design process is to develop a re-configurable product platform that can be easily modified and upgraded through the addition, substitution, and exclusion of modules to realize module-based product family. The customization stage aims at obtaining a feasible architecture of product family member through reasoning product family module space according to customer requirements (Meyer et al. 1997). There are two steps involved in this stage. First, customer requirements such as function, assembly, and reuse need to be converted to constraints (Suh 1990). Then, the reasoning is performed at two levels: namely module and attribute levels, to determine feasible product family member architecture.

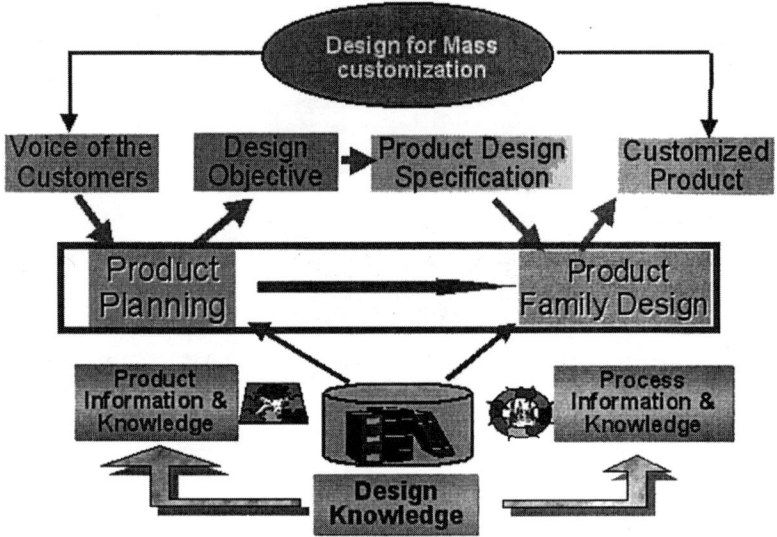

Figure 4. Knowledge support framework for CDFMC.

3.4. Knowledge support framework for CDFMC

The conceptual framework shown in Figure 1 demonstrates the process of customer-driven design for mass customization, which ranges from capturing voices of customer, analyzing market trends, generating design objectives and product design specifications (PDS) to customizing products for customer satisfaction. To assist the designer during this process, a knowledge support framework is further developed based on the rationale of customer-driven design for mass customization, as illustrated in Figure 4.

Product family design knowledge is classified into two categories: 1) product/family information and knowledge, and 2) product/family design process knowledge. These two categories of knowledge are utilized to support customer-driven design for mass customization that has two application scenarios: product planning and product family design (Zha and Sriram 2004). With understanding of the fundamental issues in modular product family design, the knowledge support scheme aims to provide support for customer requirements' modeling, product architecture modeling, product platform establishment, product family generation, and product family assessment for customization. The knowledge support scheme for modular product family design and its key research issues are described in (Zha and Lu 2002b).

As shown in Figure 5, the product family design process in the context of CDFMC can actually be divided into two major stages: 1) product platform building, and 2) product variant assessment. The generation of product platform and family in the product platform building stage is implemented through product (family) planning for design specifications and modular and configuration design, while the evaluation and selection of product family for customization is implemented by assessing product

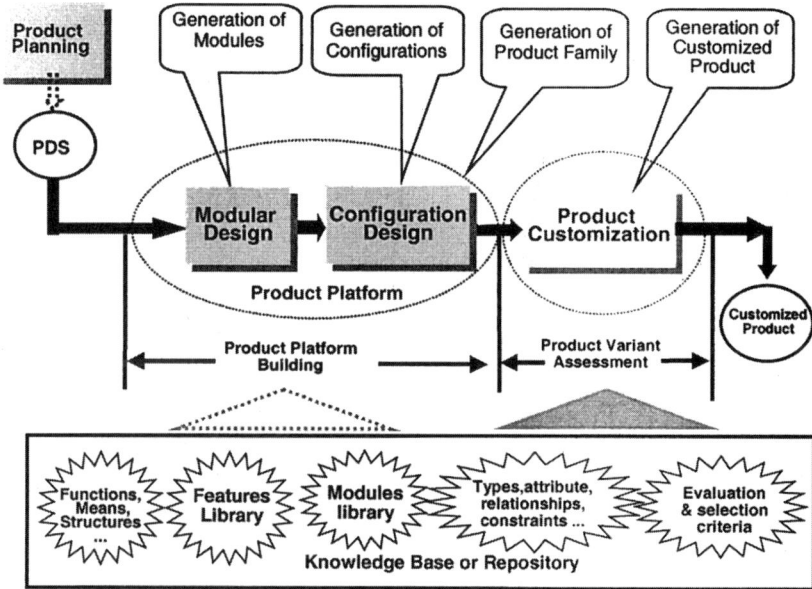

Figure 5. Modular product family design for mass customization process.

variants generated from product platform. The fundamental issues involved in product family design process have been addressed in (Zha and Sriram 2004), which include a knowledge intensive support strategy and its implementation for platform-based product design and development. During the process of modular product family design for mass customization, a family of products can vary widely by the selection and assembly of modules or pre-defined building blocks at different levels of abstraction so as to satisfy diverse customization requirements. The essence of CDFMC is to synthesize product structures by determining what modules or building blocks are in the product and how they are configured to satisfy a set of requirements and constraints: family generation, evaluation and selection. A wrong or even a poor selection of either a building block or a module can rarely be compensated for at later design stages and can give rise to a great expense of redesign costs (Pahl and Beitz 1996). Thus, product family design evaluation and selection is crucial for CDFMC. The remainder of this chapter will focus on how the decision support knowledge in product family design knowledge base or repository (Zha and Sriram 2004) supports the designer to perform product family evaluation and selection.

4. PRODUCT FAMILY DESIGN EVALUATION AND SELECTION

This section begins with a summary of knowledge decision support scheme for product family design evaluation and selection. It then presents evaluation/customization metrics applied in product family design for mass customization process. Finally, it

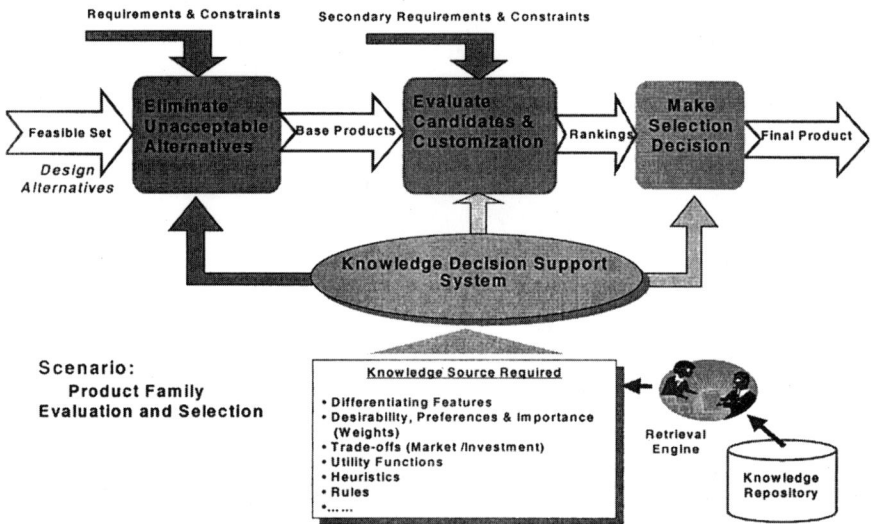

Figure 6. Knowledge decision support for product evaluation.

describes a fuzzy clustering and ranking model for classification, evaluation and selection of product family design alternatives.

4.1. Knowledge decision support scheme

The product family evaluation and selection for customization stage aims at obtaining a feasible architecture of product family members through reasoning and decision support in the product family module space according to customer requirements. The customization process includes two steps. First, the customer requirements such as functions and assemblies need to be converted to constraints and rules. Then, the reasoning or decision support is performed at two levels, namely module level and attribute level, to determine the feasible product family member architecture at the conceptual level. The design space for product configuration during module reasoning is very large for a complex system. The designer is required to consider not only the product functionality, but also some other criteria including compactness and other life-cycle issues, such as assemblability, manufacturiability, maintainability, reliability, and efficiency. Some criteria may contradict each other. Designers should analyze the trade-off among various criteria and make the "best" selection from a number of design alternatives.

In contrast to the traditional approaches (Pahl and Betiz 1996; Jiao and Tseng 1998), we propose a knowledge-based approach to product family evaluation and selection for customization. Figure 6 shows a knowledge decision support scheme. As shown in Figure 6, this stage characterizes a feasible set of products generated from product platform as an input to the final customized product as an output. It will experience the elimination of unacceptable alternatives, the evaluation of candidates for customization, and the final decision under the customers' requirements and design constraints. The knowledge resource utilized in the process may extensively include differentiating features, customers' requirements, desirabilities, preferences and importance (weights), trade-offs (e.g. market vs investment), utility functions, and heuristic knowledge, rules, etc. The kernel of the knowledge decision support scheme is based on fuzzy clustering and ranking algorithms for design evaluation and selection. These will be discussed below.

4.2. Customization/evaluation metrics

In order to evaluate a family of products for mass customization, suitable metrics are needed to assess the appropriateness of a product platform and the corresponding family of derivative products (Krishnan and Gupta 2001). The metrics should also be useful for measuring the various attributes of the product family and assessing a platform's modularity. With respect to the process of product family design and customization, we viewed the evaluation of product family design from three different level perspectives: product platform, product family and product variant (Zha and Sriram 2004). The product variant level evaluation is actually the same as or similar to the individual product design evaluation. Various traditional design evaluation approaches are applicable, and the metrics for this level evaluation include cost, time, assemblability, manufacturability, etc. The platform and family level evaluation is focused on the overall benefit of product family development and the metrics at these levels reflect the main goal of designing products/families is to maximize the benefits to the company. Currently, there are many marketing or business, econo-technical metrics that can be used for measuring performance or evaluation in customer-driven design for mass customization on the first two levels (Simpson 1998; Zha and Sriram 2004). For example, platform efficiency and platform effectiveness defined by Meyer et al. (1997) can be used to measure R&D performance, focused on platforms and their follow-on products (variants) within a product family. Other methods include cycle time efficiency, technological competitive responsiveness, and profit potential (Meyer and Lehnerd 1997). In this research, the following two typical metrics have been used in platform-based family level evaluation (Zha and Sriram 2004):

(1) *Market efficiency.* This metric embodies a tradeoff between the marketing and the engineering design, which offers the least amount of variety to satisfy the greatest amount of customers, i.e., targets the largest number of market niches with the fewest products.
(2) *Investment efficiency.* This metric embodies a tradeoff between the manufacturing and the engineering design, which invests a minimal amount of capital into machining and tooling equipment while still being able to produce as large a variety of products as possible.

Therefore, they can be represented by the following two equations:

$$\eta_M = N_{TM}/N_M \tag{1}$$

$$\eta_I = C_M/N_v, \tag{2}$$

Table 1 Various combinations of solution principles, of which hatched areas belong to the same family (group)

Solutions sub-functions		1	2	$\cdots$	j	$\cdots$	m
1	F_1	S_{11}	S_{12}		S_{1j}		S_{1m}
2	F_2	S_{21}	S_{22}		S_{2j}		S_{2m}
$\vdots$	$\vdots$	$\vdots$	$\vdots$	$\vdots$	$\vdots$	$\vdots$	$\vdots$
i	F_i	S_{i1}	S_{i2}		S_{ij}		S_{im}
$\vdots$	$\vdots$	$\vdots$	$\vdots$	$\vdots$	$\vdots$	$\vdots$	$\vdots$
n	F_n	S_{n1}	S_{n2}		S_{nj}		S_{nm}

where, N_{TM} and N_M are the number of the targetable market niches and the total market numbers, respectively; C_M and N_v are the manufacturing equipment costs and the number of the product varieties, respectively. Of course, a tradeoff also exists between the market efficiency and the investment efficiency as an increase in the investment efficiency through a decrease in product variety can cause a decrease in the market efficiency.

4.3. Fuzzy clustering and design ranking methodology

Due to the fuzziness of voice of customers (VoCs) or customer requirements/ preferences, it is difficult to model and assess the performance of a product platform/ family and product variants. In this section, a fuzzy clustering and ranking methodology is proposed for product family design evaluation and selection in the context of CDFMC. The algorithms are constructed using fuzzy sets theory to solve a fuzzy clustering/classification and multi-criteria decision-making (FMCDM) problem. The fuzzy clustering algorithm is used to classify design alternatives and determine similarity between modules and commonality between products and product families. The fuzzy multi-criteria decision-making problem can be defined as follows: given a set of design alternatives, evaluate and select a design alternative that satisfies customer needs, meets design requirements and complies with the technical capabilities of a company.

4.3.1. Fuzzy clustering analysis for design

Based on the systematic approach (Pahl and Beitz 1996), a reasonable number of possible design alternatives can be obtained using the design solution generation techniques at the conceptual design stage. Each sub-function usually corresponds to a collection of available solution principles. If there are a total of n sub-functions, each of them has m_i possible solution principles. After a complete combination, we have several theoretically possible overall solution variants as schematically illustrated in Table 1. Clustering is a widely used method for pattern recognition (Kandel 1982). In this research, the use of cluster analysis is to sort a product data set, for example, a number of possible solution principles to sub-functions or their possible combinations, into families such that the members of the same family (or group) are similar in some respect

	PV-B1	PV-B2	PV-Bi	PV-Bm
PV-A1	1	0.8	0.95	1
PV-A2	0.9	0.7	0.96	0.9
PV-Ai	0.65	0.65	0.87	0.8
PV-An	0	1	0.6	1

(a)

	PV-A1	PV-A2	PV-Ai	PV-An
PV-A1	1	0.86	0.95	0.9
PV-A2	0.86	1	0.96	0.9
PV-Ai	0.95	0.96	1	0.8
PV-An	0.9	0.9	0.8	1

(b)

Figure 7. Fuzzy matrix of similarity relations between types of product variants (PV-A, PV-B) in a family.

and unlike those from other families. This is very crucial for determining similarity between modules and also commonality between products and product families.

Assuming there are m patterns, $a_1, a_2, \ldots, a_m$, contained in the pattern spaces S. The process of clustering can be formally stated as: to seek the regions $s_1, s_2, \ldots, s_k$ such that every $a_i, i = 1, \ldots, m$ fall into one of these regions and no a_i falls into two regions, that is $s_1 \cup s_2 \cup \cdots \cup s_k = S, \forall i \neq j, s_i \cap s_j = \phi$. This definition indicates that clustering algorithms are based on natural association according to some similarity measures and the patterns are described by a set of numerical measures or linguistic variables. The similarity measure or dissimilarity measure is usually given in numerical form to indicate degree of resemblance between objects (or modules, or product variants) in a group (or family), or between an object and a group, or between object groups.

The simplest way to measure similarity is to use Euclidean distance. A design object (module, product variant or product family) in a design space may be viewed as a pattern point in a pattern space, described by a vector. The shorter the distance between two points, the more they resemble each other. However, the concept of similarity is very fuzzy. The selection of variables and similarity measures often subjectively reflects the investigator's judgment, rather than rigorous mathematical guidelines. Another practical way to measure similarity is to predefine a fuzzy similarity matrix based on some concerns and then to store it in computer. Matrix M_F (A × B) shows a fuzzy matrix to represent the similarity between types of modules or products in a family (Figure 7). Each entry in the matrix m_{ij} indicates the degree of fuzzy resemblance of

	L-R	R-L	L-L	R-R	R-LR	L-LR	LR-L	LR-R	LR-LR
L-R	1.0	0.9	0.85	0.85	0.7	0.7	0.65	0.65	0.4
R-L	0.9	1.0	0.9	0.9	0.8	0.8	0.7	0.7	0.4
L-L	0.85	0.85	1.0	0.95	0.7	0.7	0.6	0.6	0.5
R-R	0.85	0.9	0.95	1.0	0.8	0.8	0.7	0.7	0.6
R-LR	0.7	0.8	0.7	0.8	1.0	0.9	0.8	0.8	0.6
L-LR	0.7	0.8	0.7	0.8	0.9	1.0	0.8	0.8	0.7
LR-L	0.65	0.7	0.6	0.7	0.8	0.8	1.0	0.8	0.7
LR-R	0.65	0.7	0.6	0.7	0.8	0.8	0.8	1.0	0.8
LR-LR	0.4	0.4	0.5	0.6	0.6	0.7	0.7	0.8	1.0

Figure 8. Fuzzy matrix of similarity relations between types of conceptual layout variants in a gear reducer product family (L: Left, R: Right).

product variant i and j. The closer the number in the matrix is to 1, the more similar the corresponding module or product is. Figure 8 gives an instance of fuzzy similarity matrix for conceptual layout variants in a gear reducer product family (Gui 1993).

Given any two modules or product concepts at some level they will be grouped into the same cluster if these two are always kept within one group or family at all later levels. The clustering sequence or procedures are said to be hierarchical, which are divided into two distinct classes, bottom-up and top-down. The former starts with singleton clusters and forms the sequence by successively merging clusters, whereas the latter starts with all the objects in one cluster and forms the sequence by successively splitting clusters. The algorithm of clustering used in this research follows four steps:

(1) Find the smallest element in the distance matrix (d_i) to merge corresponding to two objects.
(2) Select a point as a reference in the merged group using an appropriate rule, e.g., nearest neighbor or centroid cluster.
(3) Recalculate the distance matrix between the new group and these remainders, named d_{i+1}.
(4) Repeat step 1 until all the objects merge into one group.

4.3.2. Fuzzy ranking for design

Using the design solution clustering techniques discussed above, a reasonable number of possible design alternatives can be obtained. The remaining procedure is to examine the design alternatives against marketing, econo-technical and even ergonomic criteria as well as aesthetic criteria. This is actually a multi-criteria decision-making problem. One of the well-known methods for multi-criteria decision-making is the procedure for calculating a weighted average rating $\bar{r}_i$ by use of the value analysis or cost-benefit analysis introduced in (Pahl and Britz 1996):

$$\bar{r}_i = \sum_{j=1}^{n} (w_j r_{ij}) \Big/ \sum_{j=1}^{n} w_j \tag{3}$$

where, $i = 1, 2, \ldots, m$, $j = 1, 2, 3, \ldots, n$, r_{ij} denotes the merit of alternative a_i according to the criterion C_j; w_j denotes the importance of criterion C_j in the evaluation of alternatives. The higher $\bar{r}_i$ is, the better is its aggregated performance. However, this procedure is not applicable for the situations where uncertainty exists and the information available is incomplete. For example, the terms "very important," "good," or "not good" themselves are a fuzzy set. In what follows, the problem of fuzzy ranking a set of alternatives against a set of criteria is described. Let a set of m alternatives $A = \{a_1, a_2, \ldots, a_m\}$ be a fuzzy set on a set of n criteria $C = \{C_1, C_2, \ldots, C_n\}$ to be evaluated. Suppose that the fuzzy rating r_{ij} to certain C_j of alternative a_i is characterized by a membership function $\mu_{R_{ij}}(r_{ij})$, where, $r_{ij} \in R$, and a set of weights $W = \{w_1, w_2, \ldots, w_n\}$ are fuzzy linguistic variables characterized by $\mu_{W_j}(w_j)$, $w_j \in R^+$. Consider the mapping function $g_i(z_i) : R^{2n} \rightarrow R$ defined by:

$$g_i(z_i) = \sum_{j=1}^{n} (w_j r_{ij}) \Big/ \sum_{j=1}^{n} w_j \tag{4}$$

where, $z_i = (w_1 w_2 \cdots w_n, r_{i1} r_{i2} \cdots r_{in})$. Define the membership function $\mu(z_i)$ by

$$\mu_{Z_i}(z_i) = \wedge_{j=1,\ldots,n}^{o} \mu_{W_j}(w_j) \wedge_{k=1,\ldots,n}^{o} \mu_{R_{ik}}(r_{ik}) \tag{5}$$

Thus, through the mapping $g_i(z_i) : R^{2n} \rightarrow R$, the fuzzy set Z_i induces a fuzzy rating set R_i with membership function

$$\mu_{R_i}(r_i) = \sup_{Z_i, g(z_i) = r_i} \mu_{Z_i}(z_i), \quad r_i \in R \tag{6}$$

The final fuzzy rating of design alternative a_i can be characterized by this membership function. But it does not mean the alternative with the maximal $\mu_R(r_i)$ is the best one. The following procedure further evaluates the two fuzzy sets as (Gui 1993):

(1) a conditional fuzzy set is defined with the membership function:

$$\mu_{I/R}(i|r_1, \ldots, r_m) = \begin{cases} 1 & \text{if } r_i > r_k, \forall k \in (1,2, \ldots, m) \\ 0 & \text{otherwise} \end{cases} \tag{7}$$

(2) a fuzzy set is constructed with membership function:

$$\mu_R(r_1, \ldots, r_m) = \wedge_{i=1,\ldots,m}^{\circ} \mu_{R_i}(r_i) \tag{8}$$

A combination of these two fuzzy sets induces a fuzzy set I which can determine the best design alternative with the highest final rating, i.e.,

$$\mu_I(i) = \sup_{r_1,\ldots,r_m} \mu_{I/R}(i|r_1, \ldots, r_m) \wedge^{\circ} \mu_R(r_1, \ldots, r_m) \tag{9}$$

Comparing with Eq. (3), the fuzzy ranking for design is more flexible and presents uncertainty better. Based on this method, the designer can use linguistic rating and weights such as "good," "fair," "important," "rather important," for design alternatives evaluation. Therefore it looks natural and attractive in practical use.

4.3.3. Simplified fuzzy ranking for design

In some cases, a simplified model is employed in integrating linguistic terms and fuzzy numbers into the fuzzy preference model. The universe of discourse is a finite set of fuzzy numbers used to express an imprecise level of performance rating and weight of each criterion. A range of imprecise levels is the linguistic terms, such as, "very low," "low," "fairly low," "medium," "fairly high," "high," and "very high." The linguistic scale is used to transform these linguistic terms of partial performance ratings R_{ij}, and weights w_j of the criteria into triangular or trapezoidal fuzzy numbers defined in the interval [0,1]. R_{ij} denotes the linguistic performance rating with respect to a criterion C_j for a retrieved product variant PV_i; w_j denotes the linguistic weight of a criterion C_j.

The aggregation of fuzzy numbers in an analytic form requires a complex arithmetic process. Thus, in this research, an approximate centroid-based defuzzification method is used to defuzzify the fuzzy numbers into crisp values early on, and then the defuzzified results can be aggregated easily and the execution is very fast (Zhang et al. 2002). For example, if a fuzzy set is represented as a trapezoidal fuzzy number, see Figure 9, then it can be parameterized by a quadruple (x_1, x_2, x_3, x_4) and its defuzzied crisp value using approximate centroid is $(x_1 + x_2 + x_3 + x_4)/4$. A triangular fuzzy number (x_1, x_2, x_3) can also be represented as (x_1, x_2, x_2, x_3) by a trapezoidal fuzzy number form with its crisp defuzzied value becoming $(x_1 + x_2 + x_2 + x_3)/4$.

With the approximate centroid-based defuzzification method the fuzzy linguistic performance rating R_{ij} and fuzzy linguistic weight w_j can be respectively transformed into the crisp performance rating $r_{ij} \in [0,1]$ and crisp weight $w_j \in [0,1]$. Therefore, the numerical weighted performance rating $\bar{r}_i \in [0, 1]$ of a design alternative can be calculated simply using the classic weighted average aggregation method. The key

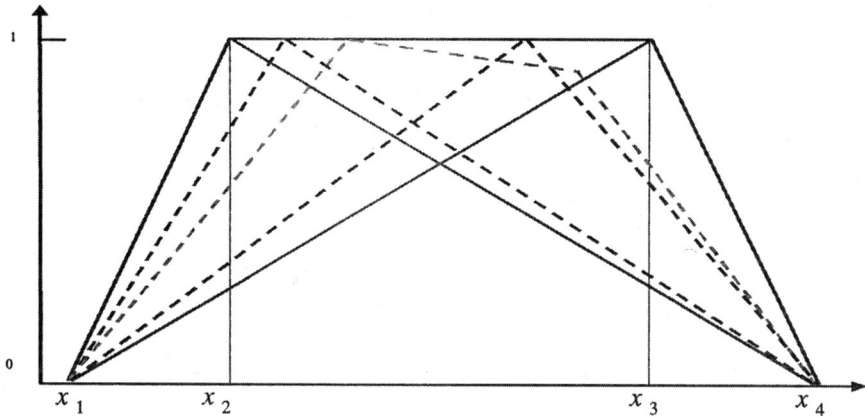

Figure 9. Linguistic scale representation for fuzzy customer preferences and performances.

points of this simplification model can be understood as: it is a simple fuzzy ranking scenario; it can also be used for defuzzification.

4.4. Evaluation of product family design alternatives

4.4.1. Heuristic evaluation function

With respect to the traditional approaches (Pahl and Betiz 1996; Jiao and Tseng 1998), we propose an approach to concept evaluation and selection for product customization from the knowledge support viewpoint. The knowledge resource utilized in the process includes differentiating features, customers' requirements, desirabilities, preferences and importance (weights), trade-offs (e.g. market vs investment), utility functions, and heuristic knowledge, rules, etc. It is important to have a powerful search strategy that will lead to a near optimum solution in a reasonable amount time. A* search (Sriram 1997) provides a method to achieve this. The system first calculates the weighted performance rating aggregation of each retrieved alternative by analyzing the trade-off among various criteria. Then it calculates the evaluation index of each design alternative used as the heuristic evaluation function by considering all the weighted performance ratings of product variants. Figure 6 shows a knowledge decision support scheme for product evaluation and customization process. The kernel of the knowledge decision support scheme is fuzzy clustering and ranking algorithms for design evaluation and selection that will be discussed below.

4.4.2. Evaluation index

After calculating the numerical weighted performance ratings of all design alternatives, the evaluation index is calculated and used as a heuristic evaluation function f_h, by considering all the weighted performance ratings $\bar{r}_i (i = 1, 2, 3, \ldots, m)$ of its constituent members and the number k of its unsatisfied customer requirements, as follows:

$$f_h = \sum_{i=1}^{m} (1/\bar{r}_i) + k \tag{10}$$

where, $\bar{r}_i \in [0,1]$ is the numerical weighted performance rating of product variants PV_i; $1/\bar{r}_i = (1, +\infty)$ is defined as the performance cost of product variants PV_i. A higher weighted performance rating of a product variant corresponds to a lower performance cost. $\sum_{i=1}^{m} (1/\bar{r}_i)$ represents the accumulated performance cost of a design alternative along the search path so far. k is a heuristic estimate of the minimal remaining performance cost of a design alternative along all the possible succeeding search paths. f_h is the estimate of the total performance costs of a design alternative, also called the evaluation index. In the above formula, a higher $\bar{r}_i$, i.e., the better-aggregated performance of each retrieved product variant PV_i, and lower m or k, i.e., higher compactness of a design alternative, will result in a lower f_h (lower evaluation index of a design alternative). Thus, at each step of the A* search process, the best design alternative, i.e., the one with the lowest value of the heuristic evaluation function is selected, by taking into account multi-criteria factors including design compactness and other life-cycle issues, such as manufacturability, assemablility, maintability, reliability, and efficiency (market vs investment).

4.5. Neural network adjustment for membership functions

Due to the complexity and uncertainty of design problems, there is a need to improve the above comprehensive fuzzy clustering and ranking methods. This improvement can be achieved through a learning technique such as neural networks. In a fuzzy set, a variable v can belong to more than one set, according to a given membership function $\mu_X(v)$. Standard membership function types as Z, λ, π and S-type can be mathematically represented as piecewise linear functions (Zimmermann 1986, 1996). It can be easily implemented and adjusted by using neural networks (Zha 2001). The fuzzy system (e.g. rule block) is the kernel of the whole fuzzy neural network model. It forms the basic scheme of knowledge representation exploited in the fuzzy evaluator.

The neuro-fuzzy hybrid approach uses neural network to optimize certain parameters of an ordinary fuzzy system, or to preprocess data and extract fuzzy rules from data (Zha 2001). The fuzzy evaluator described above is reflected in three basic elements: fuzzification, fuzzy inference and defuzzification. The fuzzification in the input interfaces translates analog inputs into fuzzy values. The fuzzy inference takes place in rule blocks that contain the linguistic control rules. The output of these rule blocks is linguistic variables. The defuzzification in the output interfaces translates them back into analog variables. Each of fuzzy rules can be interpreted as a training pattern for a multi-layer neural network, where the antecedent part of the rule is the input and the consequent part of the rule is the desired output of the neural network. There are two main approaches commonly used to implement fuzzy if-then rule blocks above by standard error back propagation network. One is to represent a fuzzy set by a finite number of its membership values (normally by linear functions). The other is to represent fuzzy numbers by finite number of α-level sets. With simplicity, but without loss of generalizity, the former approach is adopted in this research. Suppose that $[\alpha_1, \alpha_2]$ contains the support of all the A_i we might have as input to the system, and $[\beta_1, \beta_2]$ contains the support of all the B_i we can obtain as outputs from the system,

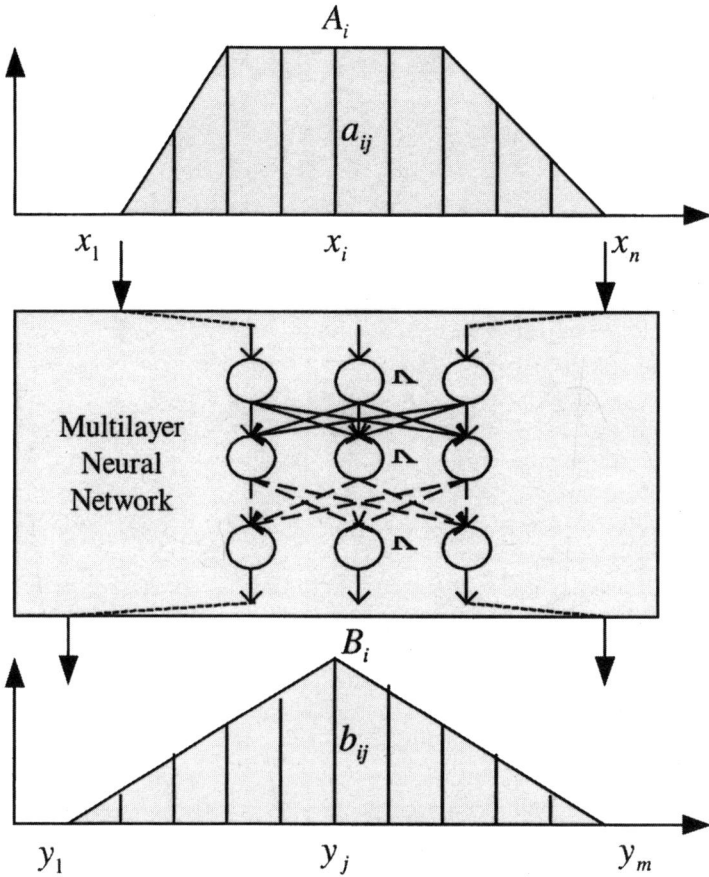

Figure 10. A network trained on membership values for fuzzy numbers.

$i = 1, 2, \ldots, n$. If $m \geq 2$ and $n \geq 2$ be positive integers, then

$$x_j = \alpha_1 + (j - 1)(\alpha_2 - \alpha_1)/(n - 1),$$

$$Y_i = \beta_1 + (i - 1)(\beta_2 - \beta_1)/(m - 1),$$

where, $1 \leq i \leq m$, and $1 \leq j \leq n$. Thus, a discrete version of the continuous training set can be composed of the following input/output pairs: $\{(A_i(x_1), \ldots, A_i(x_n)), (B_i(Y_1), \ldots, B_i(Y_m))\}$, $i = 1, \ldots, n$. Using the notations $a_{ij} = A_i(x_j)$, $b_{ij} = B_i(Y_j)$, the fuzzy neural network turns into an n inputs and m outputs crisp network, which can be trained by the generalized delta rule. Figure 10 shows a network trained on membership values of fuzzy numbers.

5. CASE STUDY AND SYSTEM PROTOTYPE

This section provides a case study of the power supply family design evaluation and selection for mass customization and introduces a prototype advisory system for product family design decision support.

5.1. Case study

Power supplies are necessary components of all electronic products. Because of diverse requirements, power supply products (http://www.artesyn.com/) are often customized (Maurice, 1993; Jiao and Tseng 1998). To illustrate and validate the proposed knowledge support scheme, a scenario illustrating the knowledge support for power supply family design evaluation and selection for customization is provided.

From a customers' point of view, a power supply product is defined on the following required features (RFs): power, output voltage (OutV), output current (OutC), size, regulator, mean time between failure (MTBF), etc. From an engineers' point of view, the power supply product is designed by determining these parameters (DPs): core of transformer (Core), coil of transformer (Coil), switch frequency (SwitchF), rectifier, heat sink type (TypeHS), heat sink size (SizeHS), control loop (Control), etc. Figure 11 shows the relationship between RFs and DPs, configurations and topologies. Three product families I, II and III are generated based on three different topologies, which have 4, 5 and 3 base products (BPs) respectively. Each topology has its own range/limitation with regard to particular product features and/or design parameters. The modularization process and modular design of power supply products are based on the work in (Zha and Sriram 2004). When the product configuration is carried out, the design requirements and constraints are satisfied especially in terms of product functions or functional features. Of course, from the assembly or disassembly/maintenance points of view, it had better that the parts with low exchange rate are placed at inside of product, but the locations of some parts are fixed in advance due to design constraints.

With reference to the knowledge decision support scheme for product evaluation (Figure 6), a scenario illustrating the knowledge support for power supply product evaluation for customization in Family I is shown in Figure 12. The customers' requirements for Family-I power supplies include AC/DC, 45 W, 5 V & ±15 V, 150 khrs, $20–50, etc. The knowledge decision support system first eliminates unacceptable alternatives and determines four acceptable alternatives, NLP40-7610, NFS40-7610, NFS40-7910, and NFS 42-7610. The final design decision can be reached based on the knowledge resources given in Figure 13, including customer preferences, differentiating features (MTBF, price, and special offer) and their utility/membership functions, fuzzy rules, and etc. The final design decision made by the system is NFS42-7610 as it has maximum MTBF, medium price and special offer of auto-start function and it is acceptable based on the rules.

5.2. System prototype

To verify and validate the knowledge support scheme, a prototype of a product family design decision support (evaluation and selection) system, called Design Advisor, has

(a) Configuration

(b) Topologies

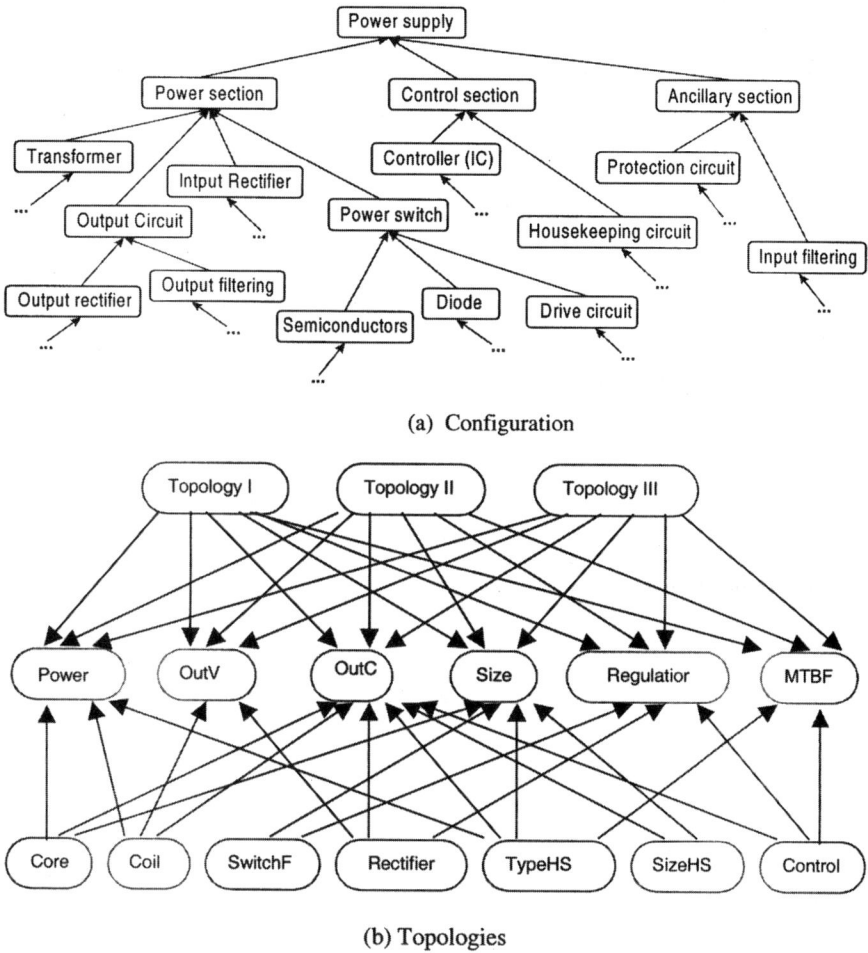

Figure 11. Configurations and topologies of power supply products (a) Configuration (b) Topologies.

been developed based on the fuzzy clustering and ranking model described above. It is a web-based multi-tier system, written in Java™, incorporating Java Expert System Shell, Jess/FuzzyJess (Ernest 1999; NRCC 2003; Samuel and Bellam 2000), consisting of the cluster analysis module, ranking module, selection module, neural-fuzzy module, and visualization and explanation facilities. The Design Advisor system is a subsystem of the knowledge intensive support system for product family design described in (Zha and Lu 2002a,b; Zha and Sriram 2004). The current capabilities of the prototype include capturing and browsing of the evolution of product families and of product variant configurations in product families, ranking and evaluation and selection of product variants in a product family.

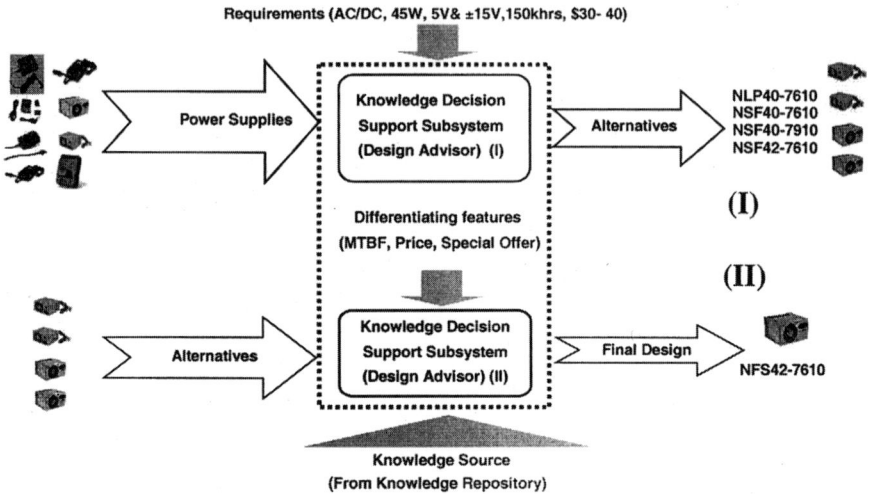

Figure 12. Scenario of knowledge support for product evaluation and selection.

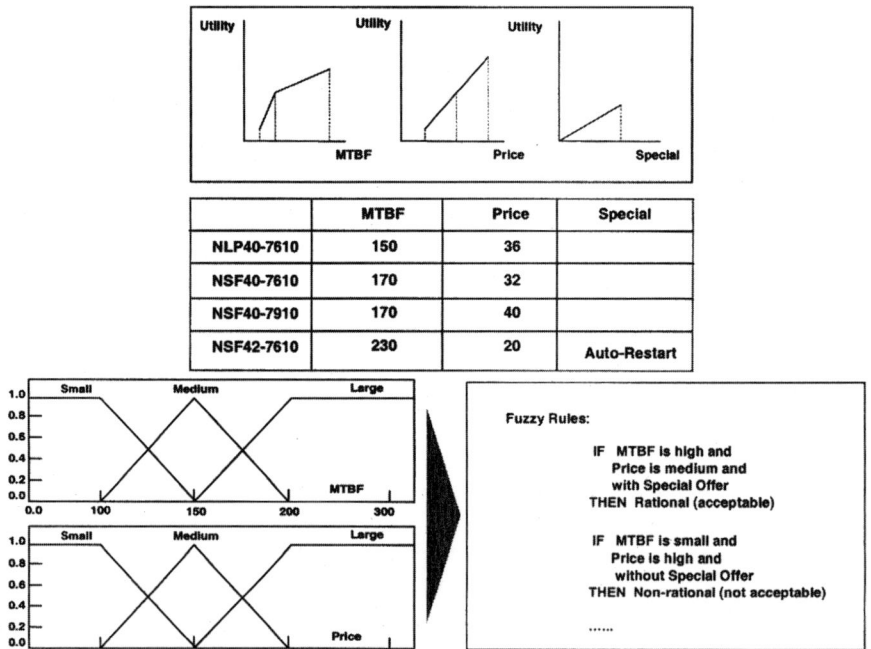

Figure 13. Knowledge used in power supply product evaluation and selection for customization.

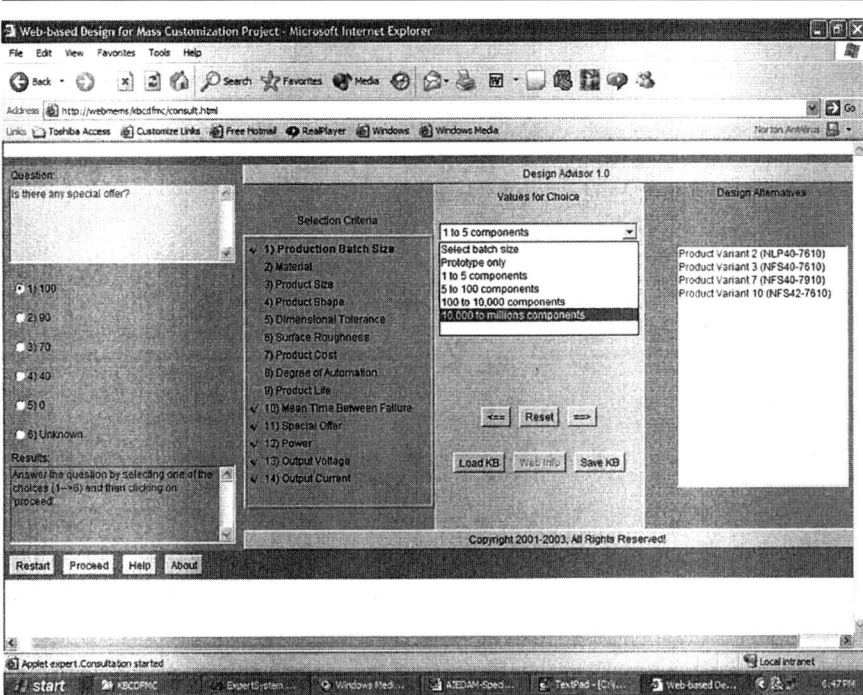

Figure 14. Screen snapshot for product family evaluation session.

The comprehensive fuzzy decision support system can visualize and explain the reasoning process and make a great difference between the knowledge support system and the traditional program. In this subsystem, a tracing approach using linear chain list (Rule_Used_No) is adopted for addressing the explanation facilities: 1) How to reach the conclusions? 2) How many rules are used in reasoning? 3) Does it use Rule X? 4) Why use Rule X? and 5) When does it use Rule X? A linear chain list records the rule number of successful rules during reasoning process and stores them in a knowledge unit. The designer/user consultation is answered by a backtracking mechanism like Prolog. With this subsystem, the designer can represent the design choices available as a fuzzy AND/OR tree. The fuzzy clustering and ranking algorithms employed in the system are able to evaluate and select the (near) overall optimal design that best satisfies customer requirements. The selected design choice is highlighted in the represented tree. Figure 14 gives a screen snapshot of the prototype system used for power supply family evaluation and selection.

6. DISCUSSION

The developed approach, which differs from existing methods and systems (e.g. Jiao and Tseng 1998), is knowledge supported and embodies an effective and efficient method and mechanism to evaluate and select design alternatives or product variants in a product family. The system described in this chapter can provide advisory service for the design of mass customized products and explain the results and what-ifs. Specifically, it is able to provide a common language at the concept level, allowing a designer to describe a design alternative or product variant so that an expert advisory system can decide and select which design alternative and product variant can satisfy the customers' requirements. This means that the system is designed as a tool for finding a "good" concept/solution for a product/product family while still at the conceptual level of design, and making a diverse catalog of design alternatives/product variants available to designers/users so that they can experiment with different requirements/technologies in business.

The "web-top" (web-based) product families can be achieved by using the technologies of e-commerce and mass customization to design and set up the mass customized systems on the web based on the remote-site customers and task requirements for reconfigurable modular systems. The widespread use of these systems is likely to lead many companies to put their products database searches on-line, allowing users to filter inventories/catalogs based on user entered requirements/preferences. Also, the system allows developers to provide intelligent knowledge services and an open environment to support and coordinate highly distributed and decentralized collaborative design and modeling activities for designers/users. Web-based interface lets designers/users customize products and submit them for review if necessary. Thus, the system provides the remote users advice that: 1) indicates which product variant is the most suited to the customers' requirement; 2) how the design could best be modified to satisfy the customers' requirements and constraints. As a result, converting a product from one task/customer to another can be very fast in order to keep up with the rapidly changing marketplaces or applications.

7. SUMMARY AND CONCLUSIONS

This chapter presented an approach to a knowledge decision support for product family evaluation and selection. A comprehensive fuzzy knowledge support scheme and the relevant technologies were developed for product family evaluation and selection in customer-driven design for mass customization. The developed systematic fuzzy clustering and ranking methodology can model the imprecision inherent in design decision-making with fuzzy preference relations and carry out fuzzy analysis and evaluation which is capable of handling linguistic as well as ordinary quantitative information thus solving the multi-criteria decision making problem. The employment of neural networks can adjust membership functions of evaluation and selection criteria, rationalize the determination of customer preferences, and incorporate them into fuzzy analysis. Thus, typical barriers to decision-making processes, including incomplete and evolving information, uncertain evaluations, inconsistency of team members' inputs, can be compensated. The results obtained from the case study illustrate the potential and feasibility of the knowledge intensive decision support scheme and the fuzzy clustering and ranking methodology in product family design evaluation and selection. This work can help bring products to market faster, and with more certainty of success.

Based on the results of assessment, industry best practices are identified that can help improve product quality, cost, and time-to-market and right-to-market. The developed methodology is generic and flexible enough to be used in a variety of decision problems, e.g., concept evaluation and selection.

Disclaimer

Commercial equipment and software, many of which are either registered or trade-marked, are identified in order to adequately specify certain procedures. In no case does such identification imply recommendation or endorsement by the National Institute of Standards and Technology, nor does it imply that the materials or equipment identified are necessarily the best available for the purpose.

REFERENCES

[1] Baudin, M. (2001). Eight strategies for mass customization, Manufacturing Management & Technology Institute, http://www.mmt-inst.com/, USA.

[2] Barkmeyer, Edward, Christopher, Neil, Feng, S., Fowler, James E., Frechette, Simon, Jones, Albert, Jurrens, Kevin K., McLean, Charles, Pratt, Mike, Scott, H. A., Senehi, M. K., Sriram, R. D., and Wallace, Evan. (1997). *SIMA Reference Architecture Part I: Activity Models*, NISTIR 5939, National Institute of Standards and Technology, Gaithersburg, MD.

[3] Boender, C. G., de Graan, J. G. and Lootsma, F. A. (1989). Multi-criteria decision analysis with fuzzy pairwise comparisons. *Fuzzy Sets and Systems*, Vol. 29, pp. 133–143.

[4] Carnahan, J. V., Thurston, D. L. and Liu, T. (1994). Fuzzy rating for multi-attribute design decision-making. *Journal of Mechanical Design, Transaction of the ASME*, Vol. 116, No. 2, pp. 511–521.

[5] Chen, S. J., Hwang, C. L. and Hwang, F. P. (1992). *Fuzzy Multiple Attribute Decision Making: Methods and Applications*. Berlin: Springer-Verlag.

[6] Clausing, D. (1994). *Total Quality Development: A Step-by-Step Guide to World Class Concurrent Engineering*, New York: ASME Press.

[7] Dhingra, A. K., Rao, S. S. and Kumar, V. (1991). Nonlinear membership functions in the fuzzy optimization of mechanical and structural systems. *AAAI 31st Structural Dynamics and Materials Conference*, Long Beach, CA, pp. 403–413.

[8] Dixon, J. R., Howe, A., Cohen, P. R., and Simmons, M. K. (1986). Dominic I: Progress towards domain independence in design by iterative redesign. *Proceedings of the ASME 1986 Computers in Engineering Conference*, Chicago, IL, Vol. 1, pp. 199–212.

[9] Dobson, G., and Kalish, S. (1993). Heuristics for pricing and positioning a product line using conjoint analysis and cost data. *Management Science*, 39(2), pp. 160–175.

[10] Du, X. H., Jiao, J. X., and Tseng, M. M. (2000). *Architecture of product family for mass customization, Proceedings of the 2000 IEEE International Conference on*, vol. 1, pp. 437–443.

[11] Ernest, J. Friedman-Hill. (1999). The Java Expert System Shell, http://herzberg.ca.sandia.gov/jess, Sandia National Laboratories, USA.

[12] Frazell, E. (1985). Suggested techniques enable multi-criteria evaluation of material handling alternatives. *Industrial Engineering*, Vol. 17, No. 2.

[13] Fujita, K. and Ishii, K. (1997). Task structuring toward computational approaches to product variety design. *Proceedings of the 1997 ASME Design Engineering Technical Conferences*, Paper No. 97DETC/DAC-3766, ASME.

[14] Fujita, K., Akagi, S., Yoneda, T., and Ishikawa, M. (1998). Simultaneous optimization of product family design sharing system structure and configuration. *CD-ROM Proceedings of the 1998 ASME Design Engineering Technical Conferences*, Atlanta, Georgia.

[15] Gaithen, N. (1980). *Production and Operations Management: A Problem-Solving and Decision-Making Approach*, The Dryden Press, New York.

[16] Gilmore, J. H. and Pine, B. J., II. (1997). The four faces of mass customization. *Harvard Business Review*, Vol. 75 (January-February): pp. 91–101.

[17] Gonzale-Zugasti, J. P. (2000). *Models for Platform-Based Product Family Design*, PhD Thesis, MIT, Cambridge.

[18] Green, P. E., and Krieger, A. M. (1985). Models and heuristics for product line selection. *Marketing. Science*, 4(1), pp. 1–19.

[19] Gui, J. K. (1993). *Methodology for Modeling Complete Product Assemblies*, PhD Dissertation, Helsinki University of Technology.

[20] Hwang, C. L. and Yoon, K. (1981). *Multiple Attribute Decision Making: Methods and Applications*, Berlin: Springer.

[21] Huang, P. and Ghandforoush, P. (1984). Procedures given for evaluating, selecting robots. *Industrial Engineering*, Vol. 16, No. 4.

[22] Jiao, J. X., and Tseng, M. M. (1998a). Fuzzy ranking for concept evaluation in configuration design for mass customization. *Concurrent Engineering: Research and Application*, Vol. 6, No. 3, pp. 189–206.

[23] Jiao, J. X., and Tseng, M. M. (1998b). Design for mass customization by developing product family architecture. *Proceedings of the 1998 ASME Design Engineering Technical Conferences*, Paper No.: DETC98/DFM-5717.

[24] Knosala, R. and Pedrycz, W. (1992). Evaluation of design alternatives in mechanical engineering. *Fuzzy Sets and Systems*, Vol. 47, No. 3, pp. 269–280.

[25] Kandel, A. (1982). *Fuzzy Techniques in Pattern Recognition*, John Wiley & Sons.

[26] Kickert, W. J. M. (1978). Fuzzy Theories on Decision Making: A Critical Review, Martinus Nijhoff Social Sciences Division

[27] Kohli, R., and Sukumar, R. (1990). Heuristics for product-line design using conjoint analysis. *Management Science*, 36(12), pp. 1464–1477.

[28] Kotler, P. (1989). From mass marketing to mass customization. *Planning Review*, Vol. 17(5): pp. 10–15.

[29] Krishnan, V. and Gupta, S. (2001). Appropriateness and impact of platform-based product development. *Management Science*, 47(1): pp. 52–68.

[30] Lee, H. L. and Tang, C. S. (1997). Modeling the costs and benefits of delayed product differentiation. *Management Science*, Vol. 43(1): pp. 40–53.

[31] Li, H., and Azarm, S. (2000). Product design selection under uncertainty and with competitive advantage. *Journal of Mechanical Design, Transactions of the ASME*, Vol. 122, pp. 411–418.

[32] Li, H., and Azarm, S. (2002). An approach for product line design selection under uncertainty and competition. *Journal of Mechanical Design, Transactions of the ASME*, Vol. 124, pp. 385–392.

[33] Maurice K. (1993). *Trends in AC/DC Switching Power Supplies and DC/DC Converters*, IEEE.

[34] Martin, M. and Ishii, K. (1996). Design for variety: a methodology for understanding the costs of product proliferation. *1996 Design Theory and Methodology Conference* (Wood, K., ed.), Irvine, CA, ASME, Paper No. 96-DETC/DTM-1610.

[35] McKay, A., Erens, F. and Bloor, M. S. (1996). Relating product definition and product variety. *Research in Engineering Design*, Vol. 8 (2): pp. 63–80.

[36] Meyer, M. H., Tertzakian, P. and Utterback, J. M. (1997). Metrics for managing research and development in the context of the product family. *Management Science*, Vol. 43(1): pp. 88–111.

[37] Mistree, F., Bras, B., Smith, W. F., and Allen, J. K. (1995). Modeling design processes: a conceptual, decision-based perspective. *Engineering Design & Automation*, Vol. 1, No. 4, pp. 209–321.

[38] Mistree, F., Hughes, O. F. and Bras, B. A. (1992). The compromise decision support problem and the adaptive linear programming algorithm. *Structural Optimization: Status and Promise*, M. P. Kamatt (ed.), AIAA, Washington D.C., Chapter 11, pp. 247–286.

[39] NRCC (National Research Council of Canada). (2003). Fuzzy Logic in Integrated Reasoning, webpage: http://www.iit.nrc.ca/IR_public/fuzzy/.

[40] Nelson, S. A., Parkinson, M. B., and Papalambros, P. Y. (1999). Multi-criteria optimization in product platform design. *CD-ROM Proceedings of DETC99*, 1999 ASME Design Engineering Technical Conferences, September 12–15, 1999, Las Vegas, Nevada.

[41] Nielsen, E. H., Dixon, J. R. and Simmons, M. K. (1986). GERES: a knowledge-based material selection program for injection molded resins. *Proceedings of the ASME 1986 Computers in Engineering Conference*, Chicago, IL, pp. 255–262.

[42] Pahl, G. and Beitz, W. (1996). *Engineering Design—A Systematic Approach*, New York: Springer.

[43] Pfaltz, J. L. and Rosenfeld, A. (1969). Web grammars. *Proceedings of First International Joint Conference on Artificial Intelligence*, Washington, D.C. pp. 609–619.

[44] Pine, B. J. (1993). *Mass Customization–The New Frontier in Business Competition*, Boston, MA, Harvard Business School Press.

[45] Prasad, B. (1996). *Concurrent Engineering Fundamentals*, Vol. 1–2, NJ: Prentice Hall PTR.

[46] Pugh, S. (1991). *Total Design: Integrating Methods for Successful Product Engineering*, Addition-Wesley Publishing Co. Inc.

[47] Samuel, A. K. and Bellam, S., (2000). http://www.glue.umd.edu/~sbellam/

[48] Sanderson, S. and Uzumeri, M. (1995). Managing product families: the case of the Sony Walkman. *Research Policy*, Vol. 24: pp. 761–782.

[49] Sanderson, S. W. (1991). Cost models for evaluating virtual design strategies in multi-cycle product families. *Journal of Engineering and Technology Management*, Vol. 8: pp. 339–358.

[50] Schile, T. and Goldhar, J. D. (1989). Product variety and time based manufacturing and business management: achieving competitive advantage through CIM. *Manufacturing Review*, Vol. 2(1): pp. 32–42.

[51] Simpson, T. W. (1998). *A Concept Exploration Method for Product Family Design*, Ph.D Dissertation, System Realization Laboratory, Woodruff School of Mechanical Engineering, Georgia Institute of Technology.

[52] Simpson, T. W., Maier, J. R. A., and Mistree, F. (2001). Product platform design: method and application. *Research In Engineering Design*, Vol. 13, pp. 2–22.

[53] Simpson, T. W., Umapathy, K., Nanda, J., Halbe, S., and Hodge, B. (2003). Development of a framework for web-based product platform customization, *Journal of Computing and Information Science in Engineering, Transactions of the ASME*, Vol. 3, pp. 119–129.

[54] Sriram, R. D. (1997). *Intelligent Systems for Engineering: A Knowledge-based Approach*, Springer.

[55] Sriram, R. D. (2002). Distributed and Integrated Collaborative Engineering Design, Sarven Publishers, Glenwood, MD 21738, USA.

[56] Suh, N. P. (1990). *The Principles of Design*, New York: Oxford University Press.

[57] Sullivan, W. (1986). Models IEs can be used to include strategic, non-monetary factors in automation decisions. *Industrial Engineering*, Vol. 18, pp. 42–50.

[58] Saaty, T. L. (1991). *The Analytic Hierarchy Process*, McGraw-Hill, New York.

[59] Siskos, J., Lochard, J. and Lombard, J. (1984). A multi-criteria decision-making methodology under fuzziness: application to the evaluation of radiological protection nuclear power plants. *TIMS/Studies in Management Sciences*, H. J. Zimmermann (ed.), Amsterdam: North-Holland, pp. 261–283.

[60] Taguchi, G. (1986). *Introduction to Quality Engineering*, Tokyo, Japan: Asian Productivity Organization.

[61] Tanino, T. (1988). Fuzzy preference relations in group decision making. *Non-Conventional Preference Relations in Decision Making*, J. Kacprzyk and M. Roubens (eds.), Berlin: Springer, pp. 54–71.

[62] Thurston, D. L. (1991). A formal method for subjective design evaluation with multiple attributes. *Research in Engineering Design*, Vol. 3, No. 2, pp. 105–122.

[63] Thurston, D. L. and Carnahan, J. V. (1992). Fuzzy rating and utility analysis in preliminary design evaluation of multiple attributes. *Journal on Mechanical Design, Transaction of the ASME*, Vol. 114, No. 4, pp. 648–658.

[64] Thurston, D. L. and Locascio, A. (1994). Decision theory for design economics. Special Issue, *Engineering Economist*, Vol. 40, No. 1, pp. 41–72.

[65] Thurston, D. L. and Crawford, C. A. (1994). A method for integrating end-user preferences for design evaluation in rule-based systems. *Journal of Mechanical Design, Transaction of the ASME*, Vol. 116, No. 2, pp. 522–530.

[66] Tong, C. and Sriram, D. (Eds.), (1991a). Artificial Intelligence in Engineering Design: Volume I—Representation: Structure, Function and Constraints; Routine Design, Academic Press.

[67] Tong, C. and Sriram, D. (Eds.), (1991b). Artificial Intelligence in Engineering Design: Volume III—Knowledge Acquisition, Commercial Systems; Integrated Environments, Academic Press.

[68] Tseng, T. Y. and Klein, C. M. (1989). New algorithm for the ranking procedure in fuzzy decision-making. *IEEE Transactions on Systems, Man and Cybernetics*, Vol. 19, No. 5, pp. 1289–96.

[69] Tseng, M. M. and Jiao, J. X. (1996). Design for mass customization. *CIRP Annals*, Vol. 45, No. 1, pp. 153–156.

[70] Tseng, M. M. and Jiao, J. X. (1998). Product family modeling for mass customization. *Computers in Industry*, Vol. 35(3-4): pp 495–498.

[71] von Neumann, J. and Morgenstern, O. (1947). *Theory of Games and Economic Behavior*, Princeton University Press.

[72] Wang, J. (1997). A fuzzy outranking method for conceptual design evaluation. *International Journal of Production Research*, Vol. 35, No. 4, pp. 995–1010.

[73] Wood, K. L., Antonsson, E. K. and Beck, J. L. (1989). Representing imprecision in engineering: comparing fuzzy and probability calculus. *Research in Engineering Design*, Vol. 1, No. 3/4, pp. 187–203.

[74] Wood, K. L. and Antonsson, E. K. (1989). Computations with imprecise parameters in engineering design: background and theory. *ASME Journal of Mechanism, Transmissions, and Automation in Design*, Vol. 111, pp. 616–625.

[75] Wortmann, H. C., Muntslag, D. R. and Timmermans, P. J. M. (1997). *Customer-Driven Manufacturing*, Chapman and Hall, London.

[76] Zha, X. F. (2001). Neuro-fuzzy comprehensive assemblability and assembly sequence evaluation. *Artificial Intelligence for Engineering Design, Analysis and Manufacturing (AIEDAM)*, Vol. 15(5), pp. 367–384.

[77] Zha, X. F. and Lu, W. F. (2002a). Knowledge support for customer-based design for mass customization. *AID'02*, J. S. Gero (ed), Kluwer Academic Press, pp. 407–429.

[78] Zha, X. F. and Lu, W. F. (2002b). Knowledge intensive support for product family design. *Proceeding of 2002 ASME DETC02*, Paper No. DETC/DAC 34098.

[79] Zha, X. F., and Sriram, R. D. (2004). Platform-based product design and development: knowledge support strategy and implementation. *Intelligent Knowledge-Based Systems: Business and Technology in New Millennium*, Cornelius T. Leondes (ed), vol. 1, chapter 1. Kluwer Academic Publishers, USA.

[80] Zimmermann, H. J. (1987). *Fuzzy Sets, Decision Making, and Expert Systems*, Boston: Kluwer Academic Publishers.

[81] Zimmermann, H. J. (1996). *Fuzzy Set Theory and Its Applications*, 3rd ed., Boston: Kluwer Academic Publishers.

[82] Zadeh, L. A. (1965). Fuzzy Sets. *Information and Control*, Vol. 8, pp. 338–353.

[83] Zhang W. Y., Tor, S. B., and Britton, G. A. (2002). A heuristic state-space approach to the functional design of mechanical systems. *International Journal of Advanced Manufacturing Technology*, Vol. 19, pp. 235–244.

GENETIC ALGORITHM TECHNIQUES AND APPLICATIONS IN MANAGEMENT SYSTEMS

CARL K. CHANG AND YUJIA GE

1. INTRODUCTION

1.1. Resource-constrained scheduling problem

Scheduling problems are NP-hard with extremely complex combinatorial optimization issues. The resource-constrained scheduling problem in its general form can be described as "Given a set of activities, a set of resources, and a measurement of performance, what is the best way to assign the resources to the activities such that the performance is maximized?" [Wall 96].

Scheduling is based on many different kinds of data, such as models of tasks, resources, processes with underlying constrains, objectives, and performance measures. Tasks can be any activity, such as assembling a product, authoring a paper, and developing a system. Machines, engineers, developers, tools, and materials can be considered resources. Objectives are some measurements for us to evaluate a schedule to determine whether it is "good" or not. For example, typical objectives of project management include minimizing the duration of the project, the number of projects which can not be completed before the deadline, and cost of the whole project. The concept of scheduling can be illustrated in Figure 1.

In a more formalized way, resource-constrained scheduling problems can be described simply as a quadruple (R, P, J, C): R is a set of resources; P is a set of products; J is a set of jobs which are to be scheduled subject to several constraints defined in C.

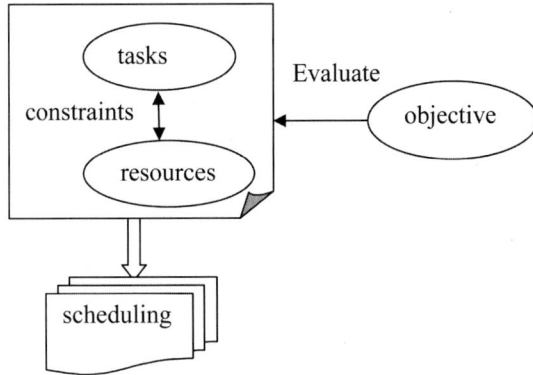

Figure 1. Concept of scheduling.

1.2. Classes of the generalized problem for resource-constrained scheduling

There are several classes in the generalized resource-constrained scheduling problems. Because of the high complexity of computability of real-world problems, they are often scaled down and simplified, such as the job-shop problems, flow-shop problems, production scheduling problems, and project scheduling problems.

First, let us examine the simplified models of those problems:

• Job-shop model: there are a finite set of n jobs and a finite set of m machines. Each job consists of some tasks and each machine can handle at most one operation at a time. Each task needs to be processed during an uninterrupted period of time with a given length on a given machine. The objective of the problem is to find a schedule with minimal length of time interval to complete all jobs.

For example, Table 1 gives a job-shop problem, and an optimal scheduling is illustrated in Figure 2.

Table 1 Example of job-shop problem

Job	Task	Machine	Duration
Job1	Task1–1	M1	4
Job1	Task1–2	M2	5
Job2	Task2–1	M1	3
Job2	Task2–2	M2	5
Job2	Task2–3	M1	6
Job3	Task3–1	M2	4

• Flow-shop model: there are a series of machines numbered 1, 2, 3, ..., m. Each job has exactly m tasks with varying durations. The first task of every job is done on machine 1, second task on machine 2 and so on. Every job goes through all m machines in a unidirectional order.

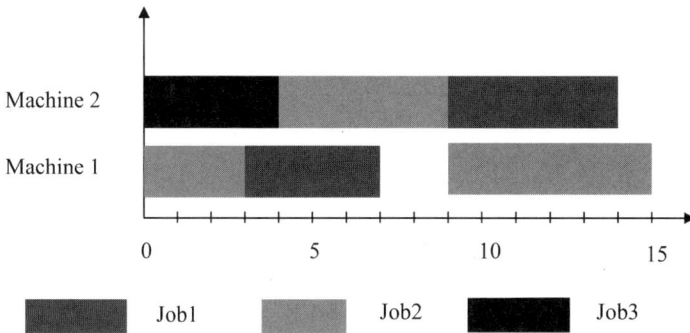

Figure 2. An optimal scheduling.

• Project scheduling model: a project consists of a set of tasks, or activities. Tasks have precedence relationships. Tasks also have estimated durations and may include various other measures such as cost. The objective is to determine a schedule with minimal *makespan* such that both the precedence and resource constraints are fulfilled. Mathematical programming formulations of the resource-constrained project scheduling problems were studied by Demeulemeester and Herroelen [Demeulemeester 92] and Mingozzi et al. [Mingozzi 98].

For example the task precedence relation of a project scheduling problem is depicted in Figure 3.

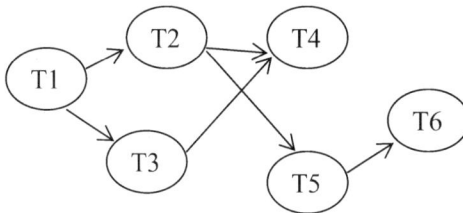

Figure 3. Example of task precedence relation.

The project consists of 6 tasks with constrains including: the required skills to finish Task1 are Java and Microsoft Project; Tom's salary is higher than Mike's; Jenny works on Monday, Tuesday, and Friday, etc.

In many industrial applications, Project Scheduling problems occur. An overview about the different models is given in the survey article "Resource-Constrained Project Scheduling: Notation, Classification, Models, and Methods" [Brucker 01].

It seems that the simplified model can be solved quite well by some exact algorithms. However, in the real-world situations, the problem is not as simple as one may think. For example, software management is a peculiar area in project scheduling. To the software development process, scheduling is so tedious, error-prone, but important that it can greatly influence the success of a project. Experiences show that project scheduling can be influenced by a lot of dynamics elements, such as skills of engineers, growth of skills and experiences, cooperation and leadership, etc. However, software project management is paid relatively little attention in the software engineering research community. The main problem is that what kind of model is sound and applicable in software engineering process. The model requires specific project information to support decision and optimization. It is clear that we cannot model every single element of the entire software engineering process. What do we need to model and how? In section 5, we will discuss it in more details.

1.3. Structure of this chapter

In section 2, we will discuss two major approaches (exact solution and heuristics) to solve scheduling problems. From section 3, we begin to focus on Genetic algorithm. Section 3 gives an introduction to genetic algorithm. Section 4 contains a survey of GA techniques on scheduling. Section 5 discusses software project management problems employing the GA solution. Finally, section 6 concludes the chapter.

2. RELATED WORK ON SCHEDULING

Research on solution of the resource-constrained scheduling problem has progressed for several decades. The methods form two distinct classes: exact methods and heuristic methods. These solutions may be categorized further into stochastic and deterministic approaches [Wall 96]. But usually exact solutions are to solve simplified problems while real problems cannot be solved exactly because of complex constrains and large scale. Therefore oftentimes we try to find "good" solutions instead the "best" one. As a result heuristic methods were introduced that contains rules that drive the optimization process in finding solutions. Stochastic methods include probabilistic operations so that they may not operate the same way twice on a given problem. Deterministic methods operate the same way each time for a given problem. Genetic algorithm combines heuristic and stochastic methods in its operation. In fact, many hybrid methods exist that combine the characteristics of these classes.

2.1. Exact solution methods

When resource-constrained scheduling solutions were first proposed, simple models were used with exact methods for solving problems. Exact methods try to find optimal solutions through some intelligent exhaustive search. They include backtracking, branch and bound [chap. 9, Murty 95], critical path method and its variations, dynamic programming, and implicit enumeration. Given a problem, the exact methods can find the best solution if it does exist. However, when constraints are added, the difficulty of solving a problem increases. In addition, significant problem size affects a lot on the feasibility of those methods. For example, critical path method was devised for finding the shortest time to complete a project, given estimates of task durations. But, the critical path method cannot solve problems that include restrictions on the number of resources that are available.

2.2. Heuristic solution methods

Although heuristic methods cannot find optimal solutions, it still can find good solution with less time, but more space, compared to exact methods. Heuristics are rules to help make a decision given a particular situation. Heuristics in scheduling are usually referred to as scheduling rules or dispatch rules. Heuristics could be deterministic or stochastic. There are several common heuristics approaches on scheduling problems. Simulated Annealing (SA) introduced by Kirkpatrick et al. [Kirkpatrick 83] is originated from the physical annealing process. It requires a schedule representation as well as a neighborhood operator for moving from the current solution to a candidate solution. In [Vidal 93], SA has been proved to be a good technique for lots of applications. Tabu Search (TS) developed by Glover [Glover 89] is essentially a steepest descent/mildest ascent method for guiding known heuristic to overcome local optimality. Genetic Algorithm (GA), inspired by the process of biological evolution, was introduced by Holland [Holland 75], and has been extensively applied in scheduling problems.

3. INTRODUCTION TO GENETIC ALGORITHM

Genetic algorithms belong to the stochastic search method introduced in the 1970s by John Holland [Holland 75] and it belongs to the evolutionary strategies developed by Ingo Rechenberg [Rechenberg 73]. They are inspired by natural genetics and evolution with Darwin's idea. Based on simplifications of natural evolutionary processes, genetic algorithms operate on a population of solutions rather than a single solution, and employ heuristics such as selection, crossover, and mutation to evolve better solutions.

3.1. The concept of genetic algorithms

Genetic algorithms begin with a group of initial solution individuals and execute iteratively to create better offspring. They can be evaluated by some criteria, such as an objective function. An individual is a candidate solution of the problem which is called *genome*. The genetic algorithms apply genetic operators such a mutation and crossover to evolve the solutions in order to find the best one. There are many different variations to improve performance or parallelize the algorithms.

The three most important aspects of using genetic algorithms are: (1) definition and implementation of the genetic representation, (2) definition and implementation of the genetic operators, (3) definition of the objective function.

For the representation of individual genomes, Holland worked primarily with strings of bits. There are other kinds of representation: arrays, tress, lists or any other object. The critical step is to define genetic operators (initialization, mutation, crossover, comparison). For example, *selection* of the parents and *crossover* (sometimes combined with *mutation*) is the construction of a child solution from the parent solutions. The selection process should choose individuals with better performance. A selection algorithm that gives little weight to performance will tend to search widely but usually will not converge quickly. A *crossover* operator mimics the step to produce children inheriting certain traits of both parents. *Mutation* is a random process that is to randomly perturb

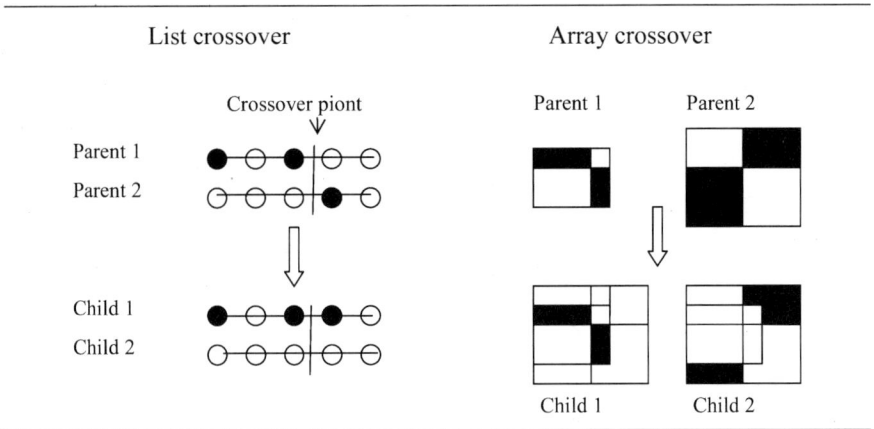

Figure 4. Crossover operator examples.

some of the solutions in the population. In the absence of mutation, no child can ever acquire parametric values that were not already present in the previous population.

Let us look at the examples of crossover operators on List and Array as Figure 4:

The objective function provides a measure of how good an individual is but can be considered for either an individual in isolation or within the context of the entire population. The objective score is a measure used to evaluate the performance of the genome. The fitness score is computed from the objective score using a scaling strategy, such as those introduced by Goldberg [Goldberg 89].

Figure 5 shows the main stages of a GA:

3.2. A simple example of genetic algorithms

For a simple example, we use simple binary string as representation of the population. Our objective is to derive 1011. The fitness function is the number of bits that matches the objective. The initial populations are 0011, 1100, 1010. They are evaluated with the score 3, 1 and 3, respectively, so 0011, 1010 are selected. By the crossover operation on 0011 and 1010, the offspring 1011 and 0010 are produced. When we found score of 1011 is 4, it signals the end of our calculation. The procedure is shown in Figure 6.

Although it is a very small example, it clearly shows that genetic algorithm can compute the result very quickly for we do not need to search the entire search space.

3.3. Packages of genetic algorithm components

Example implementation packages include GAucsd (University of California at San Diego), GALOPPS (Michigan State University), IlliGAL (UIUC Illinois Genetic Algorithms laboratory), and GAlib (MIT), LibGA (CMU Artificial Intelligence Repository).

GAucsd [GAucsd] is a genetic algorithm software package based on GENESIS. Major additions include a wrapper that simplifies the writing of evaluation functions, a facility to distribute experiments over networks of machines, and Dynamic Parameter

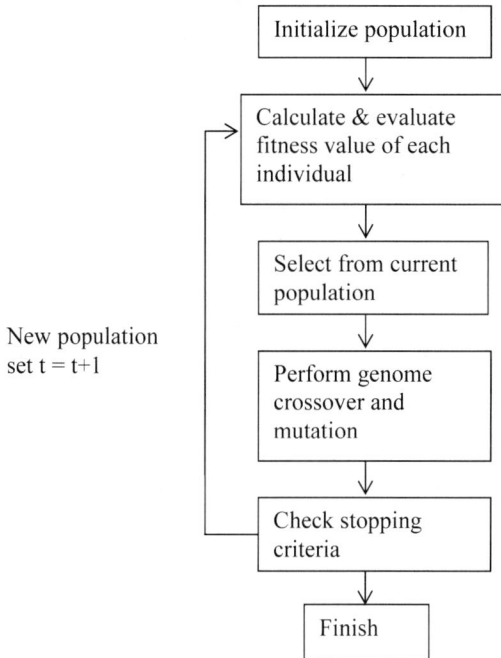

Figure 5. Main stages of a genetic algorithm.

Objective = 1011

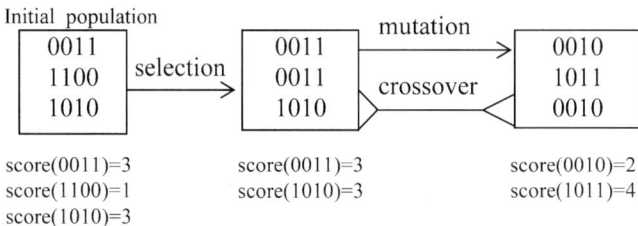

Figure 6. A simplified GA example.

Encoding, a technique that improves GA performance in continuous search space by adaptively refining the representation of real-valued genes. Experiments can be executed in parallel, and distributed to several hosts.

GALOPPS [GALOPPS] (the "Genetic Algorithm Optimized for Portability and Parallelism System") is a genetic algorithm tool writing in C language that provides a lot of options for genetic algorithm experiments. It is available for both PC and Unix systems.

Wall's GAlib [GAlib] provides rich types of Genomes and Operators. Each type can be customized to meet more complicated requirements, for instance, deterministic crowding, traveling salesman, DeJong, and Royal Road problems. Also, new genetic algorithms can be derived from base genetic algorithms class in the library.

The LibGA software package [LibGA] was developed primarily because of the noticeable deficiencies of existing GA packages at the time. LibGA is a collection of routines written in the C programming language. It can run on a variety of workstations and PC's.

3.4. Applications of GA and when not to use

Because genetic algorithm works well on certain complex practical problems compared to some other methods, many practical applications have implemented genetic algorithms and obtained quite good results. For example,

1) Optimization and planning

Genetic algorithms are naturally optimization methods. A lot of applications utilized GA for planning and scheduling.

2) Economics

Genetic algorithms are applied in game theory to find equilibrium points in non-zero sum and non-cooperative situations.

3) Business and their supportive role in decision making

Most research work focused on engineering and technologies with GA. GA can also be used in Business. For example, some papers reported work on applying GA to the design of organization.

4) Computer-aided design

Genetic algorithms use the feedback from an evaluation process to select the better designs and can generate new designs by the combination of the selected part designs.

When NOT to use a GA?

There are no common standard for evaluating this question. But we can answer it partly according to some general rules for it. When global optimization is required, GA is not satisfactory because sometimes global optimization can only be satisfied by other techniques. One of GA disadvantages is that there is no guarantee for finding exact global minimum since no mathematical proof exists. When the problem is highly constrained, much power of GA will be reduced. When the problem is smooth, we can use other optimizer, such as gradient-based optimizer. When the search space is very small, we can use exact solution to get the result.

4. SURVEY OF GA TECHNIQUES ON SCHEDULING

In the past two decades, an increasing number of research efforts have investigated the application of Genetic Algorithm techniques for the solution of scheduling problems.

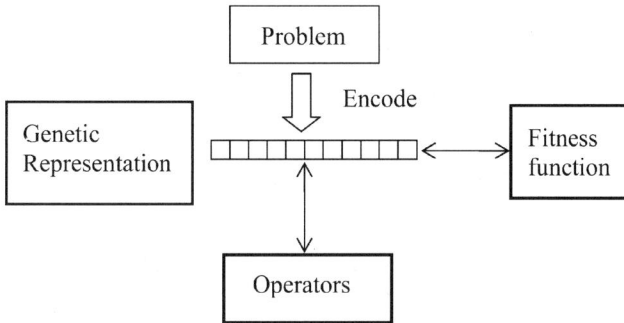

Figure 7. Representation issues of GAs.

In one of the earliest published works on the application of GAs to scheduling, Davis [Davis 85] outlines a basic scheme applied to a simplified toy problem in flow-shop scheduling. Davis also points out that there are layers of ill defined constraints in real-life scheduling problems which are very difficult to represent in the formal frameworks of operational research. Knowledge-based solutions are typically deterministic and thus easily lead to sub-optimal solutions. To avoid the sub-optimal solutions, Davis suggested genetic algorithms by their stochastic nature and used list as an indirect representation for genetic algorithm, from which the actual schedule can be derived by decoding. Since Davis' paper, numerous implementations have been suggested not only for the job-shop problem but also other variations of the general resource-constrained scheduling problem. Recently, a sharply increased number of papers are published every year. For example, in an indexed bibliography of Genetic Algorithms Papers of 1996 (in proceedings) compiled by Jarmo T. Alander [Alander 96], the statistical results shows 1470 GA papers with approximately 40% average annual growth during last twenty years.

4.1. Representation issues

Representation is the most important aspect in GAs. The operators are related to the representations as depicted in Figure 7. Usually problem-specific representations often improve the performance of GA. In some cases, a representation for one class of problems can be applied to others as well. But in most cases, modification of the constraint definitions requires a different representation. Ralf Bruns summarized the production scheduling approaches in four overlapping categories: direct, indirect, domain-independent, and problem-specific representations [Bruns 93].

4.1.1. Indirect representation

Most genetic algorithms for scheduling use an indirect representation of solutions. Indirect representation means that a schedule is not directly represented, but encoded in a certain representation. It requires transformation from genome to schedule, and in some cases requires a schedule builder as well [Bagchi 91]. Domain-independent

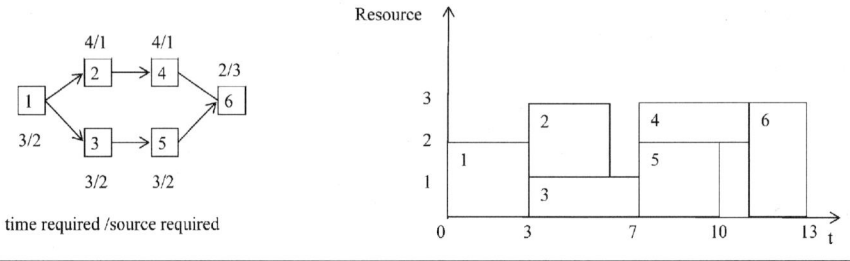

Figure 8. Example of indirect representation.

representation means domain-specific knowledge is not required for representing solutions.

There are two typical approaches:

(1) Binary representation: A solution to a scheduling problem is represented by a bit string. In [Cleveland 89], the release time of each job in a flow shop is represented as a binary integer. All such times represented in binary integers are then concatenated into one long bit string as a solution. Similar work can be found in [Nakano 91], [Tamaki 92].

(2) List or order based representations: The list of all jobs to be scheduled is represented as an individual. The ordering of the list represents the scheduling priority of the jobs. Thus, the scheduling problem is regarded as a sequencing problem, such as sequence of jobs representation [Cleveland 89, Starkweather 91, Fang 93]. For example, in *sequence of operations* representation, a solution (4, 5, 6, 4, 2, 1) means that the sequence of scheduling starts from the first part of job4, followed by job5, job6, the second part of job4, job2 and job1.

In problem-specific indirect representation, we need to define the operators and the evaluation functions based on domain knowledge. Domain knowledge was used to improve performance, such as *sequence of job-process plan* representation, *sequence of job-process plan-machines* representation [Uckun 93], and *preference list* representation [Cleveland 89].

Most of recent representations are order based:

In [Hartmann 98], considering the resource-constrained project scheduling problem with *makespan* minimization as objective, an individual is represented as $(J_1^l \dots J_J^l)$. It is a feasible activity sequence. For example, there are 6 tasks in the project with maximum source of 3. One feasible permutation is (1, 2, 3, 5, 4, 6) as shown in Figure 8.

[Hartmann 98] also proposed a new genetic algorithm approach to solve this problem. The approach made use of a permutation based genetic encoding that contains problem-specific knowledge. In his paper, he also compared their GA with the other two algorithms employing priority-value based and priority-rule based representations.

4.1.2. Direct representation

In direct representation, an individual in a complete representation is a feasible schedule itself, so a schedule builder is not necessary. A direct representation by Kanet and Filipic used a list of order-machine-time triplets for the single-operation jobs problem. However, as noted by Bruns, it was not extensible [Kanet 91] [Filipic 92]. Both of them designed unique crossover and mutation operators. A representation by Yamada [Yamada 92] used a list of completion times for each operation for the job shop problems. In [Bruns 93], he proposed a direct, problem-specific representation using a list of order assignments in which the sequence of orders was not important. In [Husbands 93], an individual is represented as: $Task_1 M_1 T_1 Task_2 M_2 T_2 G Task_3 M_3 T_3 Task_4 M_4 S_4 G \ldots$ in which "G" is used to separate interrelated groups. The whole schedule can be described as " Task1 uses machine M1 in time T1, meanwhile Task 2 uses machine M2 in time T2, etc.

In [Wall 96], a genome consists of an array of relative start times. Each time represents the duration from the latest finish time of all predecessor tasks to the start time of the corresponding task.

An example is illustrated in Figure 9.

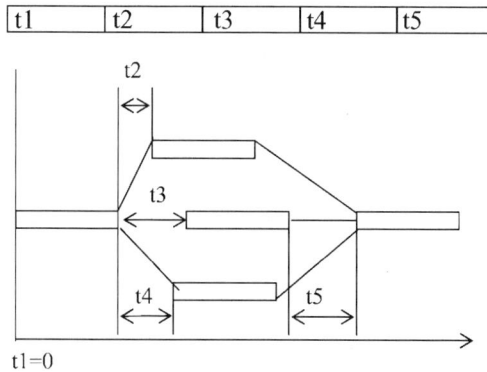

Figure 9. Example of direct representation.

4.2. Operators

Usually, operators for genetic algorithm are related to solution representation. Problem-specific operators often improve the performance of genetic algorithms. Several different sequencing operators were developed and the schedule builders used range from fairly simple ones to complex knowledge-based systems.

Initialization

Besides representation and operators, another important topics common in scheduling is non-random initialization of the population. In general it is true that using heuristics to choose better individuals for the initial population can lead to significantly faster convergence to a good solution. Therefore, using heuristic initialization [Bruns 93] is a good try. Burke, Newall and Weare [Burke 98] address the issue of heuristic initialization for the problem of timetabling. They compared a variety of different heuristics for generating good initial solutions. Based on statistical measurements of diversity, they showed that the best initialization methods can produce populations of high fitness individuals with diversity and also determine how much randomness in the heuristics is optimal.

Reordering methods

Another factor was the reordering method. In the genetic algorithm implementation, different choice of crossover can significantly affect the performance. Better performance can be achieved with appropriate operators.

Some papers investigated the effectiveness of crossover techniques. From the traditional 1-point crossover, many different crossover algorithms have been devised. [Goldberg 89] reported that usually 2-point crossover can improve the performance, but more crossover reduces the performance of GA. Other practical topics, such as mutation, can be found in [Beasley 93].

4.3. Comparison between different approaches

Some empirical evaluations have been reported to compare different evolutionary computation solutions for scheduling. Lee and Kim [Lee 96] compared a genetic algorithm (GA), a simulated annealing heuristic, and a tabu search method. Because of the variation of different GA representations and implementations on different problems, such comparisons entail a lot of work. Most papers are on the comparison of genetic algorithm with other methods. There are few papers on comparison of genetic algorithms per se. Here are two papers on comparison:

One is reported by Bruns for job shop problems:

In [Bruns 93], a direct representation with knowledge-augemented operators was compared with domain-independent representation. Several GAs were developed for the $n * m$ (minimum-makespan) job shop problem, where n denotes the number of jobs and m the number of machines. Experiments were conducted using the well-known 10*10 and 20*5 benchmarks introduced by Muth and Thompson (1963). It was found that different GAs were able to obtain very good results (close to the optimum) for these difficult scheduling problems. The best performance was achieved with a direct problem representation by Davidor 93 as shown in Table 2.

Comparisons between domain-independent and problem-specific evolutionary algorithms were conducted as well. And those results are compared with the result in [Bagchi 91]. Bagchi compared three different representations and concluded that the more problem-specific information was included in the representation, the better the algorithm would perform [Bagchi 91].

Table 2 Taken from [Bruns 93]

GA	Representation	10*10	20*5
Nakano 91	binary	965	1215
Yamada 92	direct	975	1236
Davidor 93	direct-parallel	963	1213
Fang 93	sequence of operations	977	1215
Optimal		930	1165

Table 3 Patterson instance set–taken from [Hartmann 98]

Paper	Representation	Avg. dev	optimal
Hartmann98-permutation	permutation	0.00%	100.0%
Hartmann98-Priority value	priority value	0.25%	88.4%
Hartmann98- Priority rule	priority rule	0.78%	74.6%
Leon, Ramamoorthy 1995	problem space	0.74%	75.5%

Another is reported in [Hartmann 98]:

[Hartmann 98] presented the experimental results on resource-constrained project scheduling as shown in Table 3. The *priority value* GAs can be viewed as modified versions of the GAs proposed by Lee and Kim. *Priority Rule based* Genetic Algorithm is based on a *priority rule representation*. This representation type was developed by [Dorndorf 95] for the job shop scheduling problem. *Permutation based* GA has basic scheme and the operator variants. The permutation based encoding yielded best results. Priority value based representation is in the second place and priority rule encoding has a little worse performance. Leon and Ramamoorthy [Leon 95] suggested a GA and two local search procedures. Their approach is based on the so-called *problem space based representation* which, similarly to the *priority value representation*, encodes a solution using an array of real numbers.

4.4. Other methods and issues

Hybrid solutions

Because of the popularity and limitation of GA (for example, sometimes GA is too expensive in terms of time), a lot of hybrid GA solutions have been proposed for improving better performance for some specific problems. Most of them combine GA with other heuristic methods, such as heuristic rules, gradient-based method or tabu search. [Fang 94] describes a hybrid approach to this problem which combines a genetic algorithm with simple heuristic schedule building rules. In [Al 94], GA is not used to optimize the parameters directly but to optimize the parameters of heuristic problem solving strategies. [Hilliard 88] implemented a classifier system to improve heuristics for determining the sequence of activities and found some heuristics for the simple machine shop scheduling problem. Similar works can also be found in [Nakamura 98].

Distributed parallel GAs

From the beginning of GA research, the potential for parallelization was determined. Nowadays, with the tremendous progress in computing power of hardware, researches on this direction go deeper recently. Performance can be improved dramatically using parallel computing. For example, standard sequential GA uses global population statistics to control selection, so the processing time can be shortened.

Various papers have been written describing parallel genetic algorithm implementations such as [Tamaki 92], [Yamada 96]. But most of these are straightforward extensions of serial genetic algorithms and offer small-step improvement in algorithmic performance. Parallelization by distributing computation will speed up execution, but additional evolutionary operations such as migration are required for improvements in solution quality. Kohlmorgen et al. [Kohlmorgen 96] summarize their experiences with an implementation of a GA for the RCPSP on parallel processors.

[Mcilhagga 97] describes a Distributed Genetic Algorithm which has been used to solve generic scheduling problem. It discusses more generalized large resource allocation problems. Their primary aim has been to investigate the application of GAs to a wide range of very large non-specific scheduling problems. They used GPDGA—the Generic Parallel Distributed Genetic Algorithm tool kit—to implement the evolutionary search aspect of this study.

5. APPLY GENERIC ALGORITHMS TO SOFTWARE ENGINEERING

5.1. Software project management

Software project management environment can be very dynamic where a large team of engineers work together. It is a tedious job to track project activities and the cost for tracking is quite high. Project management (PM) ensures the delivery of software that is of high quality and delivered within time and budget constraints. It requires a manager to estimate and assign the resource intelligently. Basic project management techniques include Gantt Chart, CPM and PERT chart. However, most existing project management tools can only support passive project management. Even if equipped with modern PM tool such as Microsoft project, managers still are not adequately supported to manage resource allocation, task assignments, and scheduling. The state of the art of PM requires managers make own decisions on who does what, and when, before engaging the PM tools to "track" the status. When project evolves, as that will definitely happen, such smart decisions will need to be re-made and the tools need to re-compute to track project status, often with a lot of delay and patch work. These "modern" tools are simply without a "brain".

The main problem is that we need to more faithfully model the very nature of software development. Software development is a constantly evolving organic entity where software engineers grow as project moves on and the environment changes all the time. The first paper on this research is SPMNet model [Chao 95]. SPMNet is a formal software management model offering a theoretical foundation to address a variety of issues in software project management. One of the major advantages of this model is that it provides a formal means for customers, software managers, and software developers to communicate with each other. Based on this formal model, the customers and the developers will be able to visualize and monitor the progress of the software project. Another advantage of SPMNet is that it provides the software developers a foundation to build tools that will support and enhance the software engineering process. Furthermore, a set of advanced features can be derived based on SPMNets, including: visualizing the progress of a software project, constructing a structural project plan, automated resource allocation and scheduling, and status prediction of a project.

5.2. Introduction to SPMNET

In order to capture concurrency in the software development process, SPMNets borrowed some concepts from Petri nets [Murata 89]. SPMNet closely followed the terminology used in Petri nets. However, the firing rules and information carried by tokens are different from traditional Petri nets. For brevity we only briefly introduce SPMNet here. For its full definition, please refer to [Chao 95].

A SPMNet consists of a set of places, a set of transitions, a set of constraints, and a set of arcs. There are four different place types including abstract activity, atomic activity, product, and decision. An abstract activity is a collection of atomic or abstract activities. By grouping several related lower-level atomic or abstract activities together, abstract activity provides a high-level view to software managers by hiding the underlying details in large-scale software projects. The atomic activity (P_{at}) is represented as a circle. The decision place (P_d) is represented as a diamond and it is used to represent the iterative nature of the software development. Product place (P_p) is drawn as a rectangle. Abstract activity (P_{ab}) is used for abstract activity. Each activity is associated with a set of constraints, which specifies the requirements for completing this activity. The constraints can be further classified as resource constraints (C_r) and complexity constraints (C_c). Resource constraints specify what kinds of resources are required and complexity constraints describe how much effort is needed for that activity. The dependency relations among activities are linked by transitions, product places and decision places. There are three types of transitions, T_I, T_O and T_{DO}. T_I denotes the input transition of an activity. T_O represents the output transition of an activity. T_{DO} represents the output transition of a decision place. Each transition type has different meaning and firing rules.

An example of SPM–Net is shown in Figure 10.

Based on these constraints in each activity, genetic algorithms are used to determine the resource allocation for each activity automatically. Once the resource allocation is decided, the execution time for each activity can be calculated according to the complexity constraint on that activity. Software managers may pre-execute the SPMNet to visualize the project progress in advance.

5.3. GA for software project management

5.3.1. Task-based model

Genetic Algorithms, already popular in many domains of optimization research, provide a good solution to the software project management problem. The following

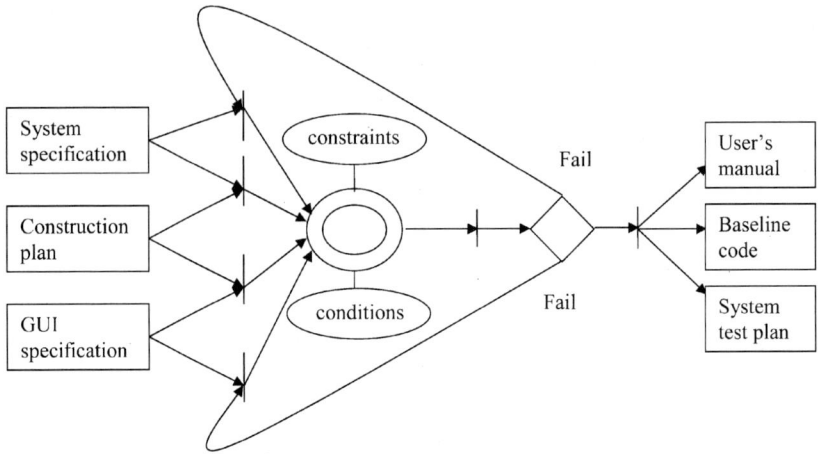

Figure 10. An example SPMNet.

model is reported in "Genetic Algorithms for Project Management" [Chang 01]. The model is proposed by improvements to the original model (i.e. SPMNet).

1. Model

The representation of the problem consists of:

1) Representation of project: TPG = (V, E)

  • The project is represented as a task precedence graph.
  • A directed a cyclic graph where the nodes represent the tasks and the edges represent the task precedence.
  • Each task is associated with an estimated effort (based on COCOMO [COCOMO]) and the required skills.

2) An employee database D_{emp} with information of skills and salary.
3) An objective function.

Genetic representation is an orthogonal 2D array with one dimension for tasks, the other for employee. GA operators are adopted from GAlib [GAlib].

In our approach, there are two stages for scheduling the project: the first stage evaluates how the genome satisfies the constraints; the second stage evaluates the schedule performance of the genome.

For the simplest objective function, it can be defined as:

Composite objective function = Validity * (OverLoadWeight / OverLoad

+ MoneyWeight / CostMoney + TimeWeight / CostTime)

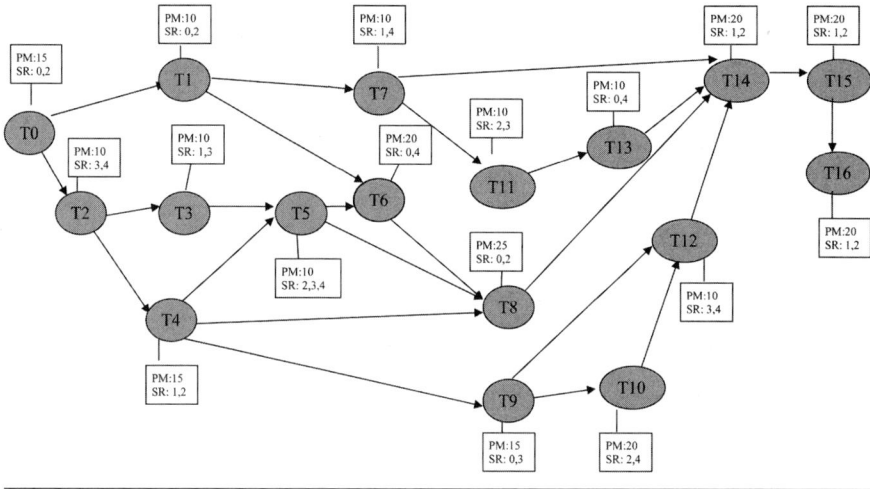

Figure 11. Task precedence graph of the test example.

Table 4 Employee table

Emp. ID	Skill 0	Skill 1	Skill 2	Skill 3	Skill 4	Salary
P1	4	—	2	4	—	7000.00
P2	1	—	2	—	—	4000.00
P3	—	4	—	—	—	4000.00
P4	2	—	—	4	—	5000.00
P5	—	3	—	—	3	5000.00
P6	—	3	—	3	3	6000.00
P7	—	—	2	—	2	5000.00
P8	—	3	3	4	—	6000.00
P9	4	—	4	—	2	7000.00

2. A Test Problem and its Results

The example is shown in Figure 11:

- The test project consists of 17 tasks, each marked with Person-Month (PM) requirement.
- There are 9 employees available to work on this project as shown in Table 4.
- The skill proficiency (Skill Required or SR) is rated on scale (0–5).
- A Sample Objective and its Schedule

In this test, the objective is to "Find the optimum valid schedule, satisfying a composite objective function, including money cost, time cost and overt time limits for loading".

The GA solution after 1000 generations is shown in Table 5.

Table 5 Result of GA test

Emp	T0	T1	T2	T3	T4	T5	T6	T7	T8	T9	T10	T11	T12	T13	T14	T15	T16
P1	0.75	0.5	0	0	1	0.75	1	0	1	1	1	0.25	0.5	0	0.75	0	0
P2	0.5	0.75	0.75	0.25	0.25	0.5	0.25	0.75	0.75	0.75	1	0.25	0.25	0.75	0.5	0.5	0.75
P3	1	0.75	1	0	0.75	1	0.75	0.5	1	0	0.75	1	0	0.75	1	0.25	0.5
P4	0.5	0.75	0.75	0	0.25	0.75	0.75	0.25	0.75	0	0.25	0.75	0.5	0.5	1	1	1
P5	0.25	1	0.25	0.5	0.5	0	1	1	1	0.75	1	0	0.75	0.25	0.25	0.75	0
P6	0.75	1	1	0	0	0	1	0.75	0.5	0.5	0	0	1	0.25	0.5	0.25	0.25
P7	0.75	0.75	1		0.5	0	0.5	1	0.75	0.75	0.5	1	0.75	0	1	0.75	0.5
P8	0	0	0	0.75	0.5	0.5	0.75	0.75	0.5	0	0.75	0.25	0.75	0	1	0.75	0.5
P9	0.5	0	0.5	0.5	0.25	0.75	0.5	0.5	0.75	0.75	0.75	1	1	0.5	0.25	1	0

5.3.2. Timeline-based model

In [Di 01], a time line was introduced to improve the original model in [Chang 01]. The time line expands the two-dimensional (task and employee) model to a three-dimensional one which shows the effort of each employee applied to each task in each time unit. The time line helped capture the dynamic nature of software management, such as reassignment of employees, learning, scheduled vacation, unexpected leave, suspension and resumption of tasks, and the introduction of hard, intermediate deadlines.

1. Model

The computational complexity is now sharply increased because of the introduction of time dimension compared to the original task-based model. In order to achieve realism, the elements, such as employee's proficiency scores, employees' technical experiences, task deadlines and task penalties are considered. Models related to employees were added, such as Employee Model (an employee represented by a numerical identifier and some properties) with Employee Compensation Model, Employee Skill List, Employee Training Model, Employee Experience Model and Availability Model. Models related to tasks (a task represented as a numerical identifier and some properties) include Task Estimated Effort, Task Importance Model, Skill List and Ancestor Tasks and Maximum Headcount.

Genetic representation is a 3D array. Figure 12 illustrates the Employee-Task Assignment Scheme.

In [Di 01], the algorithm for calculating fitness function was also provided.

2. Numerical Experiments

Additional numerical experiments were reported in Di's thesis [Di 01] to evaluate the correctness and performance of the model. The time-line based model was implemented in C++ with the GALib, an open-source Genetic Algorithms package [GALib].

6. CONCLUSION AND FUTURE WORK

Genetic algorithms have been applied successfully in some applications. In particular, plenty of research work was found in dealing with the scheduling problems. However, most of them are on simplified scheduling, such as job-shop, flow-shop and highly

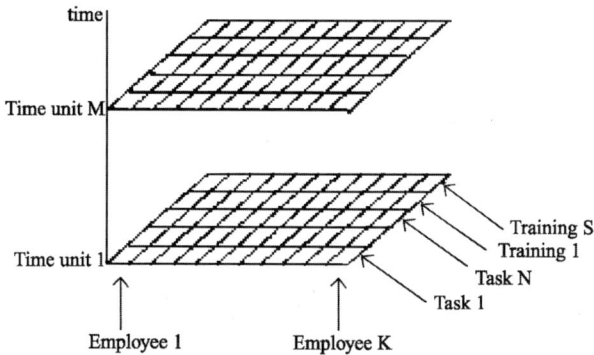

Figure 12. Assignment scheme in timeline based model.

simplified project scheduling problems. Realizing that handling various constraints encountered in the real-world scheduling problem is so difficult yet important, more and more researchers focus on modeling real-world scheduling problems at present. Chang's research group primarily focused on the software engineering domain and found interesting issues peculiar to the dynamic nature of "people", namely the software engineers.

Studies can go further on the following directions:

1. Model the real-world scheduling problem with more realistic constraints, such as employee's training and experience gaining. Those studies will involve other research fields, such as psychology, education, etc. We are yet to determine the realistic learning curve for software engineers to grow professionally and pick up both hard and soft skills.
2. Studies on more efficient genetic algorithm on problems peculiar to software engineering management problems.
3. Developing more flexible and powerful software project management tools with support on automated scheduling and consideration on capability of resources.

In sum, we believe that the results reported in this book chapter only outlined a research direction for software engineering researchers who traditionally had not paid much attention to the field of "soft computing" where genetic algorithms play a visible role. We intend to raise the awareness of good results in "soft computing" and bridge the gap between *software engineering* and *soft computing*.

REFERENCES

[AL 94] A. Al-Attar, "A Hybrid GA-Heuristic Search Strategy," AI Expert, Sept. 1994.

[Alander 96] J. Alander, "Indexed Bibliography of Genetic Algorithms Papers of 1996," Report Series No. 94-1-96PROC, University of Vaasa, 1996.

[Bagchi 91] S. Bagchi, S. Uckun, Y. Miyabe and K. Kawamura, "Exploring Problem-Specific Recombination Operators for Job Shop Scheduling," Proc. of the 4th Int'l Conf. on Genetic Algorithms, pp. 10–17, San Diego, CA, July 1991.

[Beasley 93] D. Beasley, "An Overview of Genetic Algorithms: Part 2, Research Topics," University Computing, vol. 15, no. 4, pp. 170–181, 1993.

[Brucker 01] P. Brucker, A. Drexl, R. H. Möhring, K. Neumann and E. Pesch, "Resource-Constrained Project Scheduling: Notation, Classification, Models, and Methods," European Journal of Operational Research 112, pp. 3–41, 1999.

[Bruns 93] R. Bruns, "Direct Chromosome Representation and Advanced Genetic Operators for Production Scheduling," Proc. of the 5th Int'l Conf. on Genetic Algorithms, pp. 352–359, 1993.

[Burke 98] E. Burke, J. Newall and R. Weare, "Initialization Strategies and Diversity in Evolutionary Timetabling," Evolutionary Computation, pp. 81–103, 1998.

[Chang 01] C. Chang, M. Christensen, T. Zhang, "Genetic Algorithms for Project Management," Annals of Software Engineering 11, pp. 107–139, 2001.

[Chao 95] C. Chao, "SPMNet: a New Methodology for Software Management," Ph.D. Thesis, the University of Illinois at Chicago, 1995.

[Cleveland 89] G. Cleveland and S. Smith, "Using Genetic Algorithms to Schedule Flow Shop Releases," Proc. of the 3rd Int'l Conf. on Genetic Algorithms, pp. 160–169, 1989.

[COCOMO] "COCOMO II Model Definition Manual," http://sunset.usc.edu

[Davis 85] L. Davis, "Job Shop Scheduling with Genetic Algorithms," Proc. of an Int'l Conf. on Genetic Algorithms and their Applications, Pittsburgh, Lawrence Erlbaum Associates, 1995.

[Demeulemeester 92] E. Demeulemeester and W. Herroelen, "A Branch-and-bound Procedure for the Multiple Resource Constrained Project Scheduling Problem," Management Science, vol. 38, pp. 1803–1818, 1992.

[Di 01] Y. Di, "Timeline Based Model For Job Scheduling with Genetic Algorithms," MS Thesis, University of Illinois at Chicago, 2001.

[Dorndorf 95] U. Dorndorf and E. Pesch, "Evolution based learning in a job shop scheduling environment," Computers and Operations Research, vol. 22, pp. 25–40, 1995.

[Fang 93] H. Fang, P. Ross and D. Corne, "A Promising Genetic Algorithm Approach to Job-Shop Scheduling, Rescheduling, and Open-Shop Scheduling Problems," Proc. of the 5th Int'l Conf. on Genetic Algorithms, pp. 375–382, San Mateo, CA, 1993.

[Fang 94] H. Fang, P. Ross and D. Corne, "A Promising Hybrid GA/Heuristic Approach for Open-Shop Scheduling Problems," Proc. of the 11th European Conf. on Artificial Intelligence, pp. 590–594, 1994.

[GAlib] http://lancet.mit.edu/ga/

[GALOPPS] http://garage.cps.msu.edu/software/software-index.html

[GAucsd] http://www.cs.bham.ac.uk/Mirrors/ftp.de.uu.net/EC/clife/www/Q20_gaucsd.htm

[Glover 89] F. Glover, "Tabu Search | Part I. ORSA," Journal on Computing, vol. 1, pp. 190–206, 1989.

[Goldberg 89] D. Goldberg, "Genetic Algorithms in Search, Optimization, and Machine Learning," Addison-Wesley, Reading, Massachusetts, 1989.

[Hartmann 98] S. Hartmann, "A Competitive Genetic Algorithm for Resource-Constrained Project Scheduling," Naval Research Logistics, vol. 45, pp. 773–750, 1998.

[Hilliard 88] M. Hilliard, G. Liepins and M. Palmer, "Machine Learning Applications to Job Shop Scheduling," Proc. AAAI-SIGMAN Workshop on Production Planning and Scheduling, St. Paul, 1988.

[Holland 75] H. Holland, "Adaptation in Natural and Artificial Systems," University of Michigan Press, Ann Arbor, 1975.

[Husbands 93] P. Husbands and F. Mill, "Scheduling with Genetic Algorithms," University of Edinburgh, UK, 1993.

[Kirkpatrick 83] S. Kirkpatrick, C. Gelatt, et al., "Optimization by Simulated Annealing," Science 220, pp. 671–680, 1983.

[Kohlmorgen 96] U. Kohlmorgen and H. Schmeck, "Experiences with Fine-Grained Parallel Genetic Algorithms," Proc. of Parallel Optimization Colloquium (POC'96), Versailles, pp. 217–226, March 1996.

[Lee 96] J. Lee and Y. Kim, "Search Heuristics for Resource-constrained Project Scheduling," Journal of the Operational Research Society, vol. 47, pp. 678–689, 1996.

[Leon 95] V. Leon and B. Ramamorthy, "Strength and Adaptability of Problem-space based Neighborhoods for Resource-constrained Scheduling," OR Spektrum, vol. 17, pp. 173–182, 1995.

[LibGA] http://www.cs.bham.ac.uk/Mirrors/ftp.de.uu.net/EC/clife/www/Q20_libga.htm

[Murata 89] T. Murata, "Petri Nets: Properties, Analysis and Applications," Proc. of the IEEE, pp. 541–580, Apr. 1989.

[Mingozzi 98] A. Mingozzi, V. Maniezzo, S. Ricciardelli, and L. Bianco, "An Exact Algorithm for the Resource Constrained Project Scheduling Problem Based on a New Mathematical Formulation," Management Science, vol. 44, pp. 714–729, 1998.

[McIlhagga 97] M. McIlhagga, "Solving Generic Scheduling Problems with a Distributed Genetic Algorithm," Evolutionary Computing, AISB Workshop, pp. 199–212, 1997.

[Murty 95] K. Murty, "Operations Research: Deterministic Optimization Models," Prentice Hall, 1995.

[Nakamura 98] M. Nakamura, B. Ombuki, K. Shimabukuro, and K. Onaga, "A New Hybrid GA Solution to Combinatorial Optimization Problems—An Application to the Multiprocessor Scheduling Problems," Journal for Artificial Life and Robotics, Springer Verlag, vol. 2, pp. 74–79, 1998.

[Nakano 91] R. Nakano, "Conventional Genetic Algorithm for Job Shop Scheduling," Proc. of the 5th Int'l Conf. on Genetic Algorithms, Morgan Kaufmann Publishers, pp. 474–479, 1991.

[Rechenberg 73] I. Rechenberg, "Evolution Strategy: Optimization of Technical Systems by Means of Biological Evolution," Fromman-Holzboog, 1973.

[Ramat 97] E. Ramat, G. Venturini, C. Lente, M. Slimane, "Solving the Multiple Resource Constrained Project Scheduling Problem with Hybrid Genetic Algorithm," Proc. of the 7th Int'l Conf. on Genetic Algorithms, pp. 489–496, San Mateo, CA, 1997.

[Starkweather 91] T. Starkweather, S. McDaniel, K. Mathias, D. Whitley and C. Whitley, "A Comparison of Genetic Sequencing Operators," Proc. of the 4th Int'l Conf. on Genetic Algorithms, pp. 67–76, 1991.

[Tamaki 92] H. Tamaki and Y. Nishikawa, "Paralleled Genetic Algorithm Based on a Neighborhood Model and its Application to Job Shop Scheduling," Proc. of Parallel Problem Solving From Nature II, pp. 573–582, North-Holland, 1992.

[Uckun 93] S. Uckun, S. Bagchi, K. Kawamura and Y. Miyabe, "Managing Genetic Search in Job Shop Scheduling," IEEE Expert, pp. 15–24, Oct. 1993.

[Vidal 93] R. Vidal, "Applied Simulated Annealing," Springer-Verlag, 1993.

[Wall 96] M. Wall, "A Genetic Algorithm for Resource-Constrained Scheduling," PhD Thesis, MIT, June 1996.

[Yamada 92] T. Yamada and R. Nakano, "A Genetic Algorithm Applicable to Large-Scale Job-shop Problems," Proc. of 2nd Conf. on Parallel Problem Solving From Nature, pp. 281–290, Brussels, 1992.

[Yamada 96] T. Yamada and R. Nakano, "Scheduling by Genetic Local Search with Multistep Crossover," Parallel Problem Solving From Nature (PPSN) IV, vol. 1141 of Lecture Note in Computer Science, pp. 960–970. Springer-Verlag, Berlin, 1996.

ASSEMBLY SEQUENCE OPTIMIZATION USING GENETIC ALGORITHMS

LEE H. S. LUONG, ROMEO MARIN MARIAN AND KAZEM ABHARY

1. INTRODUCTION

Assembly is part of manufacturing and an obligatory process for all multi-component products. For a long time most effort in manufacturing research was directed at primary manufacturing processes. It was recognised that one virtually untapped source to reduce costs was assembly which, with limited exceptions, was still being carried out in the same way as almost a century ago (Redford and Chal 1994).

There are two trends in today's manufacturing. The first one, due to diversified tastes of the consumers ('everything comes in at least 31 flavours' (Naisbitt 1982)) is towards mass customisation, with the direct consequence of reduction of production series. Another trend, due to globalisation of markets, is the continuous and significant pressure to reduce price and time to market. The direct result of those trends is that assembly, identified for generally being the bottleneck of the production process, will increase its share in the lead time and cost of a product.

Assembly planning offers a broad scope for improvements in assembly. Assembly Planning tries to determine a feasible method and layout to assemble a product from its components. Assembly Sequence Planning (ASP) is part of Assembly Planning. An assembly sequence is the most important part of an assembly plan and it affects other aspects of the assembly process—resources, assembly line layout, efficiency and cost—as well as various details in the product design. Automating the generation of assembly sequences and their optimisation can ensure the competitivity of manufactured goods.

This paper presents an approach to automatically generate and then optimise the assembly sequence of a mechanical product. The approach comprises an analysis of the problem, modelling aspects of the assembly processes and products from the point of view of assembly, and a series of algorithms designed to solve the ASP problem (automatic generation of feasible assembly sequences) and then to optimise it.

The paper presents aspects of assembly planning and optimisation, then the ASP problem in the next sections. A brief literature review shows a number of previous techniques attempting to S/O the ASP problem and pinpoints critical topics, not properly adapted to a constrained combinatorial problem. Section 5 introduces the approach used to S/O of ASP problem in this research.

A proper modelling of the ASP problem for solving and optimising it involves and requires:

– modelling the assembly processes—what assembly planning means in mathematical terms (Section 6);
– modelling of assembly sequences—encoded as chromosomes (Section 7);
– modelling the product for assembly purposes—encoding and storing constraints in assembly (Section 8);
– defining a framework to encode quality measures in assembly (Section 9).

All those aspects fully model and prepare the ASP problem to be solved and then optimised. The quality and extent of the modelling of the problem directly translates in the quality of the output and this justifies the ample space dedicated to modelling aspects in this paper.

The optimisation algorithm—a Genetic Algorithm (GA) specially designed to accommodate the specific requirements of the ASP problem—is a population-based search algorithm in the space of solutions and its output is a population of optimal or near-optimal assembly sequences from which the best ones are selected. It is detailed, along with an example, in section 11.

2. BACKGROUND TO ASSEMBLY PLANNING AND OPTIMISATION

Assembly is product-oriented. An assembly plan and layout have to be developed for each product. Even a minor change in the configuration of a product usually completely changes the assembly plan and layout, with important implications in costs and lead time (Nof, Wilbert et al. 1997; Tichem, Storm et al. 1999). As a result, it is necessary to formalise the process of automatically generating feasible assembly plans, a task which, to this day, has been essentially manual.

On the other hand, due to the importance of assembly in the final cost and lead time of a product, generating good/optimum assembly plans for assembled products becomes a necessity. Optimising the ASP problem is considered to be more an art than a science. A feasible assembly plan can be easily devised for a product, but, due to the character of the problem, it is virtually impossible to determine its real value and how it compares with other plans. It is, therefore, essential to define a methodology to optimise assembly sequences and plans.

The ASP problem is a large-scale combinatorial problem and is highly constrained. The number of potential assembly sequences is proportional to the factorial of the number of parts in the assembly (Combinatorial Explosion (CE) (Wolter 1991)). Absolute constraints—geometrical, precedence, accessibility and other types of constraints—severely limit the number of feasible assembly sequences. In general terms, automatically generating feasible assembly sequences is, in its full generality, an extraordinarily difficult task, shown to be NP-complete (Wilson and Watkins 1990) in both two-dimensional and tri-dimensional cases (Kavraki, Latombe et al. 1993; Wilson, Kavraki et al. 1995). As a result, most of the past and present work in this area focuses on restricted variants of the problem (Kaufman, Wilson et al. 1996), (Romney, Goddard et al. 1995).

The ASP, as a theoretical problem, has to cope with the extraordinarily diverse character of assembly. Assembly, as shown below, can address sequential or non-sequential, linear or non-linear, monotone or non-monotone, coherent or non-coherent assembly sequences and plans or any combination of those, involving rigid, elastic, non elastic, solid, liquid or gaseous components or subassemblies. To be applicable in practice and useful, an assembly sequence planning and optimisation system has to be general enough to accommodate or offer the provision to consider any type of assembly plan and component, quality measures and requirements. Often, previous attempts to optimise the ASP problem simplified the nature of the assembly process to render it manageable by the techniques used. The adaptation of the problem has been done to such extent than the results are often non-representative for the initial problem and requirements.

This paper presents an approach to Solve and Optimise (S/O) the full-scale, unabridged ASP problem. To achieve this, it is necessary to thoroughly analyse and model the assembly processes, the products of which the assembly sequences are to be optimised and the conditions and criteria for optimisation.

Solving the ASP problem is an essential step prior to its optimisation. The ASP problem is solved by generating a feasible sequence to assemble an n-part product given its description and a number of supplementary constraints. To optimise it, Genetic Algorithms (GA) were used in this research to search an optimum or near optimum assembly sequence.

The ASP problem is related to other two well-known combinatorial problems: the Travelling Salesman Problem (TSP) and the Job Shop Scheduling Problem (JSSP) (Gen, Zhou et al. 1998). Comparatively, the ASP problem is much more constrained than the TSP. Considering the analogy part (ASP problem)/city (TSP), the assembly sequence cannot start with any part (tour can start with any city), not all parts may be reached from/connected to any other part (any non-visited city may be) and not any valid connection between two parts can be done at any time (any valid connection between two cities can be done at any time). Also when comparing TSP and JSSP with ASP problem, the quality measures are well defined and invariant for TSP (distances between cities) and JSSP (the processing time for operations are known and do not change), whereas for ASP problem they are dependent on the operations already carried out. In conclusion, there are essential differences between the three problems, which makes difficult, if not impossible, the direct transfer of the algorithms and approaches to S/O the TSP and JSSP to the ASP problem. Hence, S/O the ASP problem requires a special approach.

3. THE ASSEMBLY SEQUENCE PLANNING PROBLEM

Different authors have different definitions for the ASP problem. A formal definition for the ASP problem, as considered in this paper, is given below (Marian, Luong et al. 2003):

Given:
A mechanical product A composed of n components, $A = \{c_1, c_1, \ldots c_n\}$, that is to be assembled in a finite number m of Assembly Operations, $O = (o_1, o_1, \ldots o_m)$, $m \geq n$, and described in sufficient detail to permit the extraction and definition of the following information:

I1. The contact/connection information: on O a set of relations C is defined, so as if $(o_i, o_j) \in C$, it is said that o_i and o_j have a connection; Also, $(o_i, o_j) \in C \Leftrightarrow (o_j, o_i) \in C$;

I2. The precedence information: on O a set of relations P is defined: a binary relation $(o_i, o_j) \in P$ means o_i has to be performed before o_j. If $(o_i, o_j) \in P$, then $(o_j, o_i) \notin P$;

I3. The optimisation criteria: on A is defined a set of optimisation criteria QM_k, $k \in N$;

I4. The optimisation function (or objective function) to be maximised, F;

Determine:
An Assembly Sequence (sequences) $S = \{s_1, \ldots s_i, \ldots s_n / s_i \in O\}$ so as the following conditions:

C1: $\forall s_i \in S$, $i = 1, \ldots n$, $\exists s_j \in S$, $j \in N$ and $j < i$, so that $(s_i, s_j) \in C$ (coherence condition);

C2: $\forall s_i, s_j \in S$, $i, j = 1, \ldots n$, $(s_i, s_j) \in P$ (precedence condition);

C3: An assembly sequence S that maximises the value of F (optimisation);

are fulfilled, in the following manner:

a. Generating an assembly sequence S that satisfies conditions C1 and C2 means solving the ASP problem (a feasible assembly sequence);

b. Finding an assembly sequence that satisfies conditions C1, C2 and C3 means optimising the ASP problem (an optimum assembly sequence).

If the assembly sequence concerns only assembly of components—i.e. if an assembly operation represents a complex of elementary tasks that add a component to the partial assembly—the number of assembly operations equals the number of components: m = n.

4. LITERATURE REVIEW ON ASP

S/O the ASP problem has been attempted, using various approaches, with mixed results. Due to CE, classic optimisation methods failed to optimise industrial-size problems.

AND/OR graphs and a hybrid A* algorithm were used to represent and select, through an iterative and interactive process, the optimal assembly sequence in Archimedes, a software package (Kaufman, Wilson et al. 1996; Jones, Wilson et al. 1998). The planner uses Non-Directional Blocking Graphs-NDBG (Wilson 1992)— of each subassembly to determine the assembly operations that might be performed to construct a subassembly then it adds constraints.

AND/OR graphs with weighted hyperarcs were also used to store feasible assembly operations for assembly in HighLAP—High Level Assembly Planning, another assembly software package. It selects an assembly plan minimising the costs from the initial nodes up to the goal node (Rohrdanz, Mosemann et al. 1996).

The representations used for the optimisation approaches presented above utilize the AND/OR graph to store and evaluate all assembly sequences for a given assembly or to interactively select an assembly sequence by applying a number of constraints. They are limited either by the maximum number of sequences that can be stored (CE) or risk to lose valuable solutions by artificially limiting the extent of the graph through a number of initial artificial, simplifying, hypotheses.

Simulated Annealing has been proposed by Milner et al. (Milner, Graves et al. 1994) to search a best assembly sequence. Being based on the totality of assembly sequences (to be generated, and represented in a directed-diamond-graph), and due to CE, the method is limited to reduced search spaces.

Sebaaly and Fujimoto (Sebaaly and Fujimoto 1996) used a Genetic Planner for assembly automation. The information for assembly is stored in an implicit, and very compact, form in a reference and a connectivity matrix. To overcome the constrained character of the ASP problem, the complete search space consisting of all possible parts combination is clustered into families of similar sequences, where every family contains only one feasible sequence satisfying the problem constraints. The assembly sequences are generated without searching the complete domain of solutions. Even if CE is overcome using this approach, valuable solutions in the optimisation process are lost.

From this literature review it can be concluded that the ASP problem has only been considered and S/O in a reduced format, generally for Sequential, Linear, Monotone and Coherent (SLMC) assembly plans (Wolter 1989) and/or for reduced size problems (generally less than 15 components). Often, due to massive simplifications, the results obtained are non-representative and can not be translated for real-life and industrial size products.

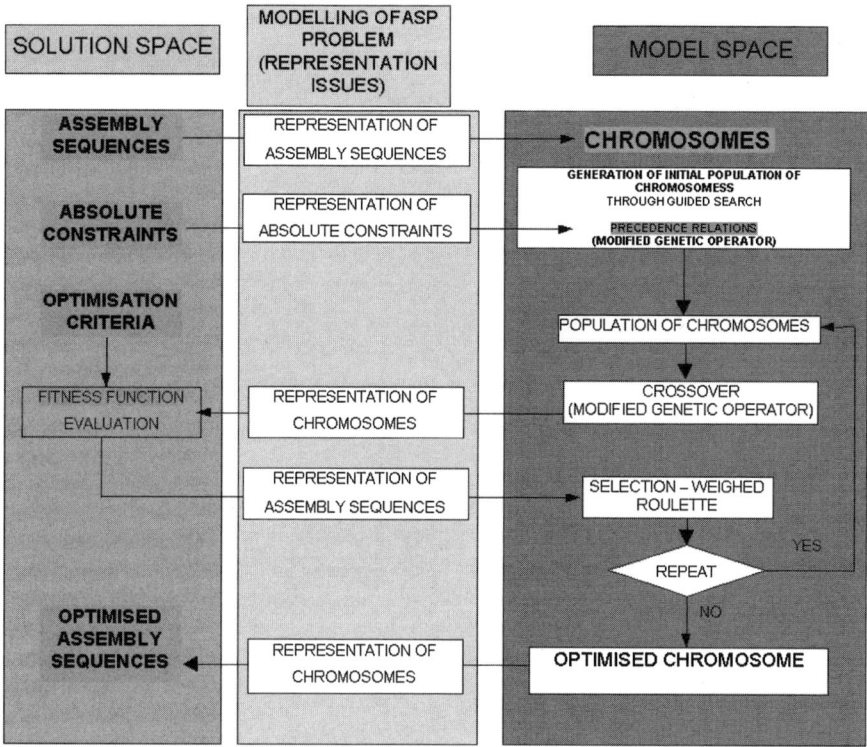

Figure 1. The approach used to solve and optimise the ASP problem using genetic algorithms (adapted from (Marian, Luong et al. 2003)).

To optimise the ASP problem, a special Genetic Algorithm working on the whole population of feasible assembly sequences is proposed.

5. THE APPROACH USED TO S/O THE ASP PROBLEM

The methodology used in this research to S/O the ASP problem is presented with reference to Fig. 1. All elements and operations are briefly explained here and will be detailed in the remaining of the paper.

Prior to optimising, the ASP problem has to be solved. The ASP problem is solved by generating an initial population of solutions or feasible assembly sequences (a succession of operations to assemble the product from its components). An assembly sequence is feasible if it satisfies absolute constraints.

Optimising the ASP problem involves searching for an optimum or near optimum feasible assembly sequence according to an objective function based on optimisation criteria. GA were chosen for the optimisation of ASP problem for two reasons. The first reason is their ability to handle large-scale problems (population based, ergodic, with probabilistic transition rules). The second reason is the flexibility in defining an objective function (use of payoff information, not derivatives or other auxiliary information to define the fitness function) (Goldberg 1989), (Haupt and Haupt 1998).

The structure of the proposed GA is classic (Gen and Cheng 1997). To handle the CE and the constrained character of the problem, modified genetic operators that work only with feasible chromosomes were used (detailed in (Marian, Luong et al. 1999), (Marian, Luong et al. 1999), (Marian, Luong et al. 2000), (Marian, Luong et al. 2000). Other approaches, including penalty, reject and repairing strategy, were attempted by the authors in earlier stages of the research (Marian, Luong et al. 1999). They proved to be effective only for assemblies with a reduced number of components (<15), and/or highly artificially constrained problems. In both cases, the solution space was relatively limited.

GA work, in an iterative process, alternatively in the coding or model space and in the solution space. Thus, modelling and representation are the interface between the real problem, defined in the solution space, and the abstract replica of the problem defined in the model space. Prior to S/O the ASP problem, a number of representations have to be considered and defined: the representation of the assembly sequences (as chromosomes), the representation of the product for assembly purposes (representation of constraints) and a framework for the definition of quality measures (fitness function).

The generation of the initial population of chromosomes is performed through a guided search (Marian, Luong et al. 1999), (Marian, Luong et al. 2000). It is a modified genetic operator, designed to overcome the CE by transforming the combinatorial problem of randomly generating an assembly sequence in a polynomial one (by generating and working only with feasible sequences). By generating the initial population, the first part of the problem (solving the ASP problem) is resolved.

The initial population undergoes crossover operations, (Marian, Luong et al. 2000), also a modified genetic operator. The crossover heavily relies on the guided search and is designed to produce only feasible chromosomes. After crossover, the chromosomes are translated back to the solution space and are evaluated using a fitness function based on the optimisation criteria and quality measures defined on the solution space (Marian, Abhary et al. 2000). Once the assembly sequences have been evaluated, the best ones are selected. The selection is a classical operation, through a weighed roulette algorithm. It operates on an extended population of parent and child chromosomes (Gen and Cheng 1997).

The optimisation is an iterative process. The result of the optimisation is a population of assembly sequences with a high fitness value (corresponding to better assembly sequences) from which the one(s) with the highest fitness can be selected.

6. A MODEL OF THE ASSEMBLY PROCESS

This section shows how a product and its associated assembly process can be modelled with graphs and the associated table of liaisons, what a feasible assembly sequence is in mathematical terms and how this can be converted in steps leading to S/O the ASP problem. Being a complex problem, the modelling stage is of paramount importance for the ASP problem. The modelling of ASP problem with graphs will facilitate the representation and generation of assembly plans, generalisations for different degrees of detail and initial hypothesis and the definition and generalisation of precedence relations.

Modelling of the TSP (Wilson and Watkins 1990) was used as a starting point for modelling the ASP problem: the cities to be visited are vertices in a graph and pairs of cities are connected with edges. In mathematical terms, solving the TSP requires finding a Hamiltonian cycle for each vertex of the corresponding graph. Optimising it means finding the smallest length Hamiltonian cycle (Ronald 1995).

6.1. The graph of liaisons and the table of liaisons

The graph model of the assembly and assembly process is an intuitive method to represent the ASP problem (Bourjault 1984). The graph of liaisons can be extracted, in a more or less automated manner, from the solid model of the assembly (Golabi 1996).

The graph of liaisons (GL) is defined as a simple, connected, undirected graph, $GL = G(A, L)$ where $A = \{a_i, i = 1 \cdots n\}$ is a nonempty set of vertices a_i representing the components c_i of the assembly. A vertex is, initially, the graphical representation of a component or a subassembly considered from the point of view of assembly as a part (e.g. a roller bearing). $L = \{l_{ij})$ are the edges of the graph, where

$$l_{ij} = \begin{cases} 1 & \text{if there is a liaison between } a_i \text{ and } a_j \\ 0 & \text{otherwise} \end{cases} \tag{1}$$

The term "liaison" will be used in a flexible manner throughout the paper. A liaison, in this case, represents a connection between components that touch each other. The model refers, initially, to the assembly of a mechanical product from its n components in a sequential, linear, monotone, coherent (SLMC) manner.

An assembly plan is Sequential if it can be decomposed into a sequence of steps such that, during each step, only one component is added (a so-called two-handed plan). A plan is Coherent when each component that is inserted (except the first) will effectively touch some other previously placed component. A plan is Linear when all components are added to the assembly one at a time (i.e. it never forms subassemblies). A plan is Monotone when each component is inserted immediately into its final position relative to the remainder of the assembly and an n-component assembly is executed in exactly $n - 1$ operations. An assembly plan can be coherent or non-coherent, sequential or non-sequential, linear or non-linear, monotone or non-monotone, or any combination of those situations (Wolter 1991).

When a component is added to the partial assembly, all its corresponding liaisons with the partial assembly are established. An assembly operation in step $j, j = 2 \cdots n$ involves the addition of a component c_i (vertex a_i) and the establishment of all liaisons between c_i and all components assembled previously, in steps $1 \cdots (j - 1)$ (establishment of all

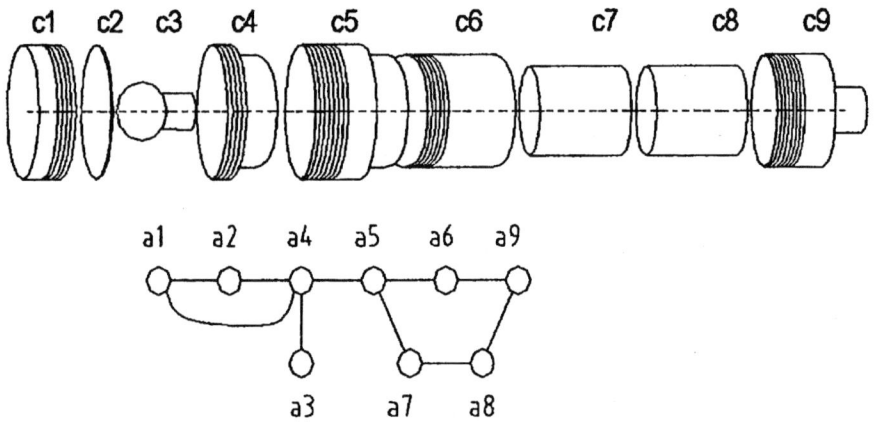

Figure 2. The electric torch and its graph of liaisons.

edges—but at least one (coherence)—between ai and the corresponding sub-graph of the partial assembly). In graph terms, this means that the graph of liaisons is connected. This model will be generalised in the Section 7.

The graph of liaisons has the following properties (Wilson and Watkins 1990):

- GL is simple—between two vertices there is only one edge representing a liaison that includes all contacts;
- GL has no loops—there is no liaison joining a vertex to itself (it is impossible to assemble a component to itself);
- GL is connected—if a component belongs to the product it has at least a liaison with another component of the assembly; as a result, a vertex belonging to GL is connected through at least one edge to another vertex in GL;
- GL is an directed—if a component ai can be assembled to ai, the reverse is also true (a liaison is commutative).

Figure 2 presents the electric torch, a classic example encountered, with some variations, in the assembly literature, and its graph of liaisons (c1-cap, c2-lens, c3-bulb, c4-reflector, c5-connector, c6-handle, c7, c8-batteries, c9-rear cap).

The contact information between components is also stored in the table of liaisons. The table of liaisons is the translation in table format of liaisons of a product, in fact of the adjacency matrix of the graph of liaisons (Wilson and Watkins 1990). The graph representation of the liaisons is very intuitive for a human but difficult to process by a computer, which, in turn, can easily handle the information in matrix form. Cell ij contains the value of lij, as defined in (1): if there is a liaison between components ai and aj in the graph of liaison, it will be designated by "1" in the corresponding cell ij (intersection of row ai with column aj) otherwise it is 0. The table of liaison is

Table 1 Table of liaisons for the assembly in Fig. 2. (the electric torch).

	a1	a2	a3	a4	a5	a6	a7	a8	a9
a1	0	1	0	1	0	0	0	0	0
a2	1	0	0	1	0	0	0	0	0
a3	0	0	0	1	0	0	0	0	0
a4	1	1	1	0	1	0	0	0	0
a5	0	0	0	1	0	1	1	0	0
a6	0	0	0	0	1	0	0	0	1
a7	0	0	0	0	1	0	0	1	0
a8	0	0	0	0	0	0	1	0	1
a9	0	0	0	0	0	1	0	1	0

symmetric: if there is a liaison between ai and aj, there is also one between aj and ai. Table 1 is the table of liaisons for the electric torch.

6.2. The wave model of the assembly process

The assembly process can be modelled as building up the graph of liaisons. This model of the assembly process of a product is derived and transformed from the Huygens' Principle in Physics (Young 1992) for the waves. Huygens' Principle offers a geometrical method for finding, from the known shape of a wave front at some instant, the shape of the wave front at some later moment. Let's consider the analogy: fluid contained within the closed wave front—partial subassembly (subgraph). This model, adapted from the graph representation (component = vertex, liaison = edge) to assembly processes, permits to determine, at each stage, what components can be added to the partial assembly in the next stage so that the assembly process is feasible (coherence condition). In case only liaisons are taken into account, the wave model for assembly can be expressed, in the solution space, as follows:

Each component of a partial assembly may be considered the element to which is added, in the next step, a component with which it has a liaison and has not yet been assembled. All liaisons between the newly added component and those of the partial assembly are established during this operation. The cycle is repeated until all components are assembled. The assembly process is equivalent to the addition of vertices and edges to the graph of liaisons until all vertices and edges have been included. This process, when represented graphically, is similar to the propagation of a wave.

The wave model of assembly is the foundation for the guided search algorithm, used to generate feasible assembly sequences, and is widely applied within the genetic operators proposed below.

The assembly process starts with the first component to be assembled. The graph of liaisons is, at this stage, a null graph—has only the first vertex—and no edges (the graph has no loops). The second component is added to the partial assembly (consisting of the first component) and their liaison is established in the graph of liaisons. The corresponding vertex and edge are added. The process is repeated; in each step all liaisons between the added component and the partial assembly are established. The assembly sequence is this succession of components added until the product is assembled. Relevant information for this model and for generating assembly sequences comprise the components to be assembled, liaisons between components and a number of conditions to be satisfied—constraints or precedence relations. The process is presented graphically in Fig. 5. and the assembly process can be visualised, in the graph representation, as the propagation of a wave. A generalisation of this process and the conditions in which it can be done will be presented later. This model and the graph of liaisons permit the definition of the framework to represent assembly sequences and the model of the product for ASP purposes (representation of precedence relations).

7. A MODEL FOR THE ASSEMBLY SEQUENCES

The goal for modelling assembly sequences is to provide a framework able to represent and encode any solution of the ASP problem, namely sequential or non-sequential, linear or non-linear, monotone or non-monotone and coherent or non-coherent. Also, the possibility to encode components with variable geometry, solids, liquids and gases is considered. Next section presents the representation of an assembly sequence for a simple case, involving SLMC assembly sequences. This representation will, then, be generalised.

7.1. Representation of SLMC assembly sequences

Let's consider for the beginning the representation of an assembly sequence only as the order in which n components are assembled together to form a product, in a SLMC manner (m = n, n operations to assemble n components). This representation and the conditions in which this can be done will be generalised in the following section.

An assembly sequence is encoded in a chromosome. The chromosome is a permutation of components of the product. A gene (a term of the sequence (Gen and Cheng 1997)) in locus j, $j = 1 \cdots n$—counted conventionally from left to right—encodes the addition of the corresponding component in the j-th step. Any partial chromosome with k genes, $k = 1 \cdots n$, represents an assembly state, where the first k components are assembled in a partial assembly and all their corresponding liaisons are established. A component, encoded as a gene, will appear in the chromosome once and only once.

Because further constraints apply, an n-term sequence of components of the assembly may be an illegal or infeasible chromosome. A simple n-term sequence is an illegal chromosome if it is not a permutation. In this case a number of components appear more than once, thus not all components are present (e.g. for the torch in Fig. 1. a1–a1–a3–a4–a4–a6–a7–a8–a9 is an illegal chromosome: a1 and a4 appear twice and a2 and a5 do not appear at all). A permutation is a legal chromosome and designates a tentative assembly sequence. All components are present but it is possible that the assembly cannot be realised because of the presence of constraints (e.g. geometry, unreachable positions—a1–a2–a3–a4–a5–a6–a7–a8–a9 is infeasible because a3 cannot be assembled to a2). A feasible chromosome represents a feasible assembly sequence. It is a constrained permutation, a permutation that complies with the assembly's specific constraints (e.g. a4–a3–a2–a1–a5–a6–a7–a8–a9 is a legal and feasible chromosome, it complies with

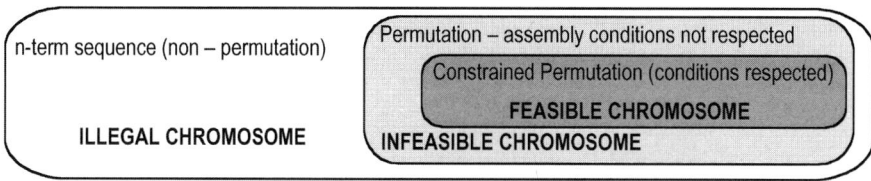

Figure 3. Relations between chromosomes and assembly sequences.

all constraints). The relations between those concepts and related conditions are presented in Fig. 3.

7.2. Generalisation of the representation for non–SLMC assembly plans

The level of detail of an assembly plan should be variable so as to accommodate the specific needs of the user. For the most abstract situation, introduced above, the chromosome represents only the order of assembly of components: a4–a5–a3–a2–a1 means the first component to be assembled is a4 to which are added a5, a3, a2 and a1 respectively. In this case a gene encodes the addition of a component to the partial assembly and symbolises the totality of operations required to assemble a component or add it to a partial subassembly. In this case the chromosome is a synthetic notation of the assembly process and each gene encodes a composite assembly operation.

The definition of a chromosome can be broadened to encode Entities Meaningful for the Assembly Sequence (EMAS), noted ai. (Marian, Kargas et al. 2003) A chromosome, in this case, becomes flexible and it can encode other types of plans (non-SLMC). A gene/EMAS can be generalised to represent more than just the addition of a component to the partial assembly. Thus, non-SLMC assembly plans can be encoded.

To encode non-SLMC assembly plans a vertex and a gene will no longer encode a composite assembly operation associated with adding a component to the partial assembly. The concept of 'liaison' changes for Non-SLMC assembly operations. It no longer represents only a contact between two parts of the product, but an edge between two adjacent vertices in the graph of assembly, representing EMAS. The resulting graph of assembly for components and operations (vertices) has the same properties as a graph of an assembly that includes only components.

Non-sequential assembly plans

A 'non-sequential assembly sequence' is a contradiction, but assembly plans with non-sequential operations are frequent, so they should be considered in the representation. To include non-sequential operations in an assembly sequence, the non-sequential set of operations should be isolated, aggregated and referred to as an EMAS (e.g. ai) and encoded as a gene. The addition of two or more components in a non-sequential assembly operation (i.e. their insertion is to be done simultaneously in a co-ordinated motion along different trajectories) can be encoded in a gene as a complex operation.

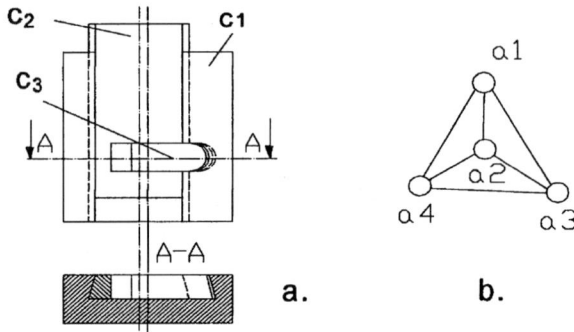

Figure 4. A product assembled with a non-monotone assembly sequence and its graph of liaisons.

In this case a chromosome represents a non-sequential assembly plan (an assembly sequence with a non-sequential element).

Non-linear assembly sequences

In case a gene/EMAS represents a subassembly previously made elsewhere and added as is, a gene encodes the addition of the subassembly to the partial assembly. In this case the chromosome represents a non-linear assembly sequence.

Non-monotone assembly sequences

A gene/EMAS can also encode special assembly operations, such as a manufacturing-like or an assembly-like operation not involving the addition of a part, for example quality checks on a partial assembly. The moment when the operation is performed may affect the quality of the assembly process. For the quality check, for instance, its complexity is different in various assembly stages as the accessibility is different. This enables the differentiation of the value of different assembly sequences. The possibility to encode diverse assembly operations permits the encoding of production line-related information. This allows also for the representation of non-monotone assembly sequences. Figure 4 presents a product requiring a non-monotone assembly sequence comprising addition of components c1, c2 and c3 and an assembly operation, a4, and its graph of liaisons. Components c1, c2 and c3 and operation a4 can be encoded as EMAS: a1, a2, a3 and a4, respectively. In this case the chromosome a2-a3-a1-a4 encodes, in a homogeneous notation, non-homogeneous information: component c2 is assembled first, to which c3 is added, then c1. In the last step c3 is pulled in the slot of c1 (an assembly operation—a4—with no component added). Each substring, a2, a2-a3, a2-a3-a1 and a2-a3-a1-a4 represents an assembly state, the last one encoding a more advanced assembly stage than the previous one. This generalisation permits even encoding the addition of fluids in a piece of equipment—an assembly-like specific operation—as a gene.

Pseudo-non-coherent assembly plans

An assembly plan is always coherent: each part that is inserted (except the first) will touch or effectively touch some other previously placed part. There are, however, two notable exceptions.

The first exception concerns non-linear plans, but in this case the assembly is subassembly-coherent. Furthermore, the coherence is respected in each subassembly and this case can be encoded and treated as presented above, for non-linear assembly plans.

The second exception occurs when an auxiliary fixture or tool is to be used, temporarily, in an early stage of the assembly process, to hold a number of parts that are not in direct contact, before a connecting part is inserted. In this circumstances, the auxiliary fixture or tool can be considered as a component (or EMAS) to be added to and then removed from (a 'negative fixture' or EMAS is added to) the assembly. Thus, the assembly sequence is transformed from a non-coherent (due to representation) into a coherent and non-monotone sequence and can be encoded as above. Consequently, all assembly sequences are coherent and this will be used for the algorithms that generate assembly sequences. The 'non-coherent' assembly sequences will be designated as Pseudo-Non-Coherent. An example involving Pseudo-Non-Coherent assembly sequences will be detailed in Section 8 in conjunction with Fig. 6.

The framework presented here can encode any type of assembly plan for any type of component or subassembly. It can even encode in an EMAS, besides rigid components with fixed geometry, components with variable geometry, even with variable volume. For example the fluid inside a heat pipe (a liquid and the vapours of that liquid) can be represented as an EMAS encoding all the elementary operations related to the addition of the fluid (as solid, liquid, vapours or double/triple-phase fluid).

The representation of SLMC assembly sequences, well studied in the literature about assembly, can, thus, be extended to other cases. The degree of abstraction of the chromosome, the definition of EMAS/genes, the chromosome, as well as liaisons, contacts and specific rules governing the optimisation process are to be stated for every situation.

8. A MODEL OF THE PRODUCT FOR ASP AND THE AUTOMATIC GENERATION OF FEASIBLE ASSEMBLY SEQUENCES

8.1. Background

The model of the product for ASP purposes aims to provide the framework able to encode the information necessary in the process of generating feasible assembly sequences, namely the assembly constraints. The constraints are encoded in an implicit manner, to avoid the CE and its effects (effects characteristic to explicit representations). The complete model of the product for ASP purposes is defined and stored using all or some of the following: contact/liaisons information stored in the graph and table of liaisons, implicit precedence relations derived from liaisons, explicit precedence relations stored in the assembly table and Boolean relations.

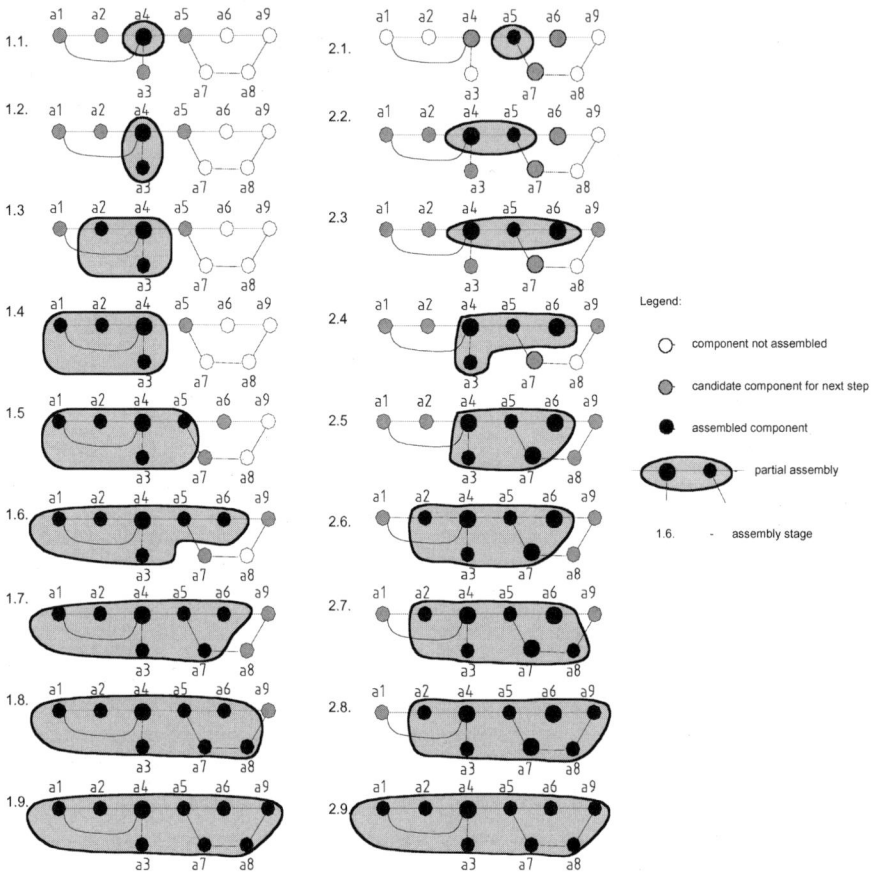

Figure 5. Illustration of IPR and the wave model for assembly for the torch in Fig. 1. (For two assembly sequences) (Marian, Luong et al. 2003).

An implicit representation is to be used in conjunction with an assembly sequence generation algorithm. The implicit representation has to enable, in each step, the extraction of the relevant information (from the pool of constraints) about which component(s) can be assembled in that particular step so as the resulting assembly sequence is feasible. The model of the product for ASP is developed in conjunction with the algorithms that generate feasible assembly sequences, presented in this section and Section 10.

Constraints in assembly are divided into several categories, the most important of which are the absolute constraints and the optimisation constraints. The violation of absolute (Jones and Wilson 1996) or hard constraints (Sebaaly and Fujimoto 1996) produce infeasible assembly sequences. The optimisation criteria (Jones and Wilson 1996), (Sebaaly and Fujimoto 1996), weak constraints (Sebaaly and Fujimoto 1996)

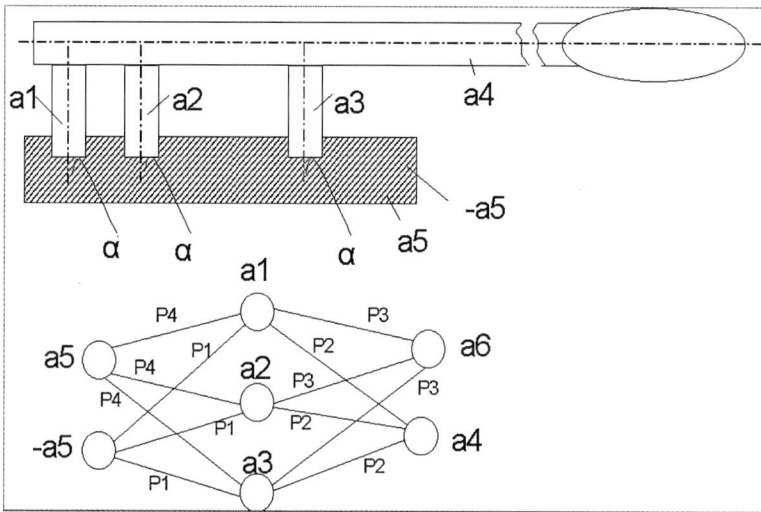

Figure 6. Assembly process involving coherent and non-monotone assembly sequences (Marian, Luong et al. 2003).

or quality measures (Jones, Wilson et al. 1998) differentiate the quality of assembly sequences and plans. As a result the constraining relations in assembly are either absolute or optimisation constraints.

Constraints on assembly plans come from a wide variety of sources: contacts and liaisons between components, design requirements, geometry, part and tool accessibility, assembly line and workcell layout, requirements of special operations, and special fixed (imposed) assembly sequences. Even supplier relationships can influence the choice of a feasible or preferred assembly sequence (Ames and Carlton 1995), (Jones and Wilson 1996), (Jones, Wilson et al. 1998). In the remaining of the paper, constraints will only refer to absolute constraints. An assembly planning system must have the ability to manage assembly constraints.

Huang & Lee in (Huang and Lee 1988) and (Huang and Lee 1991) showed that there are certain precedence constraints among assembly operations. The precedence constraints knowledge plays a very important role in assembly planning because an assembly plan cannot violate those precedence constraints. Precedence constraints include information about what component(s) can be/are to be assembled in a certain step, what component(s) can be/are to be assembled next, the precedence relations between component(s), clusters, subassemblies and so on. From the point of view of generating a feasible assembly sequence, absolute constraints can be derived and defined as precedence constraints (Marian, Luong et al. 2003). For example in Fig. 4, the impossibility of inserting c3 in the corresponding slot of c2 after c2 and c1 have been assembled, a geometrical constraint can be transformed into a precedence constraint: assemble c2-c3, then assemble c1.

The representation has to be capable of encoding all precedence constraints present in an assembly process. The logical combination of those precedence relationships constitutes a correct and complete representation for the set of all assembly sequences (Homem de Mello and Sanderson 1991)

The graph of liaisons and the coherence of the assembly process permit the definition of two broad categories of precedence relations in an assembly. Intrinsic precedence relationships are strictly specific to the liaisons between components/EMAS. Extrinsic precedence relationships, specific to the actual product and assembly process: geometry, part and tool accessibility, assembly line and workcell layout, etc. are stored in the assembly table and as Boolean relations.

8.2. Intrinsic precedence relations

Intrinsic Precedence Relations (IPR) are precedence relations in an assembly process, specific to an assembly state, derived only from the connectivity of the graph of liaisons and coherence of the assembly process (Marian, Luong et al. 2003). IPR are defined with the aid of the graph/table of liaisons and have the following properties:

♦ IPR depend on the configuration of the product—liaisons between components/EMAS;
♦ IPR depend on the state of the assembly—they are volatile, specific to a particular assembly state and change completely for the next assembly state;
♦ IPR can be used to determine candidate components for the next assembly state;

Example:
Assume the assembly process of the torch begins with a4, Fig. 2, and consider, for the beginning, only the liaisons and the associated edges, ignoring any other precedence relation. The connectivity and coherence of the graph of liaisons dictates which component can be assembled in the next state (candidate components): a1, a2, a3 or a5 and can be written:

$$(a4 < a1) \lor (a4 < a2) \lor (a4 < a3) \lor (a4 < a5) \tag{2}$$

which expresses all the precedence relations (completeness) for generating an assembly sub-sequence that is feasible (correctness).

Consider the second component to be assembled is a5. (a4–a5) is the partial assembly at state 2. In this case, candidate components for step 3 are: a1, a2, a3, a6 or a7. This can be written as:

$$((a4 - a5) < a1) \lor ((a4 - a5) < a2) \lor ((a4 - a5) < a3)$$
$$\lor ((a4 - a5) < a6) \lor ((a4 - a5) < a7) \tag{3}$$

Suppose now that the assembly starts with a5. Candidate components for the second state are a4, a6 and a7, which can be expressed as:

$$(a5 < a4) \vee (a5 < a6) \vee (a5 < a7) \tag{4}$$

A number of conclusions can be drawn from this example:

- Even if no precedence relations were defined for the product and assembly process, a number of precedence rules exist and have been defined (disjunctions (2), (3), and (4));
- Those precedence relations are different if the assembly process starts with different components;
- Those precedence relations are different for different states of the assembly process;
- Any of the expressions (2), (3) and (4) is complete (all precedence relations for the indicated state are expressed), and correct (any component added in the indicated step that complies with the conditions set by the expressions will lead to a feasible assembly step);

A representation can take advantage of this class of precedence relations and drastically reduce the amount of information to be stored and analysed. The volatile character of IPR and the size of ASP problem reduces the probability for a particular precedence relation (for a certain stage) derived from the graph of a product to be ever used in generating an assembly sequence. As a result, IPR can be defined only as needed for each stage in the assembly process and can be used to generate assembly sequences through guided search. Those assembly sequences are feasible if no other precedence constraints are present.

IPR can be used, in conjunction with an algorithm that takes advantage of the coherence of the graph of liaisons, to generate feasible assembly sequences, provided there are no other precedence relations defined for the assembly of the product.

8.3. Guided search algorithm for generation of assembly sequences considering only IPR

The guided search algorithm for randomly generating a feasible chromosome—considering only IPR—is presented below. It is the foundation for guided search of feasible assembly sequences and for the crossover operator. It is based on the wave model of assembly and works in conjunction with the table of liaisons of the assembly (Table 1 for the torch in Fig. 2):

Step 1: The first component is randomly chosen from the components of the assembly;
Step 2: The candidate components for the next assembly stage are those for which the value of aij in the corresponding rows of the components already assembled of the table of liaisons is '1'.
Step 3: Randomly select a component from the candidates;
Step 4: Delete the column of component selected in Step 3;
Step 5: Repeat steps 2–4 until all components have been placed;

The algorithm generates a perfectly random first component to be assembled. Then (using IPR), in step 2, determines candidate components for next assembly state, the ones that have a liaison with the partial subassembly and have not yet been assembled (after a components is assembled, its column is deleted, step 4), so the chromosome is a permutation constrained with IPR. The second vertex is randomly chosen from candidate components. The algorithm is very effective, at each run it adds a gene to the chromosome.

Example:

Considering the previous example, for a5 assembled in the first step, the candidates for the second locus are a4, a6 and a7. Choosing for example a4 in locus 2, the candidates for the locus 3 will be all components in contact with a5 and a4 and not already assembled, in this case a1, a2, a3, a6, a7 and so on. The algorithm for IPR will be completed with other constraints to become the guided search algorithm for generating feasible assembly sequences.

IPR and the wave model for assembly for the torch in Fig. 2., are illustrated in Fig. 5. The model only considers IPR, and no other supplementary constraint is taken into account. For two assembly sequences the wave front and IPR are completely different for each assembly state and for the same assembly state for the two cases (e.g. subassembly presented in 1.1–1.3. is: a4-a3-a2 and the subassembly presented in 2.1.–2.3. is a5-a4-a6). The model can be directly generalised for EMAS instead of components as vertices in the graph of liaisons.

IPR are easy to define, greatly reduce the size of the representation and the space needed to store it. IPR only include liaison constraints and establish the potential assembly sequences, i.e. is the maximum number of assembly sequences if no other constraint applies. The precedence relationships are stored implicitly in n^2 contact relations between components. When defining the table of liaisons, all liaisons are set by default to '0'. Then, the relevant liaisons are input and the value in the corresponding cells is changed to '1'. This way, the liaisons are stored in 2L relations, where L in the number of liaisons of the assembly. Defining additional constraints (see next section) further reduces the maximum number of feasible assembly sequences: e.g. a1 and a4 cannot be assembled unless a2 is already assembled, as it cannot be added later; same for a3.

8.4. Extrinsic precedence relations

Extrinsic Precedence Relations (EPR) are all supplementary precedence relations that can be derived from the constraints in an assembly process and are not related to the graph of liaisons.

EPR originate from constraints and requirements characterising the product—e.g. geometric and accessibility constrains—or the assembly process—e.g. assembly line layout, special operations, supply of parts. EPR are seldom assembly state-dependent and can be expressed as precedence relations between the establishment of one liaison and the establishment of another liaison (Marian, Luong et al. 2003).

The following sections present a framework developed and used to implement precedence relations (IPR and EPR), their definition, properties and auxiliary mechanisms and their implementation in the guided search algorithm.

The same precedence relations can be defined in different ways, e.g. $\{(a1 \wedge a2 \wedge a3) < a4\}$ is equivalent to $\{(a1 < a4) \wedge (a2 < a4) \wedge (a3 < a4)\}$. For this reason, the framework aims to offer straightforward tools to define and implement EPR frequently encountered in the practice of assembly rather than endeavour to offer an inflexible, exhaustive and excessively complex solution. The use of Boolean relations, for example, intends precisely to reduce the complications involved by using a rigid set of operators. The framework has an open character, new EPR can be defined as needed.

8.5. Implementation of EPR

EPR are compactly stored in a table—the assembly table—directly derived from the table of liaisons and related to the graph of liaisons. EPR are encoded by using a series of operators. If no EPR constraints are defined for the product the assembly table will be reduced to the table of liaisons.

The assembly table is a table with the following properties:

- the cell aij of the assembly table stores a collection of precedence relations between assembly of vertex/EMAS in row ai to the vertex/EMAS in column aj;
- the precedence relations in a cell of the assembly table are encoded using a set of operators;
- the relation between ai and aj is 'can be assembled to' in the conditions set by the operators in the corresponding cell (aij);
- the assembly table may be non-symmetric: in an assembly sequence if ai can be assembled to aj in certain conditions, the reverse may not be (technologically or otherwise) true (e.g.: assembling wheel to a car—i.e. holding the car and assembling the wheel to it—is a feasible operation; the reverse—holding the wheel and assembling the car to it—however, even if not impossible and not infeasible from the geometrical and accessibility point of view is not a technological solution).

EPR are implemented as filters in the guided search. They permit or prohibit assembling a vertex/EMAS. In some cases the operators trigger subroutines that will reduce the search space only to the vertices of interest for one or a limited number of assembly states (like for fixed assembly sequences or for clusters). EPR define precedence relations between two vertices adjacent to an edge ('0', '1'), between a liaison and another liaison (reference liaison 'xi' plus '>xi' and '>>xi'), Boolean relations between any two combinations of vertices/edges, between groups of liaisons and clusters, for SLMC/NON-SLMC assembly sequences.

The operators encode precedence relations frequently appearing in assembly processes.

8.5.1. EPR for individual liaisons

The operators presented here refer to individual liaisons and are defined as follows (Marian, Luong et al. 2003):

− Operator '0': if cell aij contains the operator '0', ai cannot be assembled to aj in any assembly stage;
− Operator '1': if cell aij contains the operator '1', ai can be assembled to aj at any stage;
− Reference Liaison 'xi', i ∈ N (auxiliary operator): is a labelled liaison used to define other precedence relations. It permits the definition of precedence relations between a liaison and another liaison, i.e. precedence relationships between the establishment of one liaison and the establishment of another liaison. If a liaison is commutative and if liaison aij is labelled as xi, aji is also designated as xi;
− Operator '>xi': if cell aij contains the operator '>xi', ai can be assembled to aj after the reference liaison ('x') has been established.
− Operator '>>xi': if cell aij contains the operator '>>xi', ai must be assembled to aj in the next stage after the reference liaison ('x') has been established. aim

Operators '1' and '0' define direct precedence relations between EMAS. Operators '>xi' and '>>xi', on the other hand, define precedence relations between a liaison and another liaison. Those operators are used to express precedence and are implemented as test filters that determine, at each stage, what EMAS can be assembled. If the EMAS is not present in the partial subassembly, the corresponding liaison cannot be established.

Operator '>>xi' permits the encoding of fixed assembly sequences. The edge between the first two vertices in the fixed assembly sequence is allocated xi, in the cell corresponding to which vertex to be added to the first. The subsequent liaison is imposed (>>xi) and labelled 'xi + 1,' and the cycle repeats. This facility is rarely used. A fixed assembly sequence of a subassembly is not likely to be, in itself, of any important value in the optimisation process as it does not allow for variation. It can be simply replaced with a subassembly. The fixed assembly sequences are generally to be used for the analysis of assemblies including one or more subassemblies with reduced number of parts (<5).

8.5.2. Boolean relations

Sometimes, precedence relations in assembly cannot be expressed as simple precedence relations between liaisons ('>' and '>>'' relations), but only as complex Boolean precedence relations between an EMAS/liaison or a group of EMAS/liaisons and another liaison or group of liaisons. Boolean relations are very diverse, their number is generally reduced for an assembly process and they are difficult to implement as a collection of rigid operators. Thus, they can accompany the assembly table, complete it with supplementary precedence relations that cannot be or are difficult to implement in the assembly table and be checked for every assembly state during the guided search. The following example presents a practical use of Boolean relations.

Table 2 Assembly table for the electric torch for a SLMC assembly process.

⇒	a1	a2	a3	a4	a5	a6	a7	a8	a9
a1	0	>x2	0	>x2	0	0	0	0	0
a2	>x2	0	0	x2, >x1	0	0	0	0	0
a3	0	0	0	x1	0	0	0	0	0
a4	>x2	x2, >x1	x1	0	1	0	0	0	0
a5	0	0	0	1	0	1	1	0	0
a6	0	0	0	0	1	0	0	0	1
a7	0	0	0	0	1	0	0	1	0
a8	0	0	0	0	0	0	1	0	1
a9	0	0	0	0	0	1	0	1	0

Example: Model of a product for a SLMC assembly process

For the electric torch, Fig. 2, the precedence requirements are:

EPR1: liaison a2–a4 has to be done after a3–a4 (accessibility constraint),
EPR2: liaison a1–a4 has to be done after a2–a4 (accessibility constraint);
EPR3: a5 or a9 have to be assembled after a6, a7 and a8 have been assembled.

The model of the product for SLMC assembly process includes:

– the graph of liaisons, presented in Fig. 2;
– the table of liaisons (Table 1);
– the assembly table containing operators defined as above (Table 2) for EPR1 and EPR2. The symbol '⇒' stands for 'can be assembled to';
– the following Boolean relation for EPR3: $(a5 \lor a9) > (a6 \land a7 \land a8)$.

This model encodes all precedence relations for the electric torch for a SLMC assembly process.

The assembly table, operators and Boolean relations described so far permit the definition of any precedence relation between the establishment of one liaison and establishment of another liaison or state of the assembly process (Homem de Mello and Sanderson 1991).

Other models of products for ASP for non-SLMC assembly processes are presented in (Marian, Luong et al. 2003).

8.5.3. EPR for groups of liaisons

The productivity of defining EPR can be substantially increased when considering groups of liaisons. This section presents the definition of EPR for a liaison and a component, EPR between groups of liaisons and EPR for clusters.

EPR FOR A LIAISON AND A COMPONENT. Defining reference liaisons for a component is simple: all liaisons of a component appear on a line/column in the assembly table. All non-zero cells from the table of liaisons for component ai (row and column ai) are converted to a reference liaison 'xi', Besides the increase of productivity in defining EPR, this enables the definition of precedence constraints between a liaison and the assembly state (when a certain component is assembled) (Homem de Mello and Sanderson 1991).

EPR BETWEEN GROUPS OF LIAISONS. EPR can be defined between two groups of liaisons. Let's consider a certain group G1 of m liaisons has to be established after another group G2 of n liaisons. The liaisons corresponding to group G1 are labelled xm and those in group 2 are labelled xn. The precedence relation can be expressed as a Boolean relation:

$$(\forall xm \in G1) \text{ and } (\forall xn \in G2), \quad (xm) < (xn) \tag{5}$$

The definition of EPR in this case can be encoded in the assembly table by using Priorities, as follows:

$$P1 = xm \quad \text{and} \quad P2 = xn, \text{ considering precedence relations defined in (5)}$$

A priority P2 is a set of precedence relations between a group of liaisons that all have to be established before another liaison or group P1 of liaisons. The higher the priority level, the sooner the liaison is to be made. In the process of generating the assembly sequence, the candidate vertices for a locus are those with the highest priority.

Priorities are similar to reference liaisons, but they trigger a subroutine that acts as a filter and lets only the vertices with the highest priority level to be assembled prior to considering the next priority level. Use of priorities or reference liaisons is a question of preference and implementation.

An example including priorities is presented in Fig. 6 and Table 3. Using of priorities permits the definition of (m + n) precedence relations instead of (m × n)

Example: A model for a pseudo-non-coherent assembly process using priorities

3 pegs, a1, a2 and a3 have to be assembled—projection welded—to the handle a4 (Fig. 5). Surfaces α have to be in the same plan and the position of the pegs is strictly determined. Pegs a1, a2 and a3 are, thus, inserted (order not important) in the

Table 3 EPR encoded as priorities for the assembly in Fig. 6.

⇨	a1	a2	a3	a4	a5	a6	−a5
a1	0	0	0	P2	P4	P3	P1
a2	0	0	0	P2	P4	P3	P1
a3	0	0	0	P2	P4	P3	P1
a4	P2	P2	P2	0	0	0	0
a5	P4	P4	P4	0	0	0	0
a6	P3	P3	P3	0	0	0	0
−a5	P1	P1	P1	0	0	0	0

corresponding holes in the fixture a5, their upper surface is levelled (ground)—a man-ufacturing operation, a6, then handle a4 is projection welded (assembly order not important). The assembly is then removed from the fixture (a 'negative fixture', -a5, is added. The graph of liaisons is shown in Fig. 5. EPR for this assembly are shown in Table 3. This case involves operations, negative fixtures and priorities.

EPR FOR CLUSTERS. Clusters are groups of parts that are to be assembled in an uninterrupted sequence. An assembly sequence that will assemble other components amongst those of the cluster can be a feasible one but is most likely to be less valuable. It would imply changing of tools, grippers, and so on. Information about clusters can be encoded as absolute constraints, meaning the components of a cluster are to be assembled in an uninterrupted sequence.

The appropriate liaisons are encoded as clusters: kCi, where k is the name of the cluster, $k \in N$, and i is the number of components of the cluster. Once an component of a cluster kCi has been assigned in a locus of the chromosome, the candidate components for the next $i - 1$ genes are only the components of the cluster, until all have been assigned.

Clusters are similar to priorities, but priorities can set a hierarchy of sets of parts to be assembled, whereas clusters can be assembled whenever the first component has been considered.

The definition of EPR shown here offers a framework for how to structure and represent constraints as precedence relations. The representation permits a flexible definition of EPR for different sets of initial hypothesis then the fine-tuning of the problem to answer the particular requirements of the user

The same EPR, using the relations defined so far, can sometimes be expressed in different ways, giving the user the flexibility to utilise the most appropriate relations for its particular application. A major advantage of the proposed implicit representation is that, unlike explicit representations, permits the iterative and gradual definition of relations between EMAS and assembly constraints. ASP problem can be solved initially for a simplified set of initial hypothesis, e.g. the assembly sequence considering only components of the products in a SLMC process, then this process can be expanded to incorporate operations, fixtures, subassemblies, etc. to make the process more realistic.

8.5.4. Definition of the assembly table

The assembly table is an important tool in S/O the ASP. It completes the table of liaisons and both tables, together with the Boolean relations, encode precedence information about the assembly process (as IPR and EPR). They are the database containing the pertinent data about assembly and their quality is reflected in the assembly sequences generated and then optimised using them. The assembly table contains most or all of the EPR.

Besides the normal information available and used to build the assembly table, it is useful to consider the reduction in the number of liaisons. This can be done where possible and when this does not lead to unwanted loss of assembly sequences.

In most cases a number of liaisons present in the table of liaisons cannot be executed directly. They appear as parasitic liaisons, due to contacts between components that touch each other but can never be directly assembled, e.g. a bolt-washer-nut assembly, when the bolt-nut can only be assembled after the washer-nut or bolt-nut have been assembled. The bolt-nut contact and liaison is such a parasitic liaison. Golabi proposed, for those situations, the pruning of unnecessary links (Golabi 1996) or liaisons. Once the unnecessary links are pruned, the definition of EPR is greatly simplified because EPR are defined for a reduced number of liaisons. As a consequence, the generation of feasible assembly sequences as well as the Genetic Operators can be simplified.

For the definition of the assembly table the following procedure have to be followed (Marian, Luong et al. 2003):

Step 1: Define vertices (as components, subassemblies, fixtures (pairs of vertices), operations);

Step 2: Determine liaisons—relations between related vertices;

Step 3: Draw the graph of liaisons and define the table of liaisons;

Step 4: If possible, prune unnecessary links (Golabi 1996) (seriously simplifies further definition of assembly table);

Step 5: Define precedence relations in the assembly;

Step 6: Define assembly table, initially as a copy of the table of liaisons;

Step 7: Input precedence relations in the assembly table for simple precedence relations as operators;

Step 8: Input complex precedence relations as Boolean relations;

Those steps are conceptual. Being, NP-complete, ASP problem cannot be solved automatically at this moment. A more formal and automatic approach would most probably complicate the extraction and definition of the assembly table. No fixed algorithm to construct the assembly table was developed due to the extreme variety of relations and operators that can be defined and the impossibility to anticipate them at the design stage (e.g. supplier constraints are not available when planning the assembly process). Moreover, automatic extraction of information and precedence relations about elastic elements and fluids, to name just two, has not been done yet. However, a number of those steps can be automated and the information extracted from the CAD model, especially for simple products (Golabi 1996).

From experience, building the assembly table for a product with 100 vertices takes about 0.3–1 hours for an engineer, depending on the complexity of the assembly and the degree of detail sought for the assembly sequences. It is important to note: only 2L relations have to be added to the table of liaisons, only half (L) have to be manually input (symmetry) and most products have subassemblies and clusters, speeding up the process.

9. QUALITY MEASURES FOR ASP AND THE FITNESS FUNCTION

A vital issue in any optimisation process is the definition of an objective function able to discriminate between the more and the less desirable solutions of the problem. This issue becomes critical when the quality of a solution cannot be easily expressed as a mathematical function.

For the ASP problem optimised using GA, the objective function is designated as the Fitness Function (FF). The FF has to attach a value to each assembly sequence, proportional to the worth of the sequence in the assembly process. The FF has to differentiate, using quantitative and measurable criteria, the quality of an assembly plan.

The number of optimisation criteria that can/have to be used to assess the quality of an assembly sequence is overwhelming and the definition of a 'good' or 'better' assembly sequence has, sometimes, a subjective connotation. It may depend, besides the objective differences based on the configuration of the product as such, on subjective issues, external to the product. Those external issues include, amongst others: the assembly line layout, the personal preferences and technical culture of the person who does the assembly planning, preferences of the assembly operators, socio-economic conditions and so on. An assembly sequence optimised for a product to be assembled in a developed country can be fairly poor when the same product is assembled in a developing country and vice-versa. This is due to the differences in constraints for the two cases (e.g. wages, level of automation, quality and reliability of supply and communications, to name just a few).

A framework able to define the quality of an assembly sequence, be simultaneously objective, flexible and simple, although not easy to develop, is an indispensable step towards the optimisation of the ASP problem. It is also essential for the implementation of standards in this domain so as to avoid non-desirable, subjective, approaches in S/O the ASP problem. The following principles are used in the definition of the framework for calculating the fitness function:

♦ The FF, as a final indicator, is a composite mathematical cost function of the quality of an assembly process.
♦ The quality of an assembly process depends of the quality of each assembly operation;
♦ The FF for the assembly of a product is the sum of partial fitness values corresponding to each assembly operation;
♦ The quality of the same assembly operation involving or not the establishment of a liaison/contact between two components depends on when the assembly operation takes place relative to other operations;
■ The optimisation seeks to find an assembly sequence with a maximum/near maximum value of the FF, thus a good/best sequence has a high/highest value of the fitness function;
♦ The facility to perform an assembly operation is rewarded with a high value of the corresponding partial fitness, whereas the difficulty to perform the operation is penalised accordingly;
♦ The FF should be able to accommodate a variety of quality measures (like time for assembling the product, costs involved, difficulty to assemble each of the components, etc.);

◆ The FF should be able to accommodate a singe optimisation criterion as well as multiple optimisation criteria;
◆ The FF has to have an open character such that the importance of each optimisation criteria can be modified along several optimisation runs;
◆ The FF has to have an open character, to offer the provision that other criteria can be considered, defined and added at a later stage, as need may arise;

9.1. The fitness function for a single optimisation criterion

For a single optimisation criterion, 1 the FF is defined as:

$$FF_1 = \frac{PFF_1(1) + PFF_1(2) + \cdots + PFF_1(n)}{n}, \quad 0 \le FF(i) \le 1. \tag{6}$$

where $PFF_1(i)$ is the partial FF for the criterion 1 associated with the assembly of a component/EMAS in locus i. $FF_1(i)$ is defined between 0, corresponding to an ideally bad assembly step, and 1, corresponding to an ideally good assembly step (Marian, Abhary et al. 2000).

The FF is defined as a sum of partial fitness functions, PFF(i), each corresponding to an assembly task. It indicates the facility to add an element or subassembly to the existent partial assembly. The value of the FF depends on the definition of the optimisation criterion and the position of the gene in the assembly sequence but is non-dimensional. This makes comparisons between optimisation with different criteria independent of the actual criteria and allows optimisation with different criteria to be combined together for multi-criteria optimisation.

$PFF_i(i)$ can be a obtained from any linear or non-linear, differentiable or non-differentiable, continuous or non-continuous function. The reason for this extreme elasticity in defining the fitness function is that the GA only needs a value of the fitness assigned to each individual in the population, not the way this value is obtained or varies from an individual to its neighbour.

The optimisation of the assembly process may be attempted for the fundamental final indicators: assembly cost, time and performance/reliability or for a number of specific or composite criteria (implemented in this case in partial FF functions as presented below).

The definition of the FF can use the geometrical and physical cost evaluation for assembly planning as presented in (Mosemann, Röhrdanz et al. 1997). Care should be taken to correctly assign the function so that the highest value correspond to the best assembly situation. Two evaluation criteria adapted from (Mosemann, Röhrdanz et al. 1997), used hereafter in an example, are presented below:

Separability

The *separability* is an optimisation constraint directly derived from the geometry of the assembly and is conceptually similar to the *accessibility* presented in (Hsu and Lin 1997). It quantifies the projection of the approach/depart of a component with respect to a subassembly. A better accessibility is the result of an increased projection angle:

$$A : P(C) \longrightarrow [0 \cdots 1], (A1, A2) \longrightarrow A(A1, A2) = \frac{\text{Area}[\Pi(\text{lds}(A1, A2), U]}{4\pi} \tag{7}$$

where $P(C)$ is the subset of all components of the assembly, A1, A2 the two subassemblies (in the trivial case components) to be assembled in the current step i and $\Pi(\text{lds}(A1, A2), U)$ is the projection on the unit sphere of the local depart space. An extended lds directly translates into an extended projection on the unit sphere and consequently in a better separability/accessibility and a better partial fitness.

Reorientation

The reorientation requirement is an assembly process-related constraint. In case of instability of the subassembly or need of reorientation due to the assembly cell environment, assembly costs are assigned for each reorientation $R(ai)$ corresponding to the stage when component ai is assembled:

$$R(ai) = 1 - \frac{\alpha}{\pi} \cdot \frac{m_{ai}}{M} \tag{8}$$

where α-reorientation angle, m_{ai}-mass of reoriented partial assembly before ai is assembled, M-mass of the entire product;

If the reorientation angle is zero, the reorientation cost for the selected assembly operation is also zero so the quality of the operation from the point of view of the reorientation is maximum.

A large number of similar constraints are defined in the literature (Mosemann, Röhrdanz et al. 1997). Eventually the number of criteria actually implemented will be a trade-off between the desired degree of optimality, the cost for the implementation and computation resources required.

9.2. The fitness function for multi-criteria optimisation

For multi-criteria optimisation, the FF is defined as:

$$FF_\Sigma = \alpha 1 \cdot FF_1 + \alpha 2 \cdot FF_2 + \cdots + \alpha k \cdot FF_k \tag{9}$$

$$\text{where } \alpha 1 + \alpha 2 + \cdots + \alpha k = 1. \tag{10}$$

In order to normalize and systematise the FF, the partial FF and the multicriteria FF_Σ are defined between 0 and 1. The reason is to have the possibility to make comparisons with an ideal assembly sequence for an idealised product. The relative importance of each criterion can be adjusted through the coefficients α. The fitness of the best assembly sequence may be far from the ideal value of 1 because the inherent difficulty to build certain assemblies due to the specific constraints. It is also a rough measure of the overall difficulty of the assembly derived from the difficulties to assemble each EMAS.

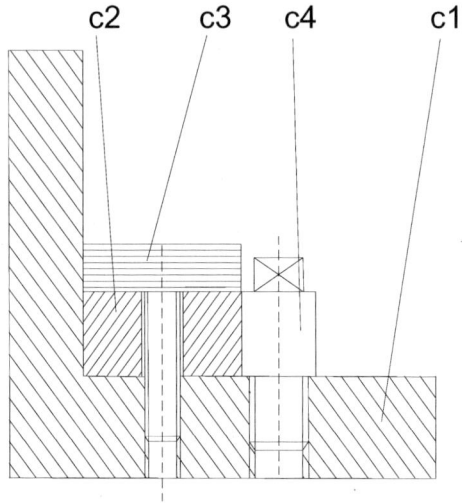

Figure 7. A 4-components product for the computation of the FF.

Example: Computation of FF

A simple example on application of the FF as defined above is presented for the 4-component product shown in Fig. 7. Components are as follows: c1—an L-shaped steel profile; c2—a steel bar with rectangular cross-section, c3—a screw with cylindrical head and socket, attaching c2 on c1, and c4 is another screw with a square head. The vertices/genes are: a1, a2, a3 and a4 corresponding to components c1, c2, c3 and c4, respectively. This example is presented to illustrate the computation of the value of the FF for 2 different chromosomes:

C1: a1–a2–a3–a4 and C2: a4–a1–a2–a3.

Mass details are: c1-10kg; c2-4kg; c3-2kg; c4-2kg.

The separability/accessibility values (application of (7)) corresponding to the assembly of components, for C1: a1-0.5 (hemisphere), a2-0.25, a3-0.25, a4-0.25 (quarter of a sphere), and for the application of (8) to the assembly for C2: a4-0.5 (hemisphere), a1-0.35 (accessibility improved because a2 not yet present), a2-0.02 (from (Rohrdanz, Mosemann et al. 1997), accessibility through a line), a3-0.25, (assuming the assembly is done downwards).

The FF is defined in this case as: $FF = \alpha 1 \cdot FF_1 + \alpha 2 \cdot FF_2$, where $\alpha 1 = \alpha 2 = 0.5$, the partial fitness functions are FF_1-accessibility and FF_2-reorientation;

$FF1(C1) = (0.5 + 0.25 + 0.25 + 0.25)/4 = 0.3125;$

$FF1(C2) = (0.5 + 0.35 + 0.02 + 0.25)/4 = 0.28;$

So from the point of view of the accessibility, the chromosome C1 is better than C2.

FF2(C1) = $(1 + 1 + 1 + 1)/4 = 1$ (no reorientation)

FF2(C2) = $(1 + 1 + (1 - (\pi \cdot 12/\pi \cdot 18)) + 1)/4 = 0.835$

From the point of view of reorientation, C1 has again a higher fitness function.

FF(C1) = $\alpha 1 \cdot$ FF1(C1) $+ \alpha 2 \cdot$ FF2(C1) $= 0.5 \cdot 0.3125 + 0.5 \cdot 1 = 0.65625$

FF(C2) = $\alpha 1 \cdot$ FF1(C2) $+ \alpha 2 \cdot$ FF2(C2) $= 0.5 \cdot 0.28 + 0.5 \cdot 0.835 = 0.5575$

The fitness of the chromosome 1 is higher than for chromosome 2, so it will have a better chance to be selected in the next generation through the weighed roulette in the GA presented in Fig. 1.

10. THE GENETIC ALGORITHM FOR THE OPTIMISATION OF ASSEMBLY SEQUENCES

This section presents the components of the GA designed for the optimisation of the ASP problem. The ASP problem has a number of particularities, as shown at the beginning of the paper, and the GA to optimise it should possess special features.

The generation of the initial population, by guided search and the crossover operator are presented in detail below. The evaluation process has been presented in section 9 and the selection process in a classical one, so they are only succinctly shown.

The structure of the GA is classic, as presented in Fig. 1. It operates on an extended population of parent and children chromosomes.

Using a sufficiently extended initial population and an extended sampling space of both parents and offspring the premature convergence was avoided without the need to use mutation. A mutation operator, although possible to develop, would be much more complicated than the guided search operator or the crossover operator, and would have disputable results. Indeed, due to the highly constrained character of the problem, to ensure the feasibility of the offspring, mutation would most likely change more than two genes, with a high probability to change all the genes at the right of the first mutation locus. An alternative to mutation, which was considered during the research and is always available if needed, was to randomly replace a feasible chromosome in the population with a new feasible chromosome generated through guided search, at a rate similar to normal mutation rates. But, so far the GA worked without the mutation operator.

10.1. Automatic generation of assembly sequences by guided search

The solutions of the ASP problem are generated by guided search, when both IPR and EPR are considered. The guided search operator for chromosomes is based on the guided search that considers only IPR. IPR define the maximum number of assembly sequences when no other constraint is present. Adding precedence constraints will reduce the number of feasible assembly sequences. Precedence relations encoded with operators in the assembly table and Boolean relations are implemented as test filters that, applied to candidate elements for assembly in a particular stage, eliminate those that would produce infeasible chromosomes. Conceptually, the guided search for chromosomes considering IPR and EPR is as follows:

Step 1: The first vertex is randomly chosen;
Step 2: Test vertex defined in step 1, if it doe not satisfy EPR, repeat step 1;
Step 3: Delete column of first vertex;
Step 4: The candidate vertices for the next assembly stage are those for which the value of aij in the corresponding rows of the elements already assembled of the table of liaisons is non-zero;
Step 5: Test vertices defined in step 4 and eliminate vertices that do not satisfy EPR;
Step 6: Randomly select a vertex from the candidates;
Step 7: Once a vertex been selected, its column is deleted;
Step 8: Repeat steps 4–8 until all vertices have been placed;

The algorithm generates a perfectly random first component to be assembled (step 1). This component is tested to determine if it satisfies EPR (step 2). If not, it is rejected and first 2 steps are repeated until a suitable vertex is found. Then, in step 3, candidate vertices for next assembly state, the ones that have a liaison with the partial subassembly (IPR), have not yet been assembled (after a components is assembled, its column is deleted, step 6 so that the chromosome is a constrained permutation) and satisfy EPR are detected. The second vertex is randomly chosen from candidate vertices. The algorithm is very effective, at each run it adds a gene to the chromosome, except for the definition of first gene. Generating and testing the first gene was faster than checking every vertex for all the EPR that appear in the assembly process.

10.2. The crossover operator

The offspring chromosomes have to satisfy two conditions: they have to be feasible and they have to keep most—if not all—the parents' properties. Due to the constrained character of the ASP problem and due to the integer representation used for chromosomes, a modified crossover operator had to be developed.

The crossover operator relies heavily on the guided search. It operates with feasible chromosomes and, from pairs of feasible parent chromosomes undergoing crossover, the result is pairs of feasible offspring chromosomes. The crossover operator is presented, conceptually, below:

Input: the population of parent chromosomes

Step 1: Randomly select pairs of parent chromosomes;
Step 2: For the first pair of parent chromosomes randomly select the cut point;
Step 3: For the first parent chromosome;

Step 4: For each locus at the right hand side of the cut point:
  – determine by guided search the candidate vertices for the gene. **If** the gene in the corresponding locus from the other parent is amongst candidates, **Then** choose it **Else** place any other candidate gene;
Step 5: Repeat step 4 for the second parent chromosome;
Step 6: Repeat Steps 3–5 for the remaining pairs of parent chromosomes;

Output: a population of feasible offspring (children) chromosomes;

This algorithm is able to produce feasible chromosomes, as the candidates for each locus are determined by guided search. Moreover, for each locus, as the corresponding gene from the other parent is the first to be chosen, if it exists amongst candidates, the crossover preserves the maximum of the parents' properties.

10.3. The fitness function

Each chromosome corresponds to an assembly sequence. After the crossover, the entire population, parents and children chromosomes, undergoes evaluation. A fitness value is associated with each chromosome. The fitness function used in the GA is as defined in Section 9.

10.4. The selection process

The sampling mechanism (how chromosomes are selected from the sampling space) used is the stochastic sampling, associated with the Holland's proportionate selection or roulette wheel selection (Holland 1975). The selection probability or the survival probability for each chromosome is proportional to its fitness value: a chromosome with fitness value f_i is allocated f_i/f_m offspring, where f_m is the average fitness value of the population. A string with a fitness value higher than the average has a chance of allocating more than one offspring, while a string with a fitness value less than average my have no offspring in the next generation. The proportionate selection allocates fractional numbers of offspring to strings.

11. A CASE STUDY

The example selected to illustrate the algorithm is the Assembled Body of a hydraulic motor, presented in Fig. 8 (Marian, Luong et al. 2001; Marian, Kargas et al. 2003) designed and built as a prototype by one of the authors. The product has the following components: c1–body, c2, c3, c4, c5–lower bushes, c6, c7, c8, c9–middle bushes and c10, c11, c12, c13—upper bushes. The bushes are essentially cylindrical and are pressed (press fit) into the corresponding holes bored into the block.

The model of the Assembled Body for ASP:

The graph of liaisons of the Assembled Body is presented in Fig. 9. The vertices correspond to the components of the product; c1, c2 ⋯ c13 are represented as vertices a1, a2 ⋯ a13. Table 4 is the table of liaisons of the Assembled Body.

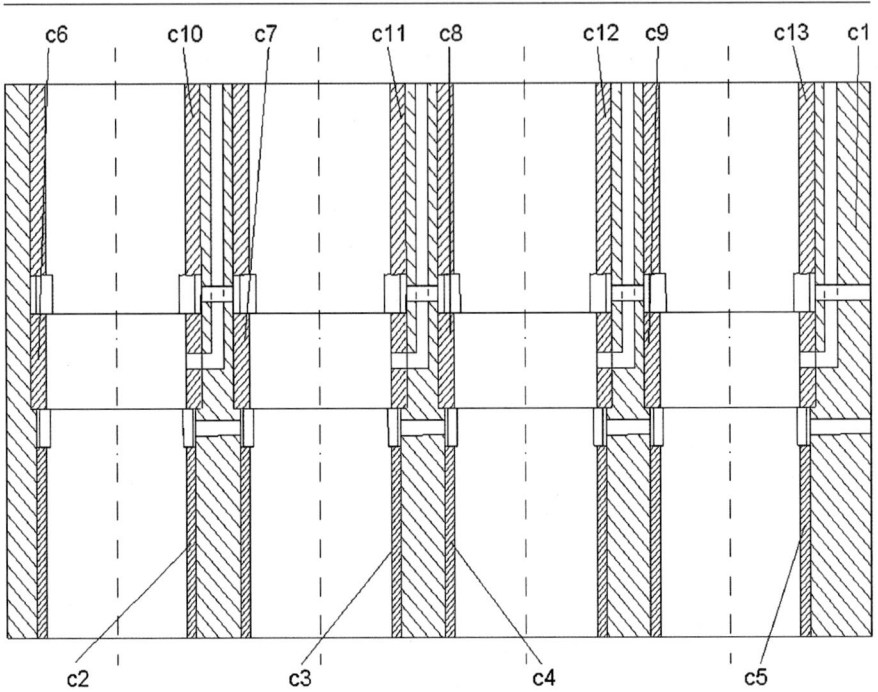

Figure 8. The assembled body of a hydraulic motor.

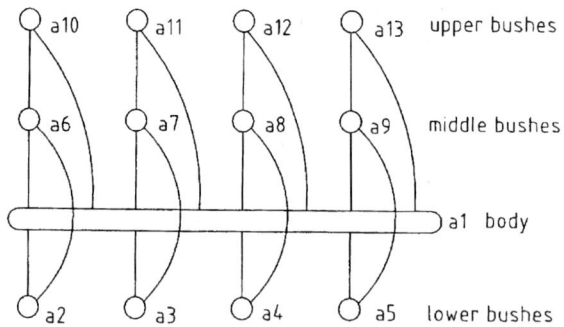

Figure 9. Graph of liaisons for the assembled body of the hydraulic motor presented in Fig. 8. (Marian, Luong et al. 2003).

Table 4 Table of liaisons for the assembled body presented in Fig. 8.

	a1	a2	a3	a4	a5	a6	a7	a8	a9	a10	a11	a12	a13
a1	0	1	1	1	1	1	1	1	1	1	1	1	1
a2	1	0	0	0	0	1	0	0	0	0	0	0	0
a3	1	0	0	0	0	0	1	0	0	0	0	0	0
a4	1	0	0	0	0	0	0	1	0	0	0	0	0
a5	1	0	0	0	0	0	0	0	1	0	0	0	0
a6	1	1	0	0	0	0	0	0	0	1	0	0	0
a7	1	0	1	0	0	0	0	0	0	0	1	0	0
a8	1	0	0	1	0	0	0	0	0	0	0	1	0
a9	1	0	0	0	1	0	0	0	0	0	0	0	1
a10	1	0	0	0	0	1	0	0	0	0	0	0	0
a11	1	0	0	0	0	0	1	0	0	0	0	0	0
a12	1	0	0	0	0	0	0	1	0	0	0	0	0
a13	1	0	0	0	0	0	0	0	1	0	0	0	0

Table 5 Assembly table for the assembled body presented in Fig. 8.

	a1	a2	a3	a4	a5	a6	a7	a8	a9	a10	a11	a12	a13
a1	0	1	1	1	1	x1	x2	x3	x4	>x1	>x2	>x3	>x4
a2	1	0	0	0	0	1	0	0	0	0	0	0	0
a3	1	0	0	0	0	0	1	0	0	0	0	0	0
a4	1	0	0	0	0	0	0	1	0	0	0	0	0
a5	1	0	0	0	0	0	0	0	1	0	0	0	0
a6	x1	1	0	0	0	0	0	0	0	1	0	0	0
a7	x2	0	1	0	0	0	0	0	0	0	1	0	0
a8	x3	0	0	1	0	0	0	0	0	0	0	1	0
a9	x4	0	0	0	1	0	0	0	0	0	0	0	1
a10	>x1	0	0	0	0	1	0	0	0	0	0	0	0
a11	>x2	0	0	0	0	0	1	0	0	0	0	0	0
a12	>x3	0	0	0	0	0	0	1	0	0	0	0	0
a13	>x4	0	0	0	0	0	0	0	1	0	0	0	0

For this example, the assembly process is SLMC, each gene corresponds to the addition of a component to the partial subassembly.

The conditions for assembly (EPR) are the following: upper bushes are to be assembled after middle bushes are assembled to body (geometric conditions derived into precedence conditions). Those EPR are implemented in the assembly table as follows:

– Liaisons between middle-bushes—body are allocated references $\times 1 \cdots \times 4$;
– Liaisons upper bushes-middle bushes are to be done after $\times 1 \cdots \times 4$, so they are allocated $(>\times 1) \cdots (> \times 4)$
– The relations are symmetric;

Table 5 is the assembly table for the Assembled body.

THE FITNESS FUNCTION. It is assumed that components are assembled vertically, downwards. Bushes have to be assembled (pressed) in the body, even if the reverse is possible.

The body, being heavy and difficult to manipulate (around 15 kg), should be the base component, to which other components, the bushes (0.2–0.4 kg) are added/pressed into, not vice-versa. Assembling body to bushes, rotating the body or changing the type of bushes to be assembled carries a penalty.

The FF for the assembly process of the Assembled body is defined as:

$$FF = \frac{PFF(1) + PFF(2) + \cdots + PFF(13)}{13} \tag{11}$$

The PFF(i) are defined as follows: $PFF(i) = (1 - PF(i))$ \hfill (12)

Where PF(i) is a penalty function corresponding to adding a particular component to the partial subassembly in step i. The penalty function approach was chosen because the penalties are easy to define, realistically capture the difficulties associated with the assembly process, the number of penalties to consider is relatively reduced and the evaluation is simple and straightforward.

The values of the PF are:

– if the body is assembled to a bush: PF = 0.8;
– changing type of bush: penalty of PF = 0.3;
– rotating block PF = 0.5;

The body has to be rotated at least once and this operation carries a penalty of 0.5. Changing the type of bushes carries a penalty of 0.2 and will occur at least twice in the assembly process. The penalty function is 0.8 for adding the body to a bush but this can be avoided if the block is the first to be assembled.

The results of a representative run of the GA are shown in Fig. A5. The population is 50 chromosomes and generally the best chromosomes appear before the 30-th generation.

The best results correspond to a sequence starting with a1, then a2, a3, a4 and a5, in any order (4! = 24 possibilities), then the body is turned—penalty of 0.5—followed by assembling bushes a6, a7, a8, a9 in any order (4! possibilities)—penalty of 0.2 for changing type of bushes—then a10, a11, a12, a13 in any order (4! possibilities)—penalty of 0.2 for changing type of bushes.

The maximum value of the FF is FFmax = (13 − 0.5 − 0.2 − 0.2)/13 = 0.93 and is the fitness of $(4!)^3 = 13824$ 'best' sequences. The number of best sequences could be further reduced, by using supplementary penalties, but in this case this would complicate matters without being of much benefit.

The results obtained by optimising the assembly sequence with GA were consistent with the actual assembly sequence used when physically building the hydraulic motor the assembled body was part.

12. CONCLUSIONS

This chapter has presented a methodology to optimise the Assembly Sequence of a product using Genetic Algorithms. The ASP problem is particularly difficult to

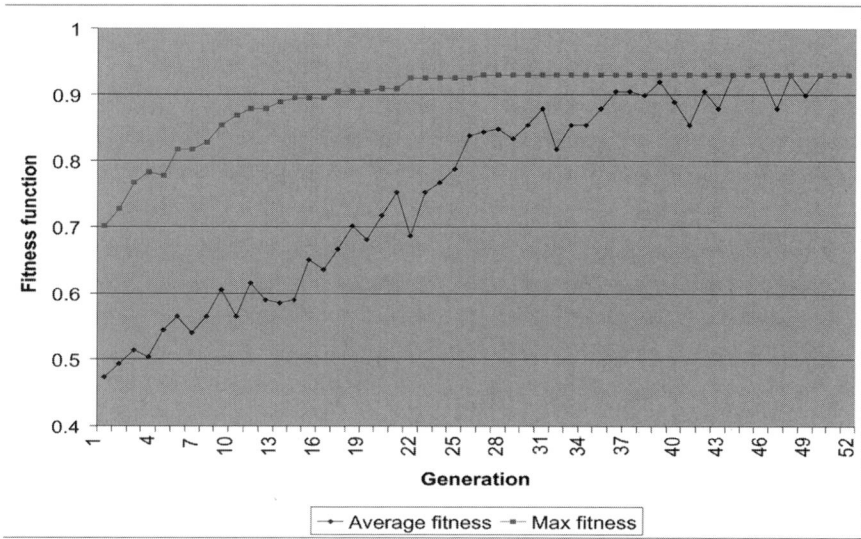

Figure 10. Evolution of fitness function for the optimisation of the Assembled Body (Marian, Luong et al. 2003).

optimise for two reasons. The first reason is the extraordinary variety of the assembly as a technological problem which has to address any type of assembly sequence and plan involving components and subassemblies with a fixed or variable geometry and volume (solid, liquid, gaseous or multiphase). The second reason comes from the large scale, highly constrained, combinatorial character of the problem as a mathematical abstraction.

An integrated methodology has been conceived, to model, then solve and optimise a full-scale, unabridged ASP. A number of models were developed: a model of assembly processes (what assembly planning means in mathematical terms), a model for assembly sequences (encoded as chromosomes), a model of products for assembly purposes (encoding and storing of constraints in assembly) and a framework to encode quality measures in assembly. Those models, even if very comprehensive, have an open character, so that they can be further expanded to accommodate other situations as need may arise.

The ASP problem has been solved by randomly generating feasible assembly sequences using a guided search algorithm. The algorithm is very effective, works in polynomial time, produces a gene and adds it to the chromosome at each iteration.

The ASP is optimised using a GA that works with and produce feasible assembly sequences/chromosomes. GA have the advantage of being able to handle large-scale problems as a direct consequence of being parallel in nature. Another advantage is the flexibility in defining the fitness function from optimisation constraints. The GA has a classical structure but with specially designed operators that rely on the guided search.

13. REFERENCES

1. Ames, A. L. and T. L. Carlton (1995). Lessons Learned from a Second Generation Assembly Planning System. IEEE International Symposium on Assembly Task Planning.
2. Bourjault, A. (1984). Contribution a une Approche Methodologique de l'Assemblage Automatise. Sciences Physiques, Universite de Franche Comte.
3. Gen, M. and R. Cheng (1997). Genetic algorithms and engineering design, John Wiley & Sons, Inc.
4. Gen, M., G. Zhou, et al. (1998). A Comparative Study of Tree Encodings on Spanning Tree Problems. IEEE World Congress on Computational Intetelligence.
5. Golabi, S. i. (1996). Automatic generation of all geometrically feasible assembly sequences using solid modelling, University of South Australia.
6. Goldberg, D. E. (1989). Genetic Algorithms in Search, Optimization & Machine Learning, Addison Wesley Publishing Company, Inc.
7. Haupt, R. L. and S. E. Haupt (1998). Practical Genetic Algorithms. New York, John Wiley & Sons, Inc.
8. Holland, J. (1975). Adaptation in Natural and Artificial Systems. Ann Arbor, University of Michigan Press.
9. Homem de Mello, L. S. and A. C. Sanderson (1991). "Representation of Mechanical Assembly Sequences." IEEE Transactions on Robotics and Automation 7, no. 2 (April 1991): 211–227.
10. Hsu, H.-Y. and G. C. I. Lin (1997). On the Assemblability of a Product. International Conference on Manufacturing Automation (ICMA'97), Hong Kong.
11. Huang, Y. F. and C. S. G. Lee (1988). Precedence Knowledge in Feature Mating Operation Assembly Planning. West Lafayette, Indiana, Engineering Research Center for Intelligent Manufacturing Systems, School of Engineering, Purdue University.
12. Huang, Y. F. and C. S. G. Lee (1991). A Framework of Knowledge-based Assembly Planning. IEEE International Conference on Robotics and Automation, Sacramento, California.
13. Jones, R. E. and R. H. Wilson (1996). A Survey of Constraints in Automated Assembly Planning. IEEE International Conference on Robotics and Automation.
14. Jones, R. E., R. H. Wilson, et al. (1998). "On Constraints in Assembly Planning." IEEE Transactions on Robotics and Automation 16(Nr. 6, December 1998).
15. Kaufman, S. G., R. H. Wilson, et al. (1996). The Archimedes 2 Mechanical Assembly Planning System. IEEE International Conference on Robotics and Automation, Minneapolis, Minnesota.
16. Kavraki, L., J.-C. Latombe, et al. (1993). "On the Complexity of Assembly Partitioning." Information Processing Letters 48(5): 229–235.
17. Marian, R., K. Abhary, et al. (2000). On the Definition of Fitness Function for the Optimisation of Assembly Sequences using GA. ICME 2000—The Eight International Conference on Manufacturing Engineering, Sydney.
18. Marian, R., L. Luong, et al. (2001). Modelling of a Linear Hydraulic Motor. 5-th Intl & 9-th Annual Mechanical Engineering Conference, Rasht—Iran.
19. Marian, R., L. H. S. Luong, et al. (1999). Applications of Genetic Algorithms in Design for Assembly. EDA Conference '99, Vancouver.
20. Marian, R., L. H. S. Luong, et al. (1999). Chromosome Generation for Assembly Planning Using a Guided Search. The Third Australia-Japan Joint Workshop on Intelligent and Evolutionary Systems, Canberra, Australia.
21. Marian, R., L. H. S. Luong, et al. (1999). Optimisation of Assembly Sequences Using Genetic Algorithms. 10-th International DAAAM Symposium, Viena, Austria.
22. Marian, R., L. H. S. Luong, et al. (2000). A new crossover technique for Assembly Sequence Planning Using GA. Computer Integrated Manufacturing CIM 2000, Singapore.
23. Marian, R. M., A. Kargas, et al. (2003). A Genetic Algorithm for the Optimisation of Assembly Sequences. 32nd International Conference on Computers and Industrial Engineering, Limerick, Ireland.
24. Marian, R. M., L. H. S. Luong, et al. (2000). Assembly Sequence Representation and Optimisation Using GA. The First Japanese-Australian Joint Seminar, Adelaide, Australia (proceedings to appear).
25. Marian, R. M., L. H. S. Luong, et al. (2003). "Assembly Sequence Planning and Optimisation Using Genetic Algorithms. Part I: Automatic Generation of Feasible Assembly Sequences." Applied Soft Computing(2/3F): 223-253.
26. Milner, J. M., S. C. Graves, et al. (1994). Using Simulated Annealing to Select Least-Cost Assembly Sequences. IEEE International Conference on Robotics and Automation.

27. Mosemann, H., F. Röhrdanz, et al. (1997). Geometrical and Physical Cost Evaluation for Robot Assembly Sequence Planning. IEEE International Conference on Intelligent Engineering Systems, Budapest, Hungary.
28. Naisbitt, J. (1982). Megatrends—Ten New Directions Transforming Our Lives.
29. Nof, S., W. Wilbert, et al. (1997). Industrial Assembly, Chapman & Hall.
30. Redford, A. and J. Chal (1994). Design for Assembly. Principles and practice. London, McGraw-Hill Book company.
31. Rohrdanz, F., H. Mosemann, et al. (1996). HighLAP: A High Level System for Generating, Representing and Evaluating Assembly Sequences. IEEE International Joint Symposium on Intelligence and Sistems.
32. Rohrdanz, F., H. Mosemann, et al. (1997). Constraint Evaluation for Assembly Sequence Planning. IEEE International Symposium on Assembly Task Planning, Marina del Rey.
33. Romney, B., C. Goddard, et al. (1995). An Efficient System for Geometric Assembly Sequence Generation and Evaluation. ASME International Computers in Engineering Conference, Boston, Massachussets.
34. Ronald, S. P. (1995). Genetic Algorithms and Permutation-Encoded Problems. Diversity Preservation and a Study of Multimodality. School of Computer and Information Science. Adelaide, University of South Australia: 213.
35. Sebaaly, M. F. and H. Fujimoto (1996). A Genetic Planner for Assembly Automation. 5th International Conference on Concurrent Engineering Research and Applications, Tokyo, Japan.
36. Tichem, M., T. Storm, et al. (1999). How to Achieve a Breakthrough in Industrialisation of Flexible Assembly Automation. 9-th International Flexible Automation and Intelligent Manufacturing (FAIM) Conference, Tilburn, The Netherlands.
37. Wilson, R. H. (1992). On geometric assembly planning, Stanford University.
38. Wilson, R. H., L. Kavraki, et al. (1995). "Two-Handed Assembly sequencing." International Journal of Robotics Research 14(4): 335–350.
39. Wilson, R. J. and J. J. Watkins (1990). Graphs—An Introductory approach. New York, John Wiley and Sons.
40. Wolter, J. D. (1989). On the automatic generation of assembly plans. IEEE International Conference on Robotics and Assembly Planning, Scottsdale, Arizona.
41. Wolter, J. D. (1991). A Combinatorial Analysis of Enumerative Data Structures for Assembly Planning. IEEE International Conference on Robotics and Automation, Sacramento, California, USA.
42. Young, H. D. (1992). University physics. Reading, Massachusetts.

KERNEL-BASED SELF-ORGANIZED MAPS TRAINED WITH SUPERVISED BIAS FOR GENE EXPRESSION DATA MINING

STERGIOS PAPADIMITRIOU

1. INTRODUCTION

Clustering is a popular data analysis technique that aims to provide insight into the structure of the data and aids at the discovery of functional classes. Gene expression analysis, utilizes clustering techniques extensively. These techniques accomplish the grouping of genes with similar expression patterns into clusters [6, 11, 18, 19]. Such approaches unravel relations between genes and help to deduce their biological role, since genes of similar function tend to display similar expression patterns.

Most of the so far developed algorithms perform the clustering of the expression patterns in an unsupervised manner [11, 16, 22], although in many application areas already exists valuable domain knowledge. For example, collections of genes knowing to encode proteins of similar biological function, e.g. genes that code for ribosomal proteins, constitute useful a priori knowledge [7]. This means that existing information is not fully explored in order to deduce the correct expression characteristics of genes that make them part of functional groups. Additionally the frequent case that genes of similar function become allocated to different clusters and are therefore known to be erroneously grouped cannot be handled by a pure unsupervised approach. Despite of the need to integrate a priori knowledge, most of the widely clustering methods, like hierarchical clustering [11], K-means clustering, Bayesian clustering [12, 13] and the Self-Organizing Map (SOM) [22] usually ignore any existing class information. In addition many kernel-based developments of the SOM approach, do not have provision for incorporating supervised labeling [3, 1].

The standard SOM algorithm has a number of properties, which render it to a candidate of particular interest as a basis framework for building more advanced algorithms for clustering applications. SOMs can be implemented easily, are fast, robust and scale well to large data sets. They allow one to impose partial structure on the clusters and facilitate visualization and interpretation. In the case hierarchical information is required, it can be implemented on top of SOM, as in [24].

Recently, several dynamically extended schemes have been proposed that overcome the limitation of the fixed non-adaptable architecture of the SOM. Some examples are the Dynamic Topology Representing structures [21], the Growing Cell Structures [12, 9], Self-Organized Tree Algorithms [8, 16], the joint entropy maximization approach [2] and the Adaptive Resonance Theory [5].

The presented approach has many similarities to these dynamically extended schemes. However, we focus on the design of such types of algorithms that aim to explore effectively existing *a priori supervised class labeling,* for multi-class and *multi-labeled* data. The multiple labeling, i.e. the possible assignment of more than one class label at each pattern, perplexes the clustering and classification tasks.

Also, in contrast to the complexity of some of these schemes, we built simple algorithms that through the restriction of growing on a rectangular grid, can be implemented easily and the training of the models is very efficient. The benefits of the more complex alternatives of dynamical extension are still retained.

We call the proposed model KSDG-SOM from Kernel Supervised Dynamic Grid SOM, since it is a model trained in kernel space and although it is SOM based it tightly integrates unsupervised and supervised learning components. Additionally, the KSDG-SOM has been designed in order to automatically detect the *appropriate level of expansion,* so that the number of clusters is controlled by a properly defined measure of the algorithm itself, with no need for any a priori specification.

The paper is outlined as follows: Section 2 deals with the definition of error measure minimization in kernel space. Section 3 deals with the learning algorithms that adapt both the structure and the parameters of the KSDG-SOM. The expansion phase of the KSDG-SOM learning is described in Section 4 separately since it is rather lengthy. Section 5 deals with the automatic detection of the appropriate expansion level. Section 6 discusses results obtained from an application of the KSDG-SOM to a gene expression data analysis task. Finally, Section 7 presents the conclusions along with some directions onto which further research can proceed for improvements.

2. KERNEL-BASED SELF-ORGANIZED MAP ADAPTATION

Denote by L a lattice of N neurons and by $I \subset \Re^d$ the input space. Each node $i \in L$ is characterized by its weight vector $\mathbf{w_i} = [\mathbf{w_{i1}} \ldots \mathbf{w_{id}}] \in \mathbf{I}$ and by a lattice coordinate $\mathbf{r_i} \in \mathbf{L_A}$, where L_A is the lattice space.

Instead of directly computing the activation of a node with weight vector $\mathbf{w_i}$ from the input vector $\mathbf{x}$ by the inner product $\langle \mathbf{x}, \mathbf{w_i} \rangle$, we utilize a kernel function $K(\mathbf{x}, \mathbf{w_i}) =$

$\langle \Phi(\mathbf{x}), \Phi(\mathbf{w_i}) \rangle$. The selected kernel is the Gaussian one:

$$K(\mathbf{x}, \mathbf{w_i}, \sigma_i) = \exp\left(-\frac{\|\mathbf{x} - \mathbf{w_i^2}\|}{2\sigma_i^2}\right)$$

We want to minimize the distortion between the mapping of the input $\Phi(\mathbf{x})$ and the mapping of the node $\Phi(\mathbf{w_i})$. Therefore we perform gradient descent with respect to $\mathbf{w_i}$.

$$\frac{\partial}{\partial \mathbf{w}_i}\|\Phi(x) - \Phi(\mathbf{w_i})\|^2 = \frac{\partial}{\partial \mathbf{w}_i}K(\mathbf{w_i}, \mathbf{w_i}, \sigma_i) + \frac{\partial}{\partial \mathbf{w}_i}K(\mathbf{x}, \mathbf{x}, \sigma_i) - 2\frac{\partial}{\partial \mathbf{w}_i}K(\mathbf{x}, \mathbf{w_i}, \sigma_i)$$

$$= -2\frac{\partial}{\partial \mathbf{w}_i}\exp\left(-\frac{\|\mathbf{x} - \mathbf{w}_i\|^2}{2\sigma_i^2}\right) \tag{1}$$

Therefore the update rule for the kernel centers $\mathbf{w_i}$ should be of the following form:

$$\Delta\mathbf{w_i} = \mu_w \frac{(\mathbf{x} - \mathbf{w_i})}{\sigma_i^2}K(\mathbf{x}, \mathbf{w_i}, \sigma_i) \tag{2}$$

with μ_w the learning rate for the kernel centers.

The next step is to derive the learning rule for the kernel radii σ_i, $\forall i \in L$. By performing gradient descent on $\|\Phi(\mathbf{x}) - \Phi(\mathbf{w_i})\|^2$, with respect to σ_i, we obtain:

$$\Delta\sigma_i \propto \frac{\|\mathbf{x} - \mathbf{w}_i\|^2}{\sigma_i^3}K(\mathbf{x}, \mathbf{w_i}, \sigma_i)$$

Therefore the update rule for the Gaussian centers will be of the form:

$$\Delta\sigma_i = \mu_\sigma \frac{\|\mathbf{x} - \mathbf{w}_i\|^2}{\sigma_i^3}K(\mathbf{x}, \mathbf{w_i}, \sigma_i) \tag{3}$$

with μ_σ the learning rate for the kernel variances (i.e. radii).

Typical values that we have used for μ_w and μ_σ are $\mu_w = 0.1$ and $\mu_\sigma = 0.1$. However, the convergence of the algorithm is not sensitive to the exact values of these parameters.

3. THE KSDG-SOM ALGORITHM

The KSDG-SOM is initialized with four nodes arranged in a 2×2 rectangular grid and grows nodes to represent the input data. This type of initialization is somehow arbitrary and different starting configurations can be used, e.g. 9 nodes arranged as a 3×3 grid. Weight values of the nodes are self-organized according to a new method inspired by the SOM algorithm. The self-organization process maps properties of the original high-dimensional data space onto the lattice consisted of KSDG-SOM nodes. The map is expanded to represent the input space by creating new nodes, either from the boundary nodes performing *boundary extension,* or by inserting whole columns (or rows) of new units with a *column extension* (or row extension).

A *training epoch* consists of the presentation of all the training gene expression patterns to the KSDG-SOM. A *training run* is defined as the training of the KSDG-SOM with a fixed number of neurons at its lattice i.e. the training between successive node insertions/deletions.

The KSDG-SOM learning aims to minimize an inhomogeneous performance measure of the form:

$$\Theta_E = \min \left(\sum_{i=1}^{K} ALE_i + r_{su} \cdot \text{Entropy}_i + MOP \right) \qquad (4)$$

where *ALE* denotes the Average Local Error, *MOP* abbreviates the Model Order Penalty and *K* is the number of nodes. Also, r_{su} is a parameter that controls the *relative significance of the supervised part.* This minimization is achieved with the formulation of SOM-like learning rules and with a dynamic expansion process.

The parameter *ALE* of Equation 4 accounts for the unsupervised (quantization) error corresponding to pattern *i* and can deal with the lack of class information. This measures tries to disperse patterns that are different according to some similarity metric, to different clusters, even if they are labeled with the same functional class label.

A commonly used measure for the local error, and the one that we minimize with the formulation of equation 1, is the Euclidean distance between the kernel mapping $\Phi(\mathbf{x_i})$ of input vector $\mathbf{x_i}$ and the representative prototype $\Phi(\mathbf{w_k})$ of its best matching node k, i.e.

$$LE_i = \| \Phi(\mathbf{x_i}) - \Phi(\mathbf{w_k}) \|^2 \qquad (5)$$

Then the ALE_i is obtained by averaging the LE_i over all the patterns of the same node. The justification for this averaging is explained in Section 4.

The available a priori information for the functional class of the patterns is considered by the *entropy measure.* This measure corresponds to the entropy of the node where the pattern is mapped. Minimization of this measure is performed by *gathering similar labels onto the same clusters.*

The *MOP* (ModelOrderPenalty) term punishes any increase in the model complexity. In this framework, the model complexity relates to the number of KSDG-SOM nodes that correspond to clusters of patterns. It also punishes models of low complexity. A term of the following form is exploited:

$$MOP = \gamma \cdot M(K - 3 \cdot K_{label})^2 - c_1 \cdot \Delta ALE - c_2 \cdot \Delta \text{Entropy} \qquad (6)$$

where $M(x) = \begin{cases} x, & \text{if } x > 0 \\ 0, & \text{if } x \le 0 \end{cases}$, ΔALE denotes the variation of the Average Local Error parameter and K_{label} is the number of the class labels. This formulation does not punish increases at the number of nodes as long as these reduce significantly the other error terms (i.e. we benefit from these). However, when increases at the model complexity do not compensated by reductions of the error terms, the *ModelErrorPenalty* quantity endeavors for a simpler model.

With $r_{su} = 0$ we have pure unsupervised learning with model complexity penalization. As r_{su} increases, the cost $\ominus_E$ is minimized for configurations that fit better to the a priori classification. Finally, for sufficiently large values of r_{su}, the a priori component dominates completely. Clearly, since in this case the information provided by the data is demolished, care should be taken to avoid such r_{su} values.

After the preliminary discussion, we can now proceed to describe the KSDG-SOM learning algorithms in more detail.

The top-level KSDG-SOM learning in algorithmic notation can be described as:

<*Top-level KSDG-SOM learning algorithm*>

1. Initialization (sets $r_{su} = 0$, i.e. pure unsupervised learning) (Subsection 3.1)
Repeat // develop a series of models corresponding to increasing
        // consideration of the supervised parameter, r_{su}
   Repeat
      2. Training Run Adaptation phase. (Subsection 3.2)
      3. Expansion phase (Section 4)
   until criteria for stopping map expansion are satisfied (Section 5)
   4. Fine Tuning Adaptation phase (Subsection 3.4)
   5. Save configuration of the map for the current supervised/unsupervised ratio, r_{su}.
   6. Compute classification performance for the current r_{su}
   7. Increment the significance of the supervised part, i.e. increase ratio r_{su}
until *Classification Performance* ≈ 1
8. Model Selection Step (Subsection 3.6)

The details of the algorithm, i.e. the initialization, adaptation, fine tuning phases and the corresponding convergence criteria are described in detail below. The technical subleties involved in the expansion process are described in detail in section 4.

3.1. Initialization phase

The weight vectors of the four starting nodes that are arranged in a 2×2 grid are initialized with random numbers within the domain of feature values. Other initialization schemes are possible i.e. as noted we can initialize to a 3×3 grid. The supervision parameter r_{su} controls the tradeof between unsupervised and supervised training and is discussed in detail in Section 4. It is initialized to 0, i.e. pure unsupervised learning is performed for the first KSDG-SOM model being generated.

3.2. Training run adaptation phase

The purpose of this phase is to stabilize the current map configuration in order to be able to evaluate its effectiveness and the requirements for further expansion. During this phase, the input patterns are repeatedly presented and the corresponding self-organization actions are performed until the map converges sufficiently. The training run adaptation phase takes the following algorithmic form.

<*Training Run Adaptation Phase*>:
MapConverged: = **false**;
while *MapConverged* = **false do**
    for all input patterns **do**
        present and adapt the map by applying the *map adaptation rules* (Subsection 3.2.1)
    endfor
        Evaluate map *training run convergence condition* (Subsection 3.2.2) and set MapConverged accordingly
endwhile

The map adaptation rules and the training run convergence condition are described separately in the following two paragraphs.

3.2.1. Map adaptation rules

The map adaptation rules that govern the processing of each input pattern $\mathbf{x}_k$ are as follows:

1. Determination of the weight vector $\mathbf{w}_i$ for which its kernel mapping $\Phi(\mathbf{w}_i)$ is closest to the kernel mapping $\Phi(\mathbf{x}_k)$, of the input vector $\mathbf{x}_k$, according to the utilized distance measure (i.e. determination of the winner node).
2. Adaptation of the weight vectors (i.e. Gaussian centers) only for the four nodes in the direct neighborhood of the winner and for the winner itself according to the following formula:

$$\mathbf{w}_j(k+1) = \begin{cases} \mathbf{w}_j(k), & j \notin N_k \\ \mathbf{w}_j(k) + \mu_w \cdot \Lambda_k(d(i,j)) \cdot \Delta\mathbf{w}_j(k), & j \in N_k \end{cases} \tag{7}$$

3. Adaptation of the Gaussian spreads also only for the four nodes in the direct neighborhood of the winner and for the winner itself according to the following formula:

$$\sigma_j(k+1) = \begin{cases} \sigma_j(k), & j \notin N_k \\ \sigma_j(k) + \mu_\sigma \cdot \Lambda_k(d(i,j)) \cdot \Delta\sigma_j(k), & j \in N_k \end{cases} \tag{8}$$

where the learning rates $\mu_w(k)$, $\mu_\sigma(k)$, $k \in N$, are monotonically decreasing sequence of positive parameters, N_k is the neighborhood of the winner node at the kth learning step and $\Lambda_k(d(j,i))$ is the neighborhood function implementing different adaptation rates even within the same neighborhood. Also, the $\Delta\mathbf{w}_j(k)$ is defined in terms of the kernel distance metric of equation 2, and $\Delta\sigma_j(k)$ is defined according to equation 3.

The learning rates $\mu_w(k)$, $\mu_\sigma(k)$, $k \in N$ typically start from a value of 0.1 and decrease down to 0.02. These values are specified with the empirical criterion of having relatively fast convergence, without however sacrificing the stability of the map.

The KSDG-SOM starts with a much smaller size than a usual SOM. Therefore a large neighborhood is not required to train the whole map at the first learning steps (e.g. with 4 nodes initially at the map, a neighborhood of 1 only is required). As training proceeds, during subsequent training epochs, the area defined by the neighborhood becomes localized near the winning neuron, not by shrinking the vicinity radius (as in the standard SOM) but by enlarging the SOM with the dynamic growing.

The neighborhood function $\Lambda_k(d(j, i))$, can thus be defined with the following simple formula (the row and column of a node i are denoted by i_r, i_c respectively):

$$\Lambda_k(d(j, i)) = \begin{cases} 1 & \text{if } j = i \\ \alpha, \quad 0 < \alpha < 1, & \text{if } |i_r - j_r| + |i_c - j_c| = 1 \\ 0, & \text{otherwise} \end{cases}$$

3.2.2. Evaluation of the map training run convergence condition

The reduction of the *Total Growth Parameter* (*TGP*, defined in section 4) controls the training run convergence condition. The corresponding convergence test is:

$$\text{MapConverged} := \left(\frac{|TGP_b - TGP_a|}{TGP_a} < \text{ConvergenceErrorThreshold} \right)$$

where $TGP_b = \sum_i (GP_i)_b$ and $TGP_a = \sum_i (GP_i)_a$ denote respectively the sum of the Growth Parameters for all nodes before and after the presentation of patterns (i.e. one training epoch) and the *ConvergenceErrorThreshold* is a given value.

The above formula states that the map converges when the relative change of the *TGP* parameter between successive epochs drops below the threshold value. The setting of the *ConvergenceErrorThreshold* is somewhat empirical but a value in the range 0.01–0.02 performs well in assuming sufficient convergence without excessive computation.

3.3. Expansion phase

This phase constitutes the main core of the learning algorithms. It is described in detail in section 4

3.4. Fine tuning adaptation phase

The fine tuning phase aims to optimize the final KSDG-SOM configuration. This phase is similar to the training run adaptation phase described previously (sub-section 3.2) with two differences:

1. The final criterion for map convergence is more elaborated. We require much smaller change of the Total Growth Parameter for accepting the condition for map convergence.
2. The learning rate decreases to a smaller value in order to allow fine adjustments to the final structure of the map.

Typically, the *ConvergenceErrorThreshold* for the fine tuning phase is about 0.00001 and the learning rate is set to 0.01 (or to an even smaller value).

3.5. Evaluation of classification performances

Each KSDG-SOM node is assigned a *classification vector* **cl** with elements $cl_i = p_i$ where p_i is the ratio of patterns with functional label i, among all the patterns mapped to the node. This vector is considered as the predicted classification. This classification is a soft one: each cl_i expresses the probability that a node (and consequently the mapped patterns) are assigned a label i. We therefore compute performance based on a metric proposed by [20].

Specifically, for each class label i of each pattern j, a score is assigned. This score equals p_i, if the corresponding label is included in the original class assignment (i.e. $c_i = 1$) and equals $q_i = 1 - p_i$ in the other case (i.e. $c_i = 0$). In this way a total score for each pattern j is calculated as:

$$\text{TotalScore}_j = \sum_{i=1}^{N_c} sc_i, \quad \text{where } sc_i = \begin{cases} p_i & \text{if } c_i = 1 \\ q_i = 1 - p_i & \text{if } c_i = 0 \end{cases}$$

Intuitively, a small $p_i \approx 0$ for a class that does not appear as a functional label (i.e. $c_i = 0$) for an input pattern is much more a success than a failure, therefore being considered by a score $q_i \approx 1$.

The performance for each pattern j, perf_j is then obtained by dividing this score with the total number of functional class labelings, N_c, i.e.

$$\text{Perf}_j = \frac{\text{TotalScore}_j}{N_c}$$

The global measure of the performance *ClassificationPerformance* (r_{su}) for a given ratio r_{su} (i.e. the supervision weighting parameter of equation 4), is obtained by averaging the Perf_j values for all the patterns of the testing set.

3.6. Model selection step

During this step a well performing ratio r_{su} is selected by using the following criteria:

• The classification performance obtains a steep increase for the selected r_{su} parameter value at the corresponding classification performance curve and this increase is followed by a plateau. The increase at the classification performance with increasing r_{su} means that a priori information for the application was taken into account by the second (supervised) term of Equation 4 at the formation of the cluster boundaries. The plateau that we require to follow the steep increase implies that increasing further the strength of the a priori information, although it can bias the model heavily towards an imperfect domain theory, does not offer significant improvements to its generalization potential. This methodology for model selection will be illustrated better by means of an example in Section 6.
• The number of the KSDG-SOM nodes that grow for the "optimal" r_{su} value should be relatively small (small model complexity). This criterion prefers the models with the smallest complexity that offer adequate generalization performance.

We should note that these selection criteria are somewhat heuristic. However, there seem to perform an adequate model selection.

3.7. Node deletion

Nodes that are selected as winners for very few (usually one or two) training patterns, termed *uncolonized* nodes, are not deleted by our scheme although they probably correspond to noisy outliers. The patterns that consistently (three times or more) are mapped to uncolonized nodes are very unique and can either be artifacts or if not they have the potential to provide knowledge. Therefore they are amenable to further consideration. These patterns therefore are marked and isolated for further study. Nodes that are not selected as winners for any pattern are removed from the map in order to keep it compact.

4. THE EXPANSION PROCESS

The expansion is based on the detection of the neurons with large *Growth Parameter* (GP), referred to as the *unresolved neurons*. The node with the largest GP becomes the current focus of map expansion.

The Growth Parameter for node i, denoted GP_i, is based on an inhomogenous type of error, computed as:

$$GP_i = ALE_i + r_{su} \cdot \text{Entropy}_i \tag{9}$$

where we recall that the ALE denotes the Average Local Error.

We describe in turn the two components of 9, i.e. the *average local error* and the *entropy*.

A *local error* term is commonly used for implementing dynamically growing schemes [4, 16]. A general assessment of the local error, le_i, is given by

$$le_i = \sum_{x \in S_i} \text{Dist}(\mathbf{x}, \mathbf{w}_i) \tag{10}$$

where we denote by S_i the set of patterns $\mathbf{x}$ mapped to node i, $\mathbf{w}_i$ the weight vector of node i that corresponds to the average expression profile of S_i and the Dist operator denotes the corresponding distance metric.

However, the peculiarities of many application domains (e.g. the gene expression data analysis) motivated two significant modifications to the classic local error measure. Specifically:

1. Instead of the simple local error measure of Equation 10 we use the *average local error* ALE_i per pattern, defined as:

$$ALE_i = \frac{le_i}{|S_i|} \tag{11}$$

where $|S_i|$ denotes the number of elements of the set $|S_i|$.

This measure does not increase when many similar patterns are mapped to the same node.

2. The second provision applies when we have class information available (either complete or partial) and we want to exploit it in order to improve the expansion. The local error that accumulates to a winner node is amplified by a factor that is inversely proportional to the square root of the frequency ratio r_c of its corresponding class c. Specifically, let $r_c = \frac{\#\text{patterns of class } c}{\#\text{total patterns}}$ be the frequency ratio of class c. Then the amplification factor is $r_c^{-\frac{1}{2}}$.

The supervised contribution to the inhomogeneous error of Equation 4 is based on the computation of a parameter HN_i characterizing the *entropy of the class assignment content* of each node i. An advantage of the entropy is that it is relatively insensitive to the over-representation of classes. This means that independently of how many patterns of a class are mapped to the same node, if the node does not represent significantly other classes, its entropy is very small.

We first consider the simple case of each pattern belonging only to one functional class. The assignment of a class label to each neuron of the KSDG-SOM is in this case performed according to a majority-voting scheme [17]. The *entropy* parameter, that quantifies the uncertainty of the class label of neuron m, can be directly evaluated by counting the votes at each SOM neuron for every class as [15]:

$$HN(m) = -\sum_{k=1}^{N_c} p_k \cdot \log p_k \tag{12}$$

where N_c denotes the number of classes and $p_k = \frac{V_k}{V_{pattern}}$, is the ratio of votes V_k for class k to the total number of patterns $V_{pattern}$ that vote to neuron m. The parameter p_k has a probability interpretation, i.e. it is computed as the relative frequency of votes for each class k. For the single label case, the number of labeled patterns $V_{pattern}$ is also equal to the number of votes.

Clearly, the entropy $HN(m)$ is zero for unambiguous neurons and increases as the uncertainty about the class label of the neuron m increases. The upper bound of $HN(m)$ is $\log(N_c)$, and corresponds to the situation where all the classes are equiprobable (i.e. the voting mechanism does not favor a particular class).

For the multi-label case, the voting scheme remains the same, but each pattern in this case can vote for more than one class. The frequent case of having patterns not assigned to any functional class is handled as a vote to the *Unassigned* class.

A quantity $HR(m)$ is defined similarly:

$$HR(m) = -\sum_{k=1}^{N_c} r_k \cdot \log r_k \tag{13}$$

The r_k do not correspond to probabilities but they are class voting ratios defined as the p_k (i.e. $r_k = \frac{v_k}{V_{pattern}}$). However, in this case $\sum_k V_k > V_{pattern}$ and therefore

$\sum_{k=1}^{N_c} r_k > 1$. Thus, $HR(m)$ is not mathematically an entropy of a probability distribution. However, this quantity retains properties similar to the entropy.

We consider an example in order to explain the handling of multiple labeling by equation 13. Let $N_c = 3$ and suppose that 30 patterns are assigned to node m_1, all of them having as a label all the three classes and that 90 patterns are assigned to neuron m_2 one third of them having as a label class 1, another third class 2 and the last third class 3. Although in each case there are 30 patterns voting for each class, the quantity HR will be high in the case of the 90 patterns (i.e. $\log(3)$) and zero at the other case. Thus, the HR measure has quantified effectively the similarity of multiple class labeling between patterns of some cluster.

The steps of the expansion process are as follows:

<*Expansion Phase:*>

Computation of the GP_i, i.e. of the Growth Parameter for every node i.
   repeat
let $i =$ the node with the maximum GP_i measure
if IsBoundaryNode(i) **then**
   // expand at the neighbours of the boundary nodes
   JoinSmoothlyNeighbours(i)
elseif IsNearBoundaryNode(i)
   RippleWeightsToNeighbours(i)
else InsertWholeColumn(i);
endif
Re-execute the Training Run Adaptation Phase for the expanded map Reset the Growth Parameter measures for all nodes
(since possible redistribution of patterns can occur over nodes).
   until not RandomLikeClustersRemain();

We describe below shortly the main issues involved in these steps. We first explore the functionality involved in the repeat loop that controls the KSDG-SOM expansion and we concentrate on the criteria for the establishment of the proper level of expansion in the section that follows. The functions that are involved with the KSDG-SOM expansion are as follows:

- **IsBoundaryNode()** The function IsBoundaryNode() checks whether a node is a boundary node. Training efficiency and implementation simplicity were the motivations for the decision to expand mostly from the boundary nodes.
- **JoinSmoothlyNeighbours()** The expansion of the map at the boundary nodes is performed by acquiring one to three new nodes from their direct neighbourhood. The weights of the new nodes are adjusted heuristically to retain the "weight flow" with the function JoinSmoothlyNeighbours().
- **IsNearBoundaryNode()**: A node is declared as a *near boundary* node by the function *IsNearBoundaryNode()* when the boundary of the map can be reached from this node by traversing in any direction at most two nodes.

- **RippleWeightsToNeighbours()**: The map configuration is slightly disturbed when the winner node is not a boundary node but is a near boundary. For a near boundary node a percentage (usually 20–50%) of the weight of the winner node is shifted towards the outer nodes with the function *RippleWeightsToNeighbours()*. This operation alters locally the Voronoi regions of influence of each Gaussian and usually with a few weight "rippling" operations the winner node is propagated to a boundary node (which is located near).
- **InsertWholeColumn()**: Finally, if the winner is a node that is neither a boundary nor a near boundary the alternative of inserting a whole empty column is used. The rippling of weights is avoided in these cases, because usually excessive computation times are required before the winner propagates from a node placed deep in the map to a boundary node. Instead of inserting whole new columns we can insert alternatively whole new rows, or we can perform a combination of row and column insertion.
- **RandomLikeClustersRemain()**: This function evaluates the "randomness" of the distribution of patterns to a specific cluster as we shall describe in the next section. If for a cluster the allocation of patterns is found to be "random," then the cluster is considered to own unrelated patterns and therefore further decomposition is required.

5. CRITERIA FOR CONTROLLING THE KSDG-SOM DYNAMIC GROWING

The growing process of the KSDG-SOM is controlled by the fore mentioned Boolean function *RandomLikeClustersRemain()*. Ideally, the output of this function should remain true until automatically the appropriate level of expansion is reached.

Intuitively, the growing should stop when the patterns are characterized by inter pattern distances that deviate significantly (either much smaller or much larger) from the typical distances for randomly selected patterns. The problem can be concentrated to the definition of similarity (or alternatively randomness) between patterns and to the determination of the maximum percentage of "random" patterns allowed to be allocated to the cluster. Similarity between patterns is related to the distance between them.

In order to treat the problem quantitatively, we set a *randomization ratio* α. The randomization ratio controls how much of the randomized distances can be treated as non-random. From this ratio we derive distance thresholds dL_{thr} and dU_{thr}. Distances below dL_{thr} imply *positive correlation* between patterns. In a similar manner, distances larger than dU_{thr} imply *negative correlation*. Both cases imply non-random association between patterns.

The randomization ratio α has the meaning that the probability that two patterns are "random" (unrelated) is lower than α, if the distance between them is either smaller than the threshold dL_{thr} or larger than dU_{thr}. Obviously, the definition of this ratio would be only possible if the distribution of the distance between random patterns were known.

Practically, although for most applications the random distribution of inter pattern distances is unknown, it is easy to approximate it by shuffling randomly the features

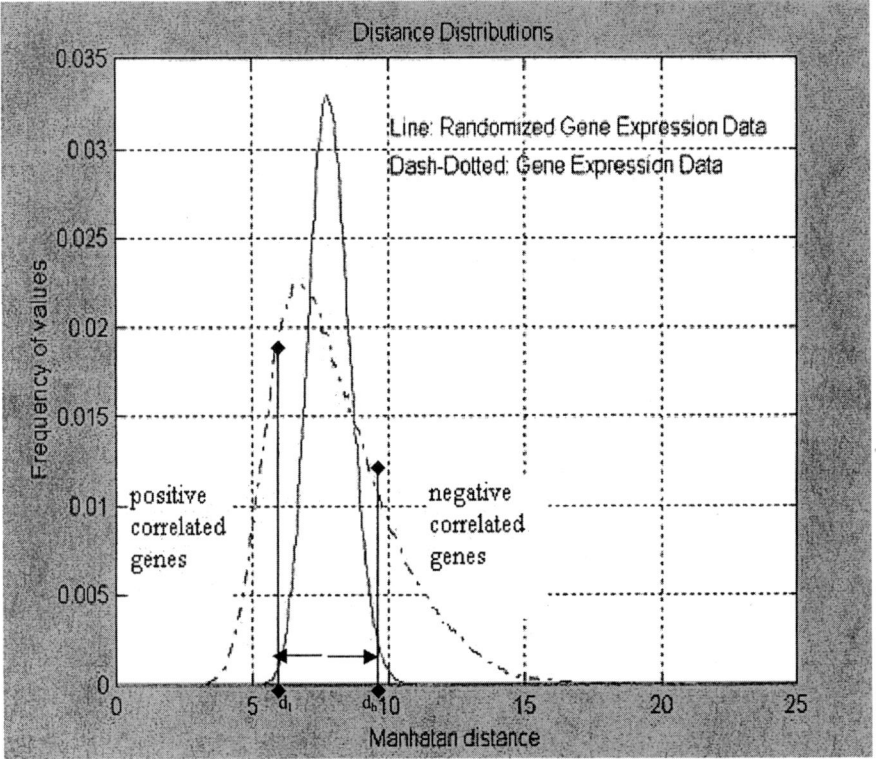

Figure 1. The results of the data shuffling illustrate that the distances between the randomized data occupy a distinct distribution. For the example case of the gene expression data positive correlation is favored while for the random the distribution has a normal form.

that constitute each pattern. This randomization destroys the correlation between the different patterns, while it retains the other characteristics of the data set (e.g. ranges and histogram distribution of values). In this way, we compute an approximation to the distribution of the distance between random patterns.

Figure 1 illustrates the distribution of the distances (with the Manhattan distance metric) between the random patterns and the actual patterns from a gene expression data experiment. In this case, we can determine an upper dU_{thr} and a lower dL_{thr} distance threshold and consider the distances lying in the interval $[dL_{thr} \, dU_{thr}]$ as random.

A parameter p is also specified, that controls the percentage of internode "random" pattern distances, i.e. patterns p_i, p_j with distances $dL_{thr} < \text{dist}(p_i, p_j) < dU_{thr}$, allowed before expansion is initiated. The parameter p is specified empirically to a value of 2%.

In conclusion, given the values of the randomization ratio α and the percentage p, the function *RandomLikeClustersRemain()* controls the growing process by taking into account the distribution of the data as illustrated in Figure 1, and as a result an appropriate number of clusters is determined automatically.

6. APPLICATION

Gene expression data are characterized by multiple functional labeling and are huge and noisy. Also, the available a priori knowledge is still very incomplete. Therefore, this application domain fits well for the application of the KSDG-SOM model.

The DNA microarray technology provides the ability to measure the expression levels of thousands of genes in a single experiment [6, 7, 10, 11]. The interpretation of such massive expression data is a new challenge for bioinformatics and opens new perspectives for functional genomics. A key question within this context is if given some expression data for a gene, this gene does belong to a particular *functional class* (i.e. it encodes for a protein of interest).

We have applied the KSDG-SOM to analyze microarray expression data from the budding yeast Saccharomyces cerevisiae. These data are public available from the Stanford web site. They were generated by studying this fully sequenced organism with microarrays, containing essentially every Open Reading Frame (ORF). The samples used were collected at various time points during the diauxic shift, the mitotic cell division cycle and sporulation. The whole data set consists of 80-element gene expression vectors for 6,221 genes. Annotation for these genes was derived from the Functional Classification Catalogue of the Munich information center for protein sequences (MIPS) Comprehensive Yeast Genome Database (CYGD) available at http://mips.gsf.de/proj/yeast/CYGD/db/index.html. The selected annotations included all the 19 *top-level functional categories*.

The gene expression data is arranged in a table whose rows correspond to the genes and columns to the individual log-transformed gene expression values of each gene in a particular experimental condition represented by the column. The weighted K-nearest neighbors imputation method presented in [23] is applied in order to fill up systematically the missing values.

The KSDG-SOM selects the model with a supervision parameter value of $r_{su} \approx 0.8$ as an appropriate model since as illustrated in Figure 2 it corresponds to a performance plateau. This selection of the model is performed according to heuristic criteria. We require acceptable classification performance, small number of nodes (i.e. model complexity control) and a plateau at the corresponding curve that indicates that further increase at the supervised gain (i.e. of parameter r_{su}) should not be performed. Another important observation is that for the smaller classes consisting of genes with functional uniformity, the convergence is much faster, e.g. for the Cellular Communication/ Signal Transduction class with 59 ORFs at $rsu \approx 0.8$ the performance approaches 1, while for the largest class of metabolism (dotted), large values of rsu ($rsu \approx 8$) are required for the same performance.

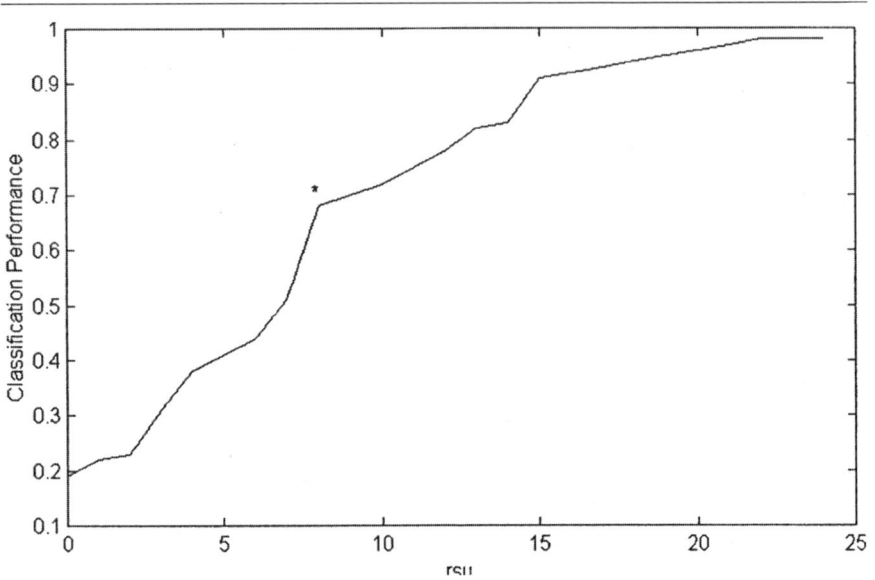

Figure 2. The selection of the appropriate ratio supervised/unsupervised parameter (rsu) by means of the classification performance plateaue.

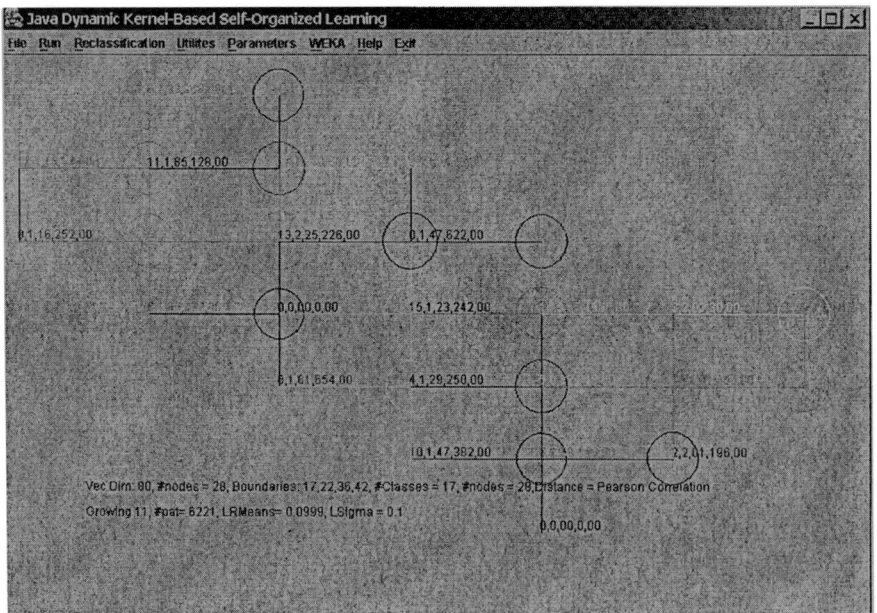

Figure 3. A snapshot of KSDG-SOM training.

Finally, Figure 3 illustrates a snapshot of KSDG-SOM learning. We can observe the dynamic extension of the map as it expands according to the rules of the growing phase. The Java based data mining tool based on KSDG-SOM is currently extended to provide modules for the extraction of fuzzy rules from the dynamically created clusters, and also a novel Support Vector Learning module is integrated to provide support for some supervised learning tasks. The current version of the software can be obtained with an email request to: sterg@teikav.edu.gr

7. CONCLUSIONS

This work has presented a new self-growing adaptive neural network model fitted to the requirements for clustering and classification of multi-labeled gene expression data. This model, called KSDG-SOM overcomes elegantly the main drawbacks of most of the existing clustering methods that impose an a priori specification at the number of clusters. The KSDG-SOM determines adaptively the number of clusters with a dynamic extension process which is able to exploit class information whenever available.

The KSDG-SOM nodes represent Gaussian kernel functions having mean and variances that are adapted on a per node basis. The model grows within a rectangular grid that provides the potential for the implementation of efficient training algorithms. The expansion of the KSDG-SOM is based on an adaptive process. This process grows nodes at the boundary nodes, ripples weights from the internal nodes towards the outer nodes of the grid, and inserts whole columns within the map. The growing algorithm is simple and computationally effective. It prefers to grow from the boundary nodes in order to minimize the map readjustment operations. However, a mechanism for whole column (row) insertion is implemented in order to deal with the case that a large map should be expanded around a point that is deep within its interior. The growing process determines automatically the appropriate level of expansion in order the similarity between the patterns of the same cluster to fulfill a designer definable statistical confidence level of not being a random event.

Multiple KSDG-SOM models are constructed dynamically each for a different unsupervised/supervised balance. Model selection criteria are used to select an KSDG-SOM model that optimizes the contribution of the unsupervised part of the patterns with the a priori knowledge (supervised part).   ·

Finally, we have presented the results of the application of the KSDG-SOM for the analysis of gene expression data sets. The methodology of exploring a priori knowledge about functional gene class labeling with gene expression data, along with the adaptive expansion process, has been used to obtain clusters of genes that balance supervised with unsupervised criteria.

8. ACKNOWLEDGMENT

This work was partially supported by the Technological Educational Institute of Kavalas, with a European Union funded EPEAK II project "Arximidis", code 04-3-001/5.

REFERENCES

[1] Van Hulle, N. M., "Kernel-Based Topographic Map Formation," Neural Computation, Vol. 14, No. 7, pp. 1560–1573, 2002.

[2] Van Hulle, N. M., "Joint Entropy Maximization in Kernel-Based Topographic Maps," Neural Computation, Vol. 14, No. 8, pp. 1887–1906, 2002.

[3] Van Hulle, N. M., "Kernel-based equiprobabilistic topographic map formation, Neural Computation, Vol. 10, No. 7, pp. 1847–1871, 2002.

[4] Alahakoon Damminda, Halgamuge Saman K., and Srinivasan Bala, "Dynamic Self-Organizing Maps with Controlled Growth for Knowledge Discovery," IEEE Transactions On Neural Networks, Vol. 11, No. 3, pp. 601–614, May 2000.

[5] Azuaje Franscisco, "A Computational Neural Approach to Support the Discovery of Gene Function and Classes of Cancer," IEEE Trans. Biomed. Eng., Vol. 48, No. 3, March 2001, pp. 332–339.

[6] Brazma Alvis, and Vilo Jaak, "Gene expression data analysis," FEBS Letters, 480 (2000) 17–24.

[7] Brown Michael P. S., Grundy William Noble, Lin David, Cristianini Nello, Sugnet Charles Walsh, Furey Terrence S., Ares Manuel, and Haussler Jr., David, "Knowledge-based Analysis of Microarray Gene Expression Data By Using Support Vector Machines," Proceedings of the National Academy of Science, Vol. 97, No. 1, pp. 262–267, 1997.

[8] Campos Marcos M., and Carpenter Gail A., "S-TREE: self-organizing trees for data clustering and online vector quantization," Neural Networks 14 (2001), pp. 505–525.

[9] Cheng Guojian and Zell Andreas, "Externally Growing Cell Structures for Data Evaluation of Chemical Gas Sensors," Neural Computing & Applications, 10, pp. 89–97, Springer-Verlag, 2001.

[10] Cheung Vivian G., Morley Michael, Aguilar Francisco, Massimi Aldo, Kucherlapati Raju, and Childs Geoffrey, "Making and reading microarrays," Nature genetics supplement, Vol. 21, January 1999.

[11] Eisen Michael B., Spellman Paul T., Patrick O. Brown, and David Botstein, "Cluster analysis and display of genome-wide expression patterns," Proc. Natl. Acad. Sci. USA, Vol. 95, pp. 14863–14868, December 1998.

[12] Friedman, N., M. Linial, I. Nachman, and D'Peier, "Using Bayesian networks to analyze expression data," J. Comp. Bio. 7, 2000, 601–620.

[13] Fritzke Bernd, "Growing Grid—a self organizing network with constant neighborhood range and adaptation strength," Neural Processing Letters, Vol. 2, No. 5, pp. 9–13, 1995.

[14] Hastie Trevor, Tibshirani Robert, Botstein David, and Brown Patrick, "Supervised Harvesting of expression trees," Genome Biology 2001, 2(1), http://genomebiology.com/2001/2/I

[15] Haykin S., Neural Networks, Prentice Hall International, Second Edition, 1999.

[16] Herrero Javier, Valencia Alfonso, and Dopazo Joaquin, "A hierarchical unsupervised growing neural network for clustering gene expression patterns," Bioinformatics, (2001) Vol. 17, no. 2, pp. 126–136.

[17] Kohonen T., Self-Organized Maps, Springer-Verlag, Second Edition, 1997.

[18] Mavroudi Seferina, Papadimitriou Stergios, and Bezerianos Anastasios, "Gene Expression Analysis with a Dynamically Extended Self-Organized Map that Exploits Class Information," Bioinformatics, Vol. 18, no. 11, 2002, pp. 1446–1453.

[19] Papadimitriou S., Mavroudi S., Vladutu L., and Bezerianos A., "Ischemia Detection with a Self Organizing Map Supplemented by Supervised Learning," IEEE Trans. On Neural Networks, Vol. 12, No. 3, May 2001, pp. 503–515.

[20] Sable, Carl L. and Vasileios Hatzivassiloglou, "Text-Based Approaches for the Categorization of Images, Proceedings of the Third Annual Conference on Research and Advanced Technology for Digital Libraries, Paris, 1999. pp. 19–38.

[21] Si J., Lin S., and Vuong M. A., "Dynamic topology representing networks," Neural Networks, 13, pp. 617–627, 2000.

[22] Tamayo, P., Slonim, D., Mesirov, J., Zhu, Q., Kitareewan, S., Dmitrovsky, E., Lander, E. S. and Golub, T. R. (1999) "Interpreting patterns of gene expression with self-organizing maps: methods and application to hematopoietic differentiation," Proc. Natl. Acad. Sci., USA, 92, pp. 2907–2912.

[23] Troyanskaya Olga, Cantor Michael, Shelock Gavin, Brown Pat, Hastie Trevor, Tibshirani Robert, Botstein David, and Altman Russ B., "Missing value estimation methods for DNA microarrays," Bioinformatics, Vol. 17, no. 6, 2001.

[24] Vesanto Juha Alhoniemi, Esa, "Clustering of the Self-Organized Map," IEEE Transactions on Neural Networks, Vol. 11, No. 3, May 2000, pp. 586–600.

COMPUTATIONAL INTELLIGENCE FOR FACILITY LOCATION ALLOCATION PROBLEMS

SHING-HWANG DOONG, CHIH-CHIN LAI AND CHIH-HUNG WU

1. INTRODUCTION

Due to the advancement of information technology and other supporting mechanisms, today's companies are doing businesses in a global market. Many international corporations accept worldwide orders via their world-wide-web (WWW) sites. By taking advantages of the Internet and WWW, companies can now operate 24 hours a day, 365 days a year, and reach as many customers as possible. This phenomenon has created a business model—the Electronic Commerce (EC) model that has caught a lot of research interests lately. No matter how an EC company is set up, its operations normally involve information flow, cash flow and goods flow; and unless goods can be packaged in a digital format such as software, music, or video, most goods still need to be distributed by some sort of physical channels. In a business to customer (B2C) EC company, the product distribution system might involve warehouse location and vehicle routing problems. On the other hand, for a business to business (B2B) EC company, the global logistic system becomes an essential part of its worldwide supply chain management system. Likewise, the logistic system can involve warehouse location and customer allocation problems.

1.1. Facility location problem

A facility location problem (*FLP*) is a planning problem to locate some useful facilities like warehouses or hospitals in such a way that the total cost for assigning facilities to satisfy the demand of customers is minimized. It is frequently considered as a site selection and resource allocation problem in Operations Research (*OR*). Suppose there are m possible sites for establishing the new facilities with the fixed opening cost of $f_i, i = 1, \ldots, m$ at each site, n existing customers each with a resource demand of $d_j, j = 1, \ldots, n$, and the unit allocation cost from the *i-th* site to the *j-th* customer is given by c_{ij}, then a *FLP* is defined as an optimization problem to select the best sites for serving customers' demand while the total cost is minimized. In terms of mathematical notation, let x_{ij} denote the fraction of the *j-th* customer's demand served by the *i-th* site and y_i the opening decision variable for the *i-th* site, then a *FLP* becomes the following optimization problem:

$$\underset{x_{ij}, y_i}{Min} \left(\sum_{i,j} x_{ij} \, d_j \, c_{ij} + \sum_i y_i f_i \right) \tag{1}$$

such that

$$\sum_{i=1}^{m} x_{ij} = 1, \quad j = 1, \ldots, n \tag{2}$$

$$x_{ij} \leq y_i, \quad i = 1, \ldots, m, j = 1, \ldots, n \tag{3}$$

$$0 \leq x_{ij} \leq 1, \quad i = 1, \ldots, m, j = 1, \ldots, n \tag{4}$$

$$y_i \in \{0, 1\}, \quad i = 1, \ldots, m \tag{5}$$

The minimization is taken over all feasible solutions of x_{ij}, y_i (decision variables) subject to the constraints in equations (2)–(5). Equation (2), called the demand constraint, states that each customer's demand must be satisfied; equation (3) says that the fractional request x_{ij} to site i cannot be greater then the opening decision variable y_i of the site, thus if the site is not selected for serving customers ($y_i = 0$), then all requests to the site should be denied. On the other hand, if a site i is selected for service ($y_i = 1$), then it is possible to allocate portions of the customers' requests to this site. Since opening a site incurs a fixed cost of f_i, which could be substantially large for some sites, it becomes obvious that we have to select the proper sites ($y_i = 1$) for service and determine the proper allocation (x_{ij}) in order to minimize the total cost in equation (1).

The problem we just stated is an un–capacitated facility location problem since there is no restriction on the amount that a site can provide. In reality, this is not the case in general. A capacitated facility location problem (*CFLP*) is a problem that each site has a limited capacity q_i; therefore in addition to the constraints in equations (2)–(5), we need to add the following capacity constraint for each site:

$$\sum_{j=1}^{n} x_{ij} d_j \leq y_i q_i, \quad i = 1, \ldots, m \tag{6}$$

If we further assume that the allocation variables x_{ij} can take only values of 0 or 1, then the *CFLP* becomes a Single Source Capacitated Facility Location Problem (*SSCFLP*).

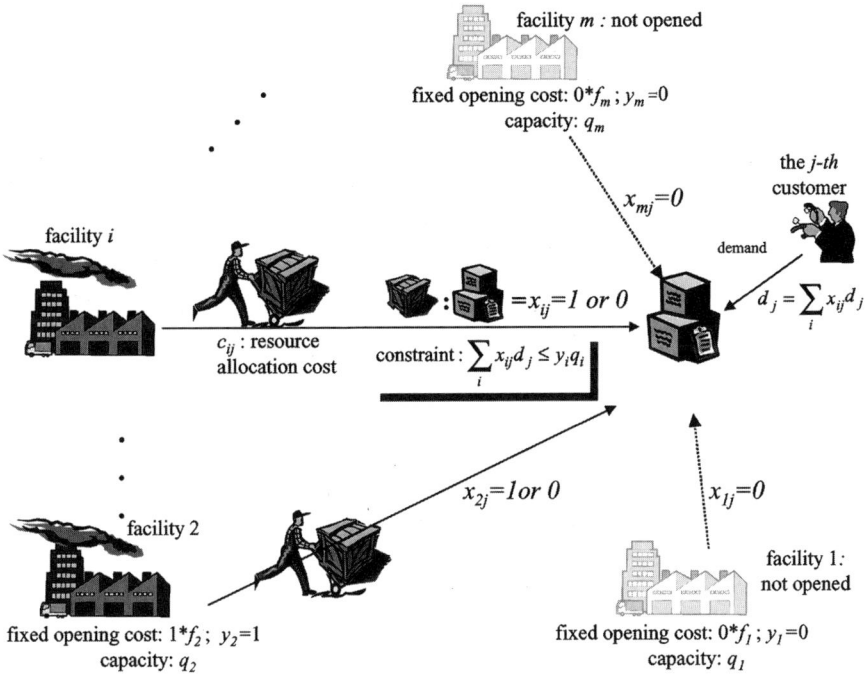

Figure 1. A single source capacitated facility problem.

A picture demonstrating this facility location problem is illustrated in Figure 1. When $x_{ij} = 1$ customer j's demand is completely fulfilled by site i, otherwise the customer is not served by the facility in any fraction. We usually rephrase a *SSCFLP* as follows:

$$\underset{x_{ij}, y_i}{Min} \left(\sum_{i,j} x_{ij}\, c_{ij} + \sum_{i} y_i\, f_i \right) \tag{7}$$

such that

$$\sum_{i=1}^{m} x_{ij} = 1, \quad j = 1, \ldots, n \tag{8}$$

$$\sum_{j=1}^{n} x_{ij}\, d_j \leq y_i\, q_i, \quad i = 1, \ldots, m \tag{9}$$

$$x_{ij} \leq y_i, \quad i = 1, \ldots, m, j = 1, \ldots, n \tag{10}$$

$$x_{ij} \in \{0, 1\}, \quad i = 1, \ldots, m, j = 1, \ldots, n \tag{11}$$

$$y_i \in \{0, 1\}, \quad i = 1, \ldots, m, \tag{12}$$

In this case, the cost coefficient c_{ij} already takes into account the quantity factor d_j therefore it is no longer necessary to include the quantity factor in the objective function in equation (7). However, equation (10) becomes redundant in the problem if we assume that each customer has a positive demand d_j. This can be verified in the following reasoning.

Proof: Suppose constraints in equation (10) are not satisfied by all i and j, then there must exist indices i', j' such that the following is true.

$$x_{i',j'} > y_{i'} \tag{13}$$

Since x_{ij}, y_i are binary (0 or 1) variables, equation (13) implies that $x_{i',j'} = 1$ and $y_{i'} = 0$. Using equation (9) for $i = i'$ and the non-negativity property of all quantities involved, we obtain

$$d_{j'} = x_{i',j'} d_{j'} \leq \sum_{j=1}^{n} x_{i'j} d_j \leq y_{i'} q_{i'} = 0 \tag{14}$$

Thus $d_{j'} \leq 0$, which violates the assumption that $d_{j'} > 0$.   □

The *FLP* we have discussed so far involves a cost factor c_{ij} for servicing customer j's demand from the facility at site i, and this cost factor is normally related to the distance between the parties. This can be fine if the customers are not too closely related geographically, for example, a B2B company needs to design its global logistic system so that it can set up a few warehouse facilities to serve its regional centers (customers). On the other hand, for a convenience store type company, the parent company may own its own fleet to deliver the products to its branch stores, which may be clustered in a few urban areas. Definitely, distance between the parties still matters in the determination of the cost factor, but a vehicle routing problem becomes obvious in this case too. In other words, if customers are clustered geographically such as the case of a B2C company, then a vehicle routing problem should also be considered in designing the facility locations. Klose and Wittmann consider this problem in [17].

1.2. Location-allocation problem

Most *OR* approaches to *FLP* assume that the site locations are already known, and the problem just needs to select the best sites to provide the service [1, 15, 17, 18]. Cooper [3] extends the problem to include the determination of the best locations as well. In other words, in addition to the site opening (y_i) and customer allocation (x_{ij}) decision variables, the facility's actual location (u_i, v_i) will also need to be determined. In this chapter, we consider a special facility location allocation problem named the Euclidean Location-Allocation Problem (*ELAP*). In the *ELAP* we need to determine the facility locations together with the site opening and customer allocation variables so that a performance measure is minimized under the constraints of a *SSCFLP*. The mathematical notation is summarized as follows:

$$\underset{x_{ij},\gamma_i,u_i,v_i}{Min} \quad (x_{ij}\,\alpha\sqrt{(u_i - a_j)^2 + (v_i - b_j)^2} + \gamma_i f_i) \tag{15}$$

such that

$$\sum_{i=1}^{m} x_{ij} = 1, \quad j = 1, \ldots, n \tag{16}$$

$$\sum_{j=1}^{n} x_{ij}\, d_j \leq \gamma_i q_i, \quad i = 1, \ldots, m \tag{17}$$

$$x_{ij},\, \gamma_i \in \{0, 1\} \tag{18}$$

Here (a_j, b_j) denotes the known location of the j-th customer, while (u_i, v_i) denotes the unknown location of the i-th facility. The cost factor c_{ij} in equation (7) is replaced by a constant α times the Euclidean distance between the facility and the customer. Equation (16) is the demand constraint, while equation (17) is the capacity constraint. Equation (18) indicates that a customer is served only by a facility (single sourcing), and a facility may or may not open for service depending on the magnitude of its opening cost f_i. Of course, we have dropped the redundant constraints of equation (10) in the ELAP. Bespamyatnikh et al. [2] discusses the location-allocation problem under different l_p norms besides the Euclidean distance which is the l_2 norm in particular.

1.3. Mathematical programming

In sections 1.1 and 1.2 we have introduced various versions of facility location problems from CFLP to SSCFLP and ELAP. All of these problems are optimization problems in operations research. However, they fall into different areas of mathematical programming, for example, CFLP is a mixed integer linear programming problem since part of its decision variables (x_{ij}) are continuous and part of the decision variables (γ_i) are discrete; SSCFLP is an integer linear programming problem since all variables are discrete; and ELAP is a mixed integer nonlinear programming (MINLP) problem since the objective function (15) involves the continuous variables (u_i, v_i) non-linearly.

All of these problems are non-convex programming problems because of the integer decision variables, thus they may present many local optima and looking for the global optimum becomes a non-trivial work. Indeed, it has been shown that these problems are all NP-hard problems [14, 18], i.e. there are no known algorithms with the polynomial growth constraint for the time complexity that can solve these optimization problems. Many NP-hard problems are caused by the facts that the search space for the discrete variables is too large, and there is no known necessary condition on these discrete variables that can be used to check for optimality efficiently. Therefore a smart enumeration of all feasible discrete solutions must be devised for (mixed) integer linear or nonlinear programming problems. For example, branch-and-bound and Lagrange relaxation [1, 5, 15, 23] methods are frequently used to solve an integer

Table 1 Characteristics of various FLPs

	CFLP	SSCFLP	ELAP
Variable types	Continuous and integer	Integer	Continuous and integer
Variable attributes	Customer allocation and facility opening decision	Customer allocation and facility opening decision	Customer allocation and facility opening decision, and facility location
Objective function	Linear in decision variables, equation (1)	Linear in decision variables, equation (7)	Nonlinear in decision variables, equation (15)
Mathematical programming classification	Mixed integer linear programming problem	Integer linear programming problem	Mixed integer nonlinear programming problem

linear programming problem in *SSCFLP*. These tools will be introduced in the next section. We summarize the characteristics of various *FLP*'s in Table 1.

1.4. Organization

The rest of this chapter is organized as follows. In section 2, we introduce some optimization tools and search techniques commonly used in operations research and artificial intelligence. Particularly, we discuss the branch-and-bound (*B&B*) algorithm, Lagrange relaxation and sub-gradient method, Genetic Algorithm (*GA*) and Simulated Annealing (*SA*) heuristic search methods. Section 3 is devoted to some hybrid methods for solving the *ELAP* viewed as a hierarchical optimization problem. We treat this mixed integer nonlinear programming (*MINLP*) problem via a two-layer procedure with *GA* as the top layer and *GA*, *B&B* or Lagrange relaxation as the bottom layer. In section 4, we treat the *MINLP* problem by using a mixed-type chromosome *GA*. In other worlds, the whole optimization problem is no longer layered as in section 3, and a single *GA* with mixed data types for genes is devised to solve the optimization problem. The traditional Alternate Location-Allocation (*ALA*) heuristic proposed by Cooper [3] will also be discussed here. Section 5 is devoted to a discussion of current optimization software, both commercial and non-commercial. In particular, we discuss the software packages and system used in this paper: PGAPack (Parallel *GA* package), UW IPMIXD (University of Wisconsin's mixed integer programming solver package), William Goffe's SA (Simulated Annealing) package, and NEOS (Network Enabled Optimization System) server. In section 6, we implement the proposed methods stated in sections 3 and 4 to solve an instance of the *ELAP*. We then compare the results with the one from the NEOS server. Finally, we conclude in section 7 with some remarks for future research.

2. BACKGROUND

This section provides the background knowledge for the tools used in this paper. Primarily, these tools come from two different areas in the research arena: operations research (*OR*) and artificial intelligence (*AI*). The *OR* based tools provide algorithmic and mathematically rigorous approach to the optimization problem, while the *AI* based tools provide heuristic and computationally intelligent search method for finding the optimum of an optimization problem.

2.1. Branch-and-bound

This is a smart partial enumeration method for solving optimization problems with discrete variables. Total enumeration of all feasible discrete solutions in a combinatorial problem is practical only when the solution space is small. If this is not true, then wise divide-and-conquer methods for partitioning the solution space are commonly needed in order to find the optimum solution quickly. Branch-and-bound (B&B) algorithm is a divide-and-conquer method, and it is traditionally the most efficient algorithm for solving integer programming problems. The idea is illustrated below.

Suppose we are dealing with the following integer linear programming problem:

$$\underset{x_i}{Min} \sum_{i=1}^{n} c_i x_i \tag{19}$$

subject to the constraints

$$A\vec{x} \leq \vec{b} \tag{20}$$

$$\vec{x} = (x_1, \ldots, x_n)^t \quad \text{integer vector} \tag{21}$$

where A is an m by n matrix defining m linear constraints on the integer variables $x_1, \ldots, x_n$. Equation (20) defines a polytope (a n-dimensional polygon) in R^n space. When we assume that the variables must be integral, then the feasible solutions consist of integer points inside the polytope.

Since there are good linear programming (LP) algorithms in OR, e.g. the simplex method or the interior point method [1, 5], that can solve the LP problem in equations (19) and (20) efficiently, we may first relax the integral condition in equation (21) to get an optimum value L_0. Because equation (21) is not considered in the relaxed LP problem, we have $L_0 \leq z^*$, the true optimum value of the integer programming problem. If all variables from this relaxed LP solution are integral, then L_0 is the optimum value to the original integer programming problem. Otherwise, this LP problem is divided into two sub-problems according to some separation rules. For example, suppose variable x_1 is non-integral, say $x_1 = 1.5$ from the relaxed LP problem, then since x_1 must be integral from the original problem, so we must have either $x_1 \leq 1$ or $x_1 \geq 2$. Thus we can implement a simple separation rule by adding these additional constraints to the LP problem and get two sub-problems. Each sub-problem consists of the same objective function (equation (19)), original linear constraints (equation (20)) and the additional linear constraint (either $x_1 \leq 1$ or $x_1 \geq 2$); these two sub-problems can be solved efficiently by the same LP solver to get two optimum values L_1 and L_2. Now suppose the first sub-problem gets an integer solution, then this sub-problem is fathomed, i.e. it is no longer necessary to search in this sub-problem. Obviously, $z^* \leq L_1$ since L_1 is the objective value of a feasible integer solution in a smaller domain, and L_1 becomes the incumbent optimum value of the original integer programming problem. A sub-problem becomes fathomed when any one of the following three conditions is met:

- The associated *LP* problem is not feasible, i.e. there is no feasible continuous solution in this case.
- The *LP* solution is integral, then this sub-problem deserves no further study since its *LP* solution provides the integer solution over the restricted domain of solution space. There are two possible outcomes from this case: (i) if the resulting optimum value is smaller than the incumbent optimum, then the incumbent optimum value is replaced by this smaller feasible objective value, the incumbent integer solution is updated, and the sub-problem is pruned from the branch-and-bound search tree; or (ii) if the resulting optimum value is larger, then the integer solution and the optimum value are discarded and this sub-problem is pruned from the branch-and-bound search tree, since we already have a better incumbent optimum solution.
- The *LP* solution is non-integral, and its optimum value is larger than the current incumbent optimum. In this case, the sub-problem should also be pruned from the branch-and-bound search tree, since we know that the integer solution of the *LP* problem over the same restricted domain of solution space should be higher than or equal to the relaxed *LP* solution. Thus there is no chance for this integer solution to beat the incumbent solution (in the minimization sense), and the sub-problem should be discarded as above.

When a sub-problem is fathomed, the branch of the search tree deriving from that sub-problem deserves no further study. We conclude that a sub-problem is not fathomed and deserves further study only when its solution is not integral and the *LP* solution offers a smaller optimum value than the incumbent optimum value. In this case, the sub-problem will need to be divided into two or more sub-problems according to the separation rules, and each sub-problem will be examined furthermore. This iterative procedure can be seen from Figure 2, which shows a branch-and-bound search tree with each node being a sub-problem derived from the original relaxed *LP* problem. The outcomes for solving a *LP* sub-problem are illustrated in Figure 3.

B&B is an exact method, i.e. it will find the optimum value if such one exists. However, from Figure 1 we see that it needs a tree search procedure to control the branching step in *B&B*. After solving a *LP* sub-problem and if it is not fathomed, then we put the resulted two or more sub-problems in a candidate list, which also includes sub-problems created from separating other non-fathomed sub-problems earlier. Which sub-problem from the candidate list becomes the next one to be examined is the important branching step in *B&B*. Since most integer programming problems are *NP*-hard, therefore if this branching step is not carefully designed, we might just search an extra ordinarily large tree before a solution is found. Besides the traditional backtracking or LIFO (last in first out) method, heuristic search methods such as Tabu search [11] may be used to improve the *B&B* algorithm. More information about *B&B* can be found in [1, 5].

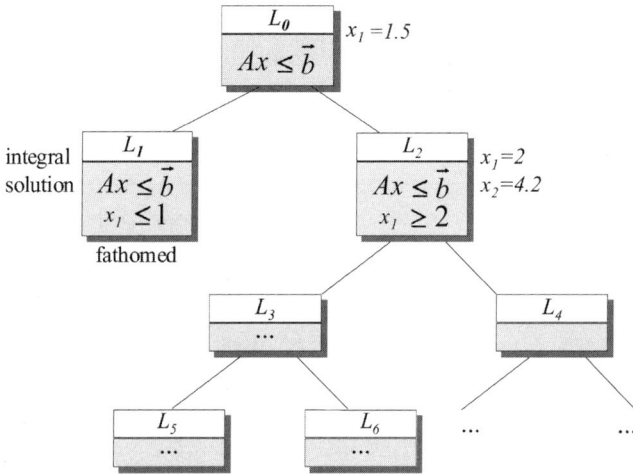

Figure 2. Branch and bound.

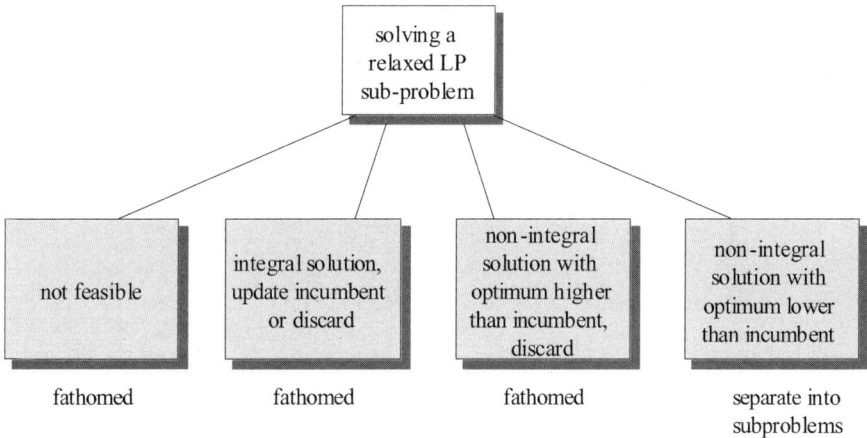

Figure 3. Outcomes for solving a relaxed *LP* sub-problem.

Cutting plane is another exact method that can be used to solve the integer programming problem in equations (19)–(21). Each separation step in *B&B* can be considered as
a partitioning of the feasible space into smaller regions (the divide step), and the branching and bounding step glues together pieces of information from these smaller regions
into a global picture (the conquer step). On the other hand, a cutting plane method
does not separate the feasible space into smaller regions, instead it shrinks the feasible
polytope into a smaller polytope such that the relaxed *LP* problem in this reduced
polytope produces an integer solution. Of course, in the process to reduce the original

polytope, we should not exclude any feasible integer solutions inside the polytope, and the way to do this is by using proper cutting planes to reduce the original polytope. Each cutting plane is represented by a linear constraint, hence finding the proper linear constraints and adding them to the constraints in equation (20) becomes crucial in the cutting plane method. Traditionally, cutting plane method converges slowly to the needed reduced polytope, i.e. we may need many linear constraints added to equation (20) before we can find a proper polytope; *B&B* method is preferred in solving integer linear programming problem. However, late development of polyhedral theory has improved this situation [19]. *B&B* may be combined with cutting plane to produce the branch-and-cut method. More information of this may be found in [1, 5, 19].

2.2. Lagrange relaxation and sub-gradient method

If branch-and-bound is said to relax the integral constraint of the integer variables, then Lagrange relaxation is used to relax the *hard* linear constraints in an integer linear programming problem. Holmberg et al. [15] devises a Lagrange heuristic for solving a *SSCFLP*. Below we introduce the Lagrange relaxation and sub-gradient optimization methods that are pertinent to one of our hybrid approaches.

Consider the following integer programming problem (P),

$$(P) \quad \underset{x_i}{Min} \sum_{i=1}^{n} c_i x_i$$

such that

$$A\vec{x} \leq \vec{b}$$
$$C\vec{x} \leq \vec{d}$$
$$\vec{x} = (x_1, \dots, x_n)^t \quad \text{integer vector}$$

In other words, we separate the constraints in equation (20) into two parts: the *hard* part $A\vec{x} \leq \vec{b}$ and the *easy* part $C\vec{x} \leq \vec{d}$. Lagrange relaxation begins with the process to relax the constraints on the hard part by constructing a Lagrangian associated with the problem (P). Suppose $\vec{u} = (u_1, \dots, u_m)^t$, $u_i \geq 0$ is a non-negative real-valued vector whose length is equal to the row number of the matrix A, i.e. the number of hard constraints. Then, the Lagrangian associated with the problem (P) for multipliers $\vec{u}$ is defined by solving the following problem $(L_{\vec{u}})$:

$$(L_{\vec{u}}) \quad L(\vec{u}) := \underset{x}{Min} \sum_{i=1}^{n} c_i x_i + \vec{u}^t (A\vec{x} - \vec{b}) \tag{22}$$

such that

$$C\vec{x} \leq \vec{d}$$
$$\vec{x} = (x_1, \dots, x_n)^t \quad \text{integer vector}$$

where the minimum is taken over *all* integral vectors $\vec{x}$ satisfying the *easy* constraints only. It is easy to show that for each $\vec{u} \geq \vec{0}$, $L(\vec{u}) \leq z^*$, the optimum value to problem (P) as follows.

Proof: Let the optimum value z^* be assumed by some integer solution $\vec{x}^*$, then $\vec{x}^*$ satisfies $\sum_{i=1}^{n} c_i x_i^* = z^*$, $A\vec{x}^* \leq \vec{b}$ and $C\vec{x}^* \leq \vec{d}$, since it is an optimum solution to problem (P). Now, because $\vec{x}^*$ is feasible to problem $(L_{\vec{u}})$ and by the definition of minimum, we have

$$\underset{x}{Min} \sum_{i=1}^{n} c_i x_i + \vec{u}^t (A\vec{x} - \vec{b}) \leq \sum_{i=1}^{n} c_i x_i^* + \vec{u}^t (A\vec{x}^* - \vec{b})$$

where the minimum is taken over the feasible space of problem $(L_{\vec{u}})$. The left hand side is $L(\vec{u})$ by definition, and the right hand side is less than or equal to $\sum_{i=1}^{n} c_i x_i^* = z^*$ since the second term is non-positive due to the facts that $\vec{u} \geq \vec{0}$ and $A\vec{x}^* \leq \vec{b}$. $\qquad\square$

Thus equation (22) provides a lower bound to z^* for any non-negative multiplier vector $\vec{u}$. Fisher [8] shows that a vector $\vec{u}^*$ solving the following Lagrange dual problem (LD),

$$(LD) \qquad l^* = \underset{\vec{u}}{Max} \, L(\vec{u}) \tag{23}$$

$$\vec{u} \geq \vec{0}$$

gives the best lower bound on z^* and that $z^{LP} \leq l^* \leq z^*$, where z^{LP} is the objective value by solving the *LP* relaxation of problem (P). The Lagrange relaxation method for the problem (P) then proceeds to solve the optimization problem posed by the dual problem (LD). Even though the dual problem (LD) is a continuous optimization problem, its objective function L may not be differentiable at every multiplier $\vec{u} \geq \vec{0}$, i.e. L may not be smooth. Common derivative based methods cannot be used to find an optimum solution for problem (LD).

The sub-gradient method proposed by Polyak [21] is frequently used to handle optimization problems with non-smooth objective functions. A vector $\vec{g}$ is called a sub-gradient of the Lagrangian function L at $\vec{u}$ if it satisfies

$$L(\vec{u}) \leq L(\vec{\bar{u}}) + \vec{g}^t (\vec{u} - \vec{\bar{u}}) \tag{24}$$

for any vector $\vec{u}$. L is sub-differentiable at $\vec{\bar{u}}$ if it has at least one sub-gradient at $\vec{\bar{u}}$. Now, suppose $\vec{\bar{x}}$ solves the optimization problem poised in equation (22) for $L(\vec{\bar{u}})$, i.e.

$$L(\vec{\bar{u}}) = \sum_{i=1}^{n} c_i \bar{x}_i + \vec{\bar{u}}^t (A\vec{\bar{x}} - \vec{b}) \tag{25}$$

We will show that the following formula yields a sub-gradient of L at $\vec{u}$.

$$\vec{g} := A\vec{x} - \vec{b} \tag{26}$$

Proof: Let $\vec{u}$ be any vector, then by the definition of $L(\vec{u})$ in equation (22) and the assumption of equation (25), we have

$$L(\vec{u}) - L(\vec{\bar{u}}) = \underset{x}{Min} \left(\sum_{i=1}^{n} c_i x_i + \vec{u}^t (A\vec{x} - \vec{b}) \right) - \left(\sum_{i=1}^{n} c_i \bar{x}_i + \vec{\bar{u}}^t (A\vec{\bar{x}} - \vec{b}) \right)$$

$$\leq \left(\sum_{i=1}^{n} c_i \bar{x}_i + \vec{u}^t (A\vec{\bar{x}} - \vec{b}) \right) - \left(\sum_{i=1}^{n} c_i \bar{x}_i + \vec{\bar{u}}^t (A\vec{\bar{x}} - \vec{b}) \right)$$

$$= (\vec{u}^t - \vec{\bar{u}}^t)(A\vec{\bar{x}} - \vec{b})$$

$$= \vec{g}^t (\vec{u} - \vec{\bar{u}})$$

Therefore L is sub-differentiable at $\vec{\bar{u}}$ and $\vec{g} = A\vec{\bar{x}} - \vec{b}$ as a sub-gradient of L at $\vec{\bar{u}}$.

$\square$

It is noted that L may have several different sub-gradients at $\vec{\bar{u}}$. Now, we illustrate these concepts in the following example.

Example: Suppose we want to solve the following integer linear programming problem,

(EP) $\underset{x_1, x_2}{Min} (3x_1 + 4x_2)$

such that

$x_1 + x_2 \leq 5$

$x_1 + 2x_2 \leq 8$

$x_1 + x_2 = 2$

x_1, x_2 are non-negative integers

Drawing the constraints of problem (EP) on the Cartesian plane (cf. Figure 4), we see that there are only 3 feasible solutions: $(x_1, x_2) = (2, 0)$, $(1, 1)$ or $(0, 2)$. Plugging these numbers into the objective function we obtain the optimum value of 6 given by the solution $(2, 0)$.

Suppose we consider the first two linear constraints *hard* and would like to relax them via non-negative Lagrange multipliers u_1, u_2, then the Lagrangian is defined as follows:

$(EL_{\vec{u}})$ $L(u_1, u_2) = \underset{x_1, x_2}{Min} \{3x_1 + 4x_2 + u_1(x_1 + x_2 - 5) + u_2(x_1 + 2x_2 - 8)\}$

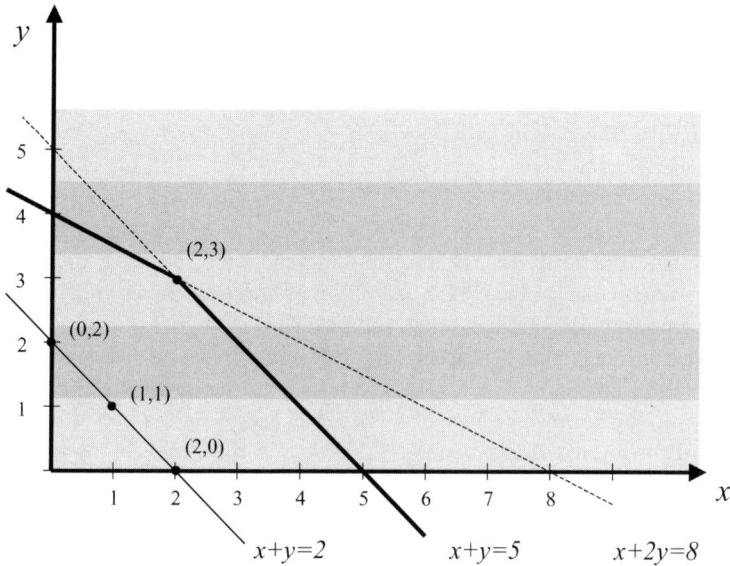

Figure 4. Feasible domain to an integer programming problem.

such that

$$x_1 + x_2 = 2$$

x_1, x_2 are non-negative integers

Constraints in problem $(EL_{\bar{u}})$ are definitely easier than those in problem (EP). Indeed, from the constraints, we immediately see that there are only 3 feasible solutions to problem $(EL_{\bar{u}})$ without drawing a graph: $(x_1, x_2) = (2, 0)$, $(1, 1)$ or $(0, 2)$. Therefore, $L(u_1, u_2)$ can be expressed as follows by substituting the feasible solutions into the objective function:

$$L(u_1, u_2) = Min \ (6 - 3u_1 - 6u_2, 8 - 3u_1 - 4u_2, 7 - 3u_1 - 5u_2)$$

Since the multipliers are non-negative, so the first term corresponding to the solution $(x_1, x_2) = (2, 0)$ gives the smallest number. Thus, the Lagrangian function is given by $L(u_1, u_2) = 6 - 3u_1 - 6u_2$, and the dual problem becomes:

$$(ELD) \quad \underset{u_1, u_2}{Max} \ L(u_1, u_2) = \underset{u_1, u_2}{Max} (6 - 3u_1 - 6u_2)$$

such that

$$u_1 \geq 0, u_2 \geq 0$$

Table 2 Sub-gradient iterative algorithm

---

choose an initial value $\vec{u}^{(0)}$
while (termination condition is not met)
{

  calculate a sub-gradient $g^{(k)}$ of $L(\vec{u})$ at $\vec{u}^{(k)}$
  $\vec{u}^{(k+1)} := \max(0, \vec{u}^{(k)} + \lambda_k \vec{g}^{(k)} / \|\vec{g}^{(k)}\|)$

}

Obviously this dual problem has an optimum value of 6, which is the same as the optimum value of the problem (*EP*). Also, the Largrangian function is differentiable at any legal point with a gradient (also, sub-gradient) of $(-3, -6)$.

Looking back at equation (24) we notice that the direction $\vec{u}$ that allows for the maximum variation of $L(\vec{u}) - L(\vec{\bar{u}})$ is given by a sub-gradient direction, i.e. $\vec{u} - \vec{\bar{u}}$ is in the same direction as $\vec{g}$. Therefore one could set $\vec{u} = \vec{\bar{u}} + \lambda \vec{g}$ for some positive λ in order to maximize the function $L(\vec{u})$. Based on this observation, a sub-gradient method is devised as an iterative method that is usually used to solve the Lagrange dual problem (*LD*) in equation (23). We list this method in Table 2.

A max of $\vec{0}$ and the adjustment along the sub-gradient direction is taken in order to guarantee that the multiplier vector is still non-negative in the next iteration:

$$\vec{u}^{(k+1)} := \max\left(\vec{0}, \vec{u}^{(k)} + \lambda_k \vec{g}^{(k)} / \|\vec{g}^{(k)}\|\right) \tag{27}$$

Commonly used termination conditions include when successive approximations do not change over a predefined threshold ($\|\vec{u}^{(k+1)} - \vec{u}^{(k)}\| < \varepsilon$) or the maximum iteration number has been reached. It is important to choose the right step size λ_k, since improper step size may make the iteration diverge. Polyak [21] proves that if the step size λ_k satisfies the following condition, then the sub-gradient algorithm converges.

$$\lambda_k \to 0 \quad \text{and} \quad \sum_{k=0}^{\infty} \lambda_k = \infty \tag{28}$$

2.3. Local search

A local search algorithm is a greedy algorithm. At any time of the local search process, there is always one incumbent point, which is assumed to be the current best solution of the problem. The procedure must define a neighborhood structure in the solution space for any given point. For example, if the decision variables are all continuous, then one might use the Euclidean distance to define a neighborhood for a solution point. On the other hand, if decision variables are discrete, the definition of a neighborhood structure becomes problem dependent. After the algorithm defines a neighborhood structure, it performs an iterative search procedure. In each iteration, the algorithm search for the best solution in the neighborhood of the incumbent solution, moves to that point and then continue the iteration. If a better solution cannot be found in

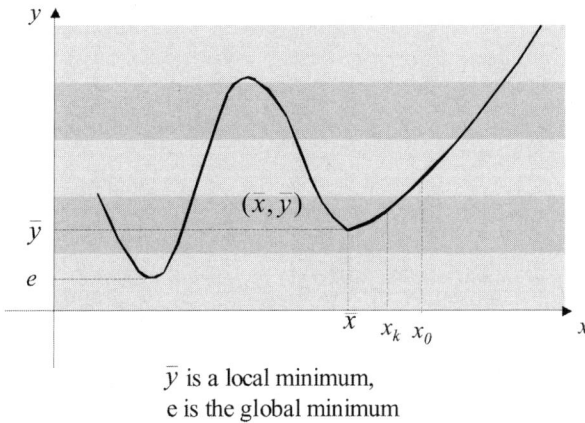

$\bar{y}$ is a local minimum,
e is the global minimum

Figure 5. Local search may be trapped at a local optimum.

Table 3 A generic local search algorithm

choose an initial solution u
while (better neighbor solution can be found)
{
    find the best point b in the neighborhood of u
    $u = b$
}

the neighborhood, then the procedure stops and the incumbent solution is returned as the best solution for the optimization problem. Since the procedure always moves to the best neighbor and stops moving when a better neighbor cannot be found, a local search algorithm may be trapped at a local optimum point as illustrated in Figure 5.

Because of the local optimality characteristics, which depend very much on the initial choice of the solution, if a local search algorithm is used to solve a global optimization problem such as *ELAP*, we may have to restart the algorithm several times with different seeds to avoid being trapped at a particular local optimum point. For some nonlinear optimization problems, there are quite a few local optimum points, thus many restarts of the local search algorithm must be done in order to get a good global optimum solution. Unfortunately, it is generally not known how many restarts must be done, and how the initial solutions must be chosen for a particular problem. A pseudo-code for the local search algorithm is given in Table 3.

2.4. Genetic algorithm

Genetic Algorithms (*GAs*) [9, 13, 20] are randomized search and optimization techniques guided by the principles of evolution and natural genetics, and have a large amount of implicit parallelism. They provide global near-optimal solutions of an

Table 4 Standard genetic algorithm

$t = 0$
evaluate population P_0
while (stopping criterion is not fulfilled)
{

   $P_{t+1} = \delta(P_t)$
   $t = t + 1$

}

objective or fitness function in complex, large, and multi-modal landscapes. In general, a GA contains a fixed-size population of potential solutions over the search space. These potential solutions of the search space are encoded as binary, integer or floating-point strings and called chromosomes. The initial population can be created randomly or based on the problem specific knowledge. In each iteration, called a generation, a new population is created based on a preceding one through the following three steps:

- Evaluation: each chromosome of the old population is evaluated using a fitness function and given a value to denote its merit
- Selection: chromosomes with better fitness are selected to generate next population
- Mating: genetic operators such as crossover and mutation are applied to the selected chromosomes to produce new chromosomes for the next generation

The above three steps are iterated for many generations until a satisfactory solution is found or a terminated criterion is met. A pseudo-code of a standard GA is shown in Table 4.

In this pseudo-code, δ denotes the so-called probabilistic transition operator that computes the next generation P_{t+1} from the current one P_t by taking the fitness of the chromosomes into account. Normally, δ is a composition of the various probabilistic operators such as selection, crossover, and mutation.

GAs have the following advantages over traditional search methods: (i) GAs directly work with a coding of the parameter set; (ii) search is carried out from a population of points instead of a single one as in the case of the local search or simulated annealing algorithm; (iii) pay-off information is used instead of derivatives or auxiliary knowledge; and (iv) probabilistic transition rules are used instead of deterministic ones [20].

2.5. Simulated annealing

Simulated Annealing (SA) is a one-point memory-less stochastic search method for finding global optimal solutions. Kirkpatrick et al. [16] presents a method of using the Metropolis Monte Carlo simulation to find the lowest energy orientation of a system. Their method simulates the annealing procedure used to make the strongest possible glass from melted glass. The SA procedure begins with an initial solution and a high temperature. Before moving to a lower temperature, SA tries a fixed number of neighbor points in random order to find a better solution with lower objective value, suppose we are solving a minimization problem. It is important that the procedure does not always move to a better solution like a greedy local search algorithm does. At times, SA allows the current point to be replaced by an inferior solution with a higher objective value. However, these kind of inferior replacements depend very much on the current temperature. Roughly speaking, when the temperature is high, then the probability of moving to an inferior solution is higher, and when the temperature is cooled down, it is less likely to make an inferior movement. This phenomenon simulates the annealing procedure of melted glass, where atoms are allowed to make bigger movements at high temperature, and stabilize within a relatively fixed region when the temperature is down.

Let $f(x)$ denote the function to be minimized, x_0 an initial solution and T_0 an initial temperature. Besides these two initial data, one needs to define the following three elements before an SA procedure can be executed:

- a neighborhood structure for each solution
- the number N of Metropolis Monte Carlo simulations performed at each temperature level
- an annealing schedule, i.e. a schedule to bring down the temperature

The procedure picks a random point from the neighborhood of the current solution. If the new objective value is lower, then movement to the new point is accepted and the current point is replaced. On the other hand, if the new point has a higher objective value, say $f(x_{new}) > f(x_0)$, then the new point is accepted and becomes the current point with the probability $e^{-(\frac{f(x_{new})-f(x_0)}{T})}$ where T is the current temperature. Notice that when the temperature T is high, then by dilution through this high temperature a larger increase $(f(x_{new}) - f(x_0))$ of objective values is allowed with a reasonable level of acceptance probability. This random neighborhood search, a Metropolis Monte

Table 5 Simulated annealing procedure for minimization

```
/* minimize f(x)*/
picks x0, T0
while (stopping criterion is not fulfilled) {
    do the following N times {
        pick a neighbor xnew of x0 randomly
        if (f(xnew) < f(x0) ) {
            x0 ← xnew
        }
        else {
            pick a random number r from the uniform distribution over (0, 1)
            if (r < e^{-(\frac{f(xnew)-f(x0)}{T0})}) {
                x0 ← xnew
            }
        }
    }
    T0 = cT0;
}
```

Carlo simulation, is repeated for a preset number of times before the temperature is lowered down. The temperature is lowered down according to an annealing schedule. A commonly used schedule is to reduce the temperature by a fixed constant, for example $T_{new} = cT_0$ where $c < 1$. The pseudo code for an *SA* procedure is illustrated in Table 5.

3. HYBRID METHOD FOR LOCATION-ALLOCATION PROBLEM

After introducing the needed tools in section 2, we proposed three hybrid methods for solving the Euclidean Location-Allocation Problem (*ELAP*) considered as a Mixed Integer Non-Linear Programming (*MINLP*) problem. The hybrid methods separate decision variables into two groups: the continuous variables for locating facilities, and the discrete variables for allocating facilities to customers. The continuous variables are treated by a top layer Genetic Algorithm (*GA*) followed by a local search method, while the discrete variables are found by solving a Single Source Capacitated Facility Location Problem (*SSCFLP*), which results from the facility locations encoded in a chromosome of the top layer *GA*, and will be solved by three different methods, namely a second layer *GA*, a branch-and-bound (*B&B*) method, and a Lagrange relaxation with sub-gradient method. A separation of variables is mathematically rigorous because of a nice property of the *Min* operator:

$$\operatorname*{Min}_{\vec{x}, \vec{y}} f(\vec{x}, \vec{y}) = \operatorname*{Min}_{\vec{x}} \left(\operatorname*{Min}_{\vec{y}} f(\vec{x}, \vec{y}) \right) \tag{29}$$

We check this in the following.

Proof: Let $m = \operatorname*{Min}_{\vec{x}, \vec{y}} f(\vec{x}, \vec{y})$ denote the minimum of the objective function over the problem domain. Since we have

$$m \le f(\vec{x}, \vec{y})$$

for all possible $(\vec{x}, \vec{y})$ in the domain, taking the minimum of the right hand side repeatedly with respective to $\vec{y}$ and then $\vec{x}$ gives us

$$m \le \operatorname*{Min}_{\vec{x}} (\operatorname*{Min}_{\vec{y}} f(\vec{x}, \vec{y}))$$

because the left hand side is a constant. This shows one direction of the inequalities needed to establish the equality in equation (29).

Now we prove the reverse inequality. Suppose the minimum m is assumed by some $\vec{x}_0, \vec{y}_0$, i.e. $f(\vec{x}_0, \vec{y}_0) = m$, then by the definition of minimum with respect to $\vec{y}$, we have

$$f(\vec{x}_0, \vec{y}_0) \ge \operatorname*{Min}_{\vec{y}} f(\vec{x}_0, \vec{y}).$$

Consider $g(\vec{x}) = \underset{\vec{y}}{Min} f(\vec{x}, \vec{y})$ as a function of $\vec{x}$, then by the definition of minimum again we have $g(\vec{x}_0) \geq \underset{\vec{x}}{Min} g(\vec{x})$, i.e.

$$\underset{\vec{y}}{Min} f(\vec{x}_0, \vec{y}) \geq \underset{\vec{x}}{Min} \left(\underset{\vec{y}}{Min} f(\vec{x}, \vec{y}) \right).$$

By the transitivity of inequality, we prove the reverse inequality

$$m = f(\vec{x}_0, \vec{y}_0) \geq \underset{\vec{x}}{Min} \left(\underset{\vec{y}}{Min} f(\vec{x}, \vec{y}) \right). \qquad \square$$

In view of equation (29) while trying to minimize the objective function in the *ELAP*, we may select to minimize the function with respect to the allocation variables (playing the role of $\vec{y}$ in equation (29)) first for a fixed set of location variables (playing the role of $\vec{x}$ in equation (29)), and then minimize the resulted function with respect to the location variables.

More specifically, the facility location variables are encoded in chromosomes of the top layer *GA*, which evolves through sufficiently many generations to get a near optimal solution to the *ELAP*. The fitness value of a chromosome is evaluated by solving a *SSCFLP* that results from the *ELAP* by substituting the encoded facility location data into equation (15). A flowchart for the hybrid methods is illustrated in Figure 6.

3.1. Nested GA (GA + GA)

The structure of a two layer *GA* is illustrated in Table 6. The method is to create and combine two different populations consistently; i.e. the approach controls and optimizes both populations of the location and allocation variables simultaneously in order to solve the *MINLP* problem. The top layer *GA* first creates a population of chromosomes for the potential facility location, and then corresponding to a chromosome in this population a bottom layer *GA* creates a population of the allocation variables. The fitness value of a chromosome in the top layer *GA* is given by the best objective value returned from the bottom *GA* specifically prepared for that top layer chromosome.

3.2. GA + Branch and Bound

Doong et al. [7] recognize that when the continuous location variables are given, one can calculate the cost factors c_{ij} and the *ELAP* becomes a *SSCFLP*, which is an integer linear programming problem. Branch-and-bound (*B&B*) is commonly used to solve an integer programming problem as indicated in section 2.1. Therefore, the second hybrid method that we propose is to combine *GA* with *B&B* for solving the *EALP*. The location variables will be encoded as a chromosome in the *GA* procedure, and its fitness value is calculated by solving the *SSCFLP* problem with the *B&B* method. *B&B* method will determine the allocation variables once the location variables are given.

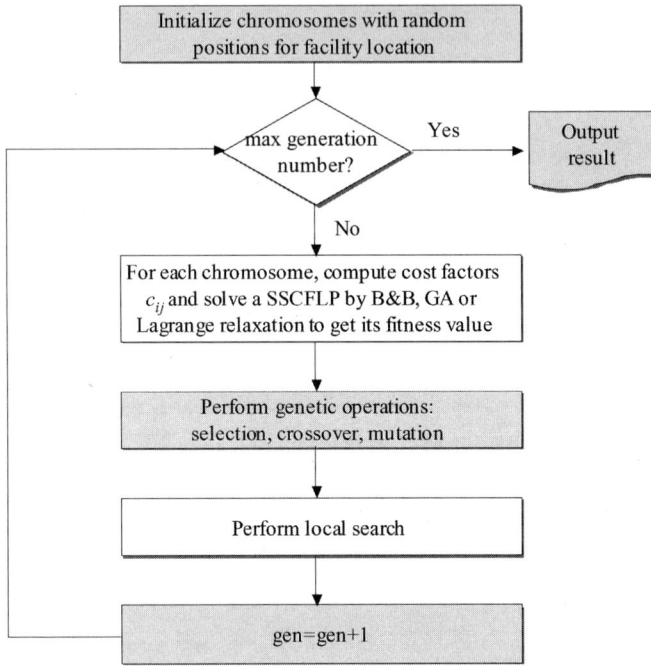

Figure 6. Flowchart for the hybrid methods.

Table 6 Two layer genetic algorithm

Top-layer genetic algorithm	Bottom-layer genetic algorithm
$t_1 = 0$	$t_2 = 0$
initialize $P(t_1)$	initialize $P(t_2)$
evaluate $P(t_1)$: **for each individual**	evaluate $P(t_2)$
do Bottom-layer genetic algorithm	while (termination condition is not met)
while (termination condition is not met)	{
{	$t_2 = t_2 + 1$
$t_1 = t_1 + 1$	select $P(t_2)$ from $P(t_2 - 1)$
select $P(t_1)$ from $P(t_1 - 1)$	recombine $P(t_2)$
recombine $P(t_1)$	evaluate $P(t_2)$
evaluate $P(t_1)$: **for each individual**	}
do Bottom-layer genetic algorithm	
}	

3.3. GA + Lagrange

Gong et al. [12] solves an *ELAP* by hybridizing *GA* with a Lagrange relaxation and sub-gradient method. However, they do not consider the fixed cost f_i and its associated decision variable y_i for opening a facility. In this section, we will show that with these quantities considered, the resulted *SSCFLP* is still solvable by a Lagrange relaxation and sub-gradient method. We summarize the *SSCFLP* as follows:

$$\underset{x_{ij}, y_i}{Min} \ (x_{ij} \ c_{ij} + y_i \ f_i) \tag{30}$$

where

$$c_{ij} = \alpha \sqrt{(u_i - a_j)^2 + (v_i - b_j)^2} \tag{31}$$

subject to the following conditions

$$\sum_{i=1}^{m} x_{ij} = 1, \quad j = 1, \dots, n \tag{32}$$

$$\sum_{j=1}^{n} x_{ij} \ d_j \le y_i q_i, \quad i = 1, \dots, m \tag{33}$$

$$x_{ij}, \ y_i \in \{0, 1\} \tag{34}$$

By considering equation (33) as the *hard* constraint and include it in the associated Lagrangian we get:

$$L(u_1, \dots, u_m) := \underset{x_{ij}, y_i}{Min} \sum_{i,j} x_{ij} \ c_{ij} + \sum_{i} y_i \ f_i + \sum_{i} u_i \left(\sum_{j} x_{ij} d_j - y_i q_i \right) \tag{35}$$

$$= \underset{x_{ij}, y_i}{Min} \sum_{i,j} x_{ij} \ (c_{ij} + u_i d_j) + \sum_{i} y_i (f_i - u_i q_i) \tag{36}$$

subject to constraints in equations (32) and (34). This Lagrangian can be easily solved for x_{ij}, y_i given any multiplier $(u_1, \dots, u_m) \ge \vec{0}$, thus we can find a sub-gradient for the Lagrangian function $L(u_1, \dots, u_m)$ and use the sub-gradient method (equations (26) and (27)) to maximize it.

The first sum in equation (36) can be rewritten as

$$\sum_{j} \left(\sum_{i} x_{ij} \ (c_{ij} + u_i d_j) \right). \tag{37}$$

Given any j we can find an $i_0 = i_0(j)$, such that $c_{i_0 j} + u_{i_0} d_j$ is the smallest, i.e.

$$c_{i_0 j} + u_{i_0} d_j = \underset{i}{Min} \ (c_{ij} + u_i d_j) \tag{38}$$

By the demand and single sourcing constraints (equations (32) and (34)), we can define

$$x_{ij} = \begin{cases} 1, & i = i_0(j) \\ 0, & i \ne i_0(j) \end{cases} \tag{39}$$

This will make equation (37) as small as possible, given c_{ij}, d_j, u_i.

After taking care of the x_{ij} variables, we can solve for the y_j variables by making the second sum of equation (36) as small as possible. The following definition of y_j will make the second sum of equation (36) the minimum, given q_i, f_i, u_i.

$$y_i = \begin{cases} 1, & f_i - u_i q_i \leq 0 \\ 0, & f_i - u_i q_i > 0 \end{cases} \tag{40}$$

Equations (39) and (40) together will solve the optimization problem in equation (36) subject to constraints in equations (32) and (34), given c_{ij}, d_j, q_i, f_i, u_i. In other words, they solve the minimization problem posed by the definition of the Lagrangian $L(u_1, \ldots, u_m)$. Hence according to equation (26), the formula

$$g_i = \sum_j x_{ij} d_j - y_i q_i \tag{41}$$

defines a sub-gradient for the Lagrangian $L(u_1, \ldots, u_m)$.

Now suppose $u_i^{(k)}$ is the k-th iterative approximation to the maximizing multiplier, $x_{ij}^{(k)}$ and $y_i^{(k)}$ are the Lagrangian solutions defined by equations (39) and (40) given this value of the multiplier, then equation (27) gives us the following iterative formula for solving the Lagrange dual (LD) problem, provided that the step size λ_k is chosen properly.

$$u_i^{(k+1)} = \max\left(0, u_i^{(k)} + \lambda_k \left(\sum_j x_{ij}^{(k)} d_j - y_i^{(k)} q_i\right) \Big/ \|\vec{q}^{(k)}\|\right) \tag{42}$$

4. MIXED TYPE CHROMOSOME AND ALTERNATE LOCATION ALLOCATION

Besides those hybrid methods in section 3 for solving the *ELAP*, we discuss two more possible approaches in this section. The first one is to utilize the highly adaptable feature of the data types encoded for chromosomes in a Genetic Algorithm (*GA*) to create a mixed type chromosome *GA* to handle the Mixed Integer Non-Linear Programming (*MINLP*) problem; and the second one is the traditional Alternate Location-Allocation (*ALA*) heuristic method proposed by Cooper [3].

Section 3 uses equation (29) to translate a *joint* multivariable minimization problem into a *repeated* multivariable minimization problem. From the separation of variables, we use a *GA* to treat the location variables, and a *GA* (section 3.1), a *B&B* (section 3.2) or a *Lagrange relaxation* (section 3.3) method to solve the allocation problem. Since *GA* is a versatile optimization algorithm, especially in its ability to encode complex data types in the chromosome, we can devise a *GA* with mixed-type genes to represent a solution vector for the *ELAP*. A mixed-type chromosome consists of real-valued genes for the facility locations, and integer-valued genes for the customer allocations. Pierrot et al. [22] used a mixed-type *GA* to solve an optimization problem with a simple objective function. In this chapter, we implement a mixed-type *GA* for the

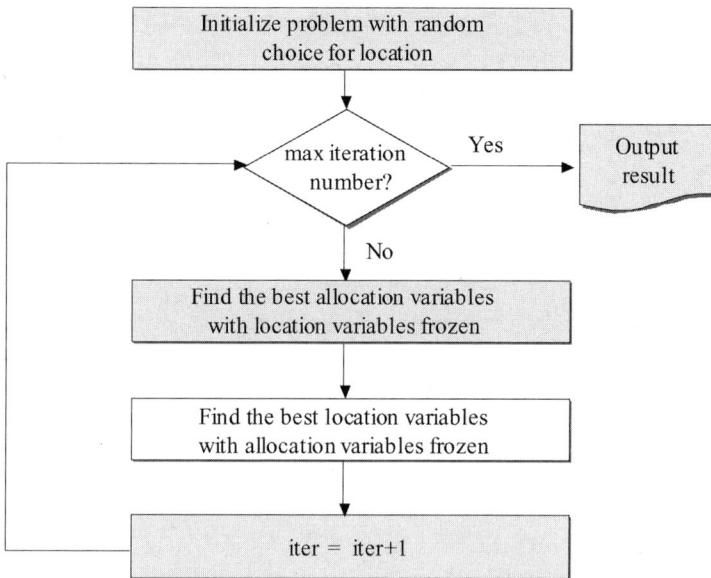

Figure 7. Flowchart for the *ALA* method.

ELAP, which has a more complicated objective function, and compare the result with the ones from other methods.

The *ALA* heuristic method proposed by Cooper [3] was considered efficient for solving location-allocation type problems. The philosophy of the method is simple: solve the location and allocation problems in alternating turns. For example, in *ALA* method, initial location variables are first randomly selected, then one solves the allocation problem with these location variables fixed. Once we get the new allocation variables, we can use them to solve for the location problem, this time with the allocation variables fixed. The procedures of solving location problem with the allocation variables fixed and solving allocation problem with the location variables fixed take turns in alternating style. Like a local search algorithm, *ALA* finds a local optimum solution that depends pretty much on the initial selection of the location variables. Therefore a couple of *ALA* procedures must be performed with different seeds to get a better global solution in *ELAP*. We will use a simulated annealing procedure (section 2.4) as the location problem solver and a branch–and–bound method as the allocation problem solver to implement the *ALA* method. A flowchart of the *ALA* method is depicted in Figure 7.

5. CURRENT OPTIMIZATION SOFTWARE

In this section we discuss some optimization software that are either commercially available with a fee or freely downloadable from the Internet. The Optimization Technology Center at Argonne National Laboratory and Northwestern University (http://www.ece.northwestern.edu/OTC/) provides a good resource for solving optimization problems. We summarize special features of a couple of optimization packages in the following. Some of them can solve mixed integer linear programming problems very well, but cannot solve the mixed integer non-linear optimization problem presented in the *ELAP*.

- CPLEX—ILOG CPLEX (http://www.ilog.com/products/cplex/) provides optimizers for solving linear, mixed integer and quadratic programming problems. It is widely used to solve large systems of mixed integer programming problems. Many heuristic method designers for mixed integer programming problems seem to prefer to compare their results with the one from the CPLEX system. However, the mixed integer programming solver in CPLEX can solve only linear and quadratic type objective function, and thus is not applicable in the *ELAP*, where the continuous location variables appear inside the square root function (equation (15)).
- LINGO—This is a commercial optimization package available from the Lindo System, Inc. (http://www.lindo.com). It is one of the software that can solve linear and nonlinear mixed integer programming problems. The package offers its own modeling language that can be easily used to represent the users' problems. The system can be used to solve the *ELAP* like the following NEOS server. However, the downloadable test version of LINGO can only solve a very small size *ELAP* due to its restriction on the number of available variables.
- NEOS—Network Enabled Optimization System (http://www-neos.mcs.anl.gov/) is an Internet-based optimization service [4]. The system is supported by the National Science Foundation and the Department of Energy, and currently maintained by Argonne National Laboratory. There are a couple of remote servers around the world to help solve the optimization problems, which can be submitted via a Web interface. NEOS solvers represent the state-of-the-art technology in optimization software, and there are a couple of optimization packages available from the system. Among these packages, *MINLP* (Mixed Integer Nonlinearly Constrained Optimization package) has interested us the most since others are not able to handle the objective function in the *ELAP* appropriately. Program inputs can be prepared in one of two formats: AMPL and GAMS. We use NEOS for the comparison purpose since it is the only system that is freely available and can do mixed integer nonlinear programming problems needed in the *ELAP*.
- PGAPack—Parallel Genetic Algorithm package is an implementation of *GA* in a parallel format. The package is developed by David Levine of the Mathematics and Computer Science Division at Argonne National Laboratory. (http://www-fp.mcs.anl.gov/ccst/research/reports_pre1998/comp_bio/stalk/pgapack.html). Objective function evaluation in a *GA* is the most tedious part of the algorithm. It is highly desirable if one can parallelize this part of the *GA* procedure. Due to the facts that fitness evaluation in a population is quite independent for each chromosome and the current information technology has improved the parallel computing technology to a very usable stage, parallel *GA* computation thus is thought to be viable lately. PGAPack uses the MPI message passing interface library to distribute

function evaluations to a cluster of computers or different CPUs in a multi-processor computer. Besides the parallel computing feature, PGAPack also has some other nice features such as

- Callable from Fortran or C
- Binary-, integer-, real-, and character-valued native data types
- Parameterized population replacement
- Multiple choices for selection, crossover, and mutation operators
- Easy integration of hill-climbing heuristics
- Fully extensible to support custom operators and new data types
- Runs on uniprocessors, parallel computers, and workstation networks

We use PGAPack as the GA procedure for solving either continuous or discrete optimization problems since it provides convenient calling procedure (from C or Fortran), versatile data structure for representing chromosomes, implementation structure (parallel or single), and the package is freely available.

- UW IPMIXD—This is a mixed integer linear programming solver developed by the Division of Information Technology (DoIT) at the University of Wisconsin – Madison. It is freely downloadable as Fortran source codes at the site: http://www.wisc.edu/mathsoft/m14e.html. The package uses a branch-and-bound ($B\&B$) method (section 2.1) to solve small to medium sized integer programming problems. User must write their Fortran main programs to call the package as a subroutine. We primarily use this package as the $B\&B$ solver in the hybrid $GA + B\&B$ method (section 3.2) and in the ALA method (section 4) for solving the allocation variables in the $ELAP$.

- William Goffe's SA—This implementation of simulated annealing was used in the 1994 paper of Goffe et al. in Journal of Econometrics. A Fortran source code is available from http://emlab.berkeley.edu/Software/abstracts/goffe895.html. It implements the continuous simulated annealing global optimization algorithm described in Corana et al.'s 1987 article "Minimizing Multi-modal Functions of Continuous Variables with the Simulated Annealing". The software requires a user to write a Fortran main program to set up the optimization environment and call the package as a subroutine. It allows the user to specify an initial solution, a temperature reduction factor, a number of Metropolis Monte Carlo simulation at each temperature level, and an acceptable tolerance for terminating the temperature reduction cycle. We use this package in the ALA method for solving the continuous location variables in the $ELAP$ (section 4).

6. EXPERIMENTS

To test the efficiency and accuracy of the proposed methods in sections 3 and 4, we prepare a set of artificial data for experiment. There are 50 customers and 5 facilities in the data. Customers' locations and demands are randomly generated as indicated in Table 7, and so are facility capacities and opening costs in Table 8. The objective function and constraints are listed in equation (15)–(18), where we set $\alpha = 4$. We summarize the parameters setting in each of the heuristic methods in the following.

Table 7 Customer locations and demands for the test set

j	1	2	3	4	5	6	7	8	9	10
a_j	439.0	340.0	314.0	365.0	393.0	591.0	119.0	381.0	458.0	869.0
b_j	360.0	548.0	261.0	597.0	493.0	571.0	700.0	962.0	750.0	740.0
d_j	12	35	20	44	43	43	17	49	37	32
j	11	12	13	14	15	16	17	18	19	20
a_j	934.0	264.0	160.0	872.0	237.0	645.0	966.0	664.0	870.0	99.0
b_j	431.0	634.0	803.0	839.0	945.0	915.0	602.0	253.0	873.0	513.0
d_j	20	49	21	24	40	11	24	28	30	15
j	21	22	23	24	25	26	27	28	29	30
a_j	137.0	818.0	430.0	890.0	734.0	687.0	346.0	166.0	155.0	191.0
b_j	732.0	422.0	961.0	721.0	553.0	292.0	858.0	335.0	680.0	534.0
d_j	47	47	33	47	17	38	18	38	36	34
j	31	32	33	34	35	36	37	38	39	40
a_j	422.0	856.0	490.0	815.0	460.0	457.0	450.0	412.0	901.0	56.0
b_j	356.0	498.0	434.0	562.0	616.0	113.0	898.0	754.0	791.0	815.0
d_j	41	23	31	16	29	44	22	15	38	32
j	41	42	43	44	45	46	47	48	49	50
a_j	297.0	492.0	693.0	650.0	983.0	552.0	400.0	198.0	625.0	733.0
b_j	670.0	200.0	273.0	626.0	536.0	595.0	890.0	271.0	409.0	474.0
d_j	41	17	46	14	35	11	45	25	23	25

Table 8 Facility capacity for the test set

i	1	2	3	4	5
q_i	500.0	300.0	300.0	200.0	400.0
f_i	500.0	400.0	400.0	600.0	700.0

• Nested GA (section 3.1)

The top layer GA for location variables has 10 real coded genes in a chromosome. A population of 20 chromosomes is maintained in each generation, and a stopping criterion of 2000 generations is implemented in a run of this nested GA hybrid method. The bottom layer GA will decide the discrete variables consisting of 50 allocation variables and 5 facility opening indicators. Because of the single sourcing condition, each customer can only be allocated to a single facility, therefore instead of using 250 binary variables x_{ij} to indicate the allocation variables, we simply use 50 integer variables z_j where each z_j is between 1 and 5 and indicates the facility number selected for the j-th customer. This layer of GA has 55 integral genes in a chromosome, and a population of 110 chromosomes is used in each generation. A stopping criterion of maximum 500 generations is implemented in a run of this GA layer. Initial populations of both GA are randomly generated. Default crossover operator and rate, and default mutation operator and rate from PGAPack in last section are used in this experiment. The fitness value of a chromosome in the top layer GA is evaluated when the bottom layer GA has found the best allocation values with the given facility locations specified in the chromosome.

- *GA + B&B* (section 3.2)

Again, the setting of the top layer *GA* procedure for the location variables is the same as the one in last paragraph. Now, once a chromosome has fixed the facility locations, we can calculate the coefficients $\alpha\sqrt{(u_i - a_j)^2 + (v_i - b_j)^2}$ in equation (15) and use a *B&B* method to solve this mixed integer programming (*MIP*) problem. The near optimum value from solving this *MIP* problem becomes the fitness value for the chromosome giving the facility locations. We use the UW IPMIXD package to solve this *MIP* problem, where there are 255 binary variables (x_{ij} and y_i) and 55 linear constraints (50 demand constraints and 5 capacity constraints).

- *GA + Lagrange relaxation* (section 3.3)

The setting of the *GA* for the continuous location variables is just the same as the last two methods. However, this time we use a Lagrange relaxation and sub-gradient method to solve the resulted *SSCFLP* from a location chromosome. A zero vector is chosen for the initial multiplier vector, and equation (27) is iterated 100000 times with the following step size

$$\lambda_k = \frac{1}{10000 + k}.$$

This choice of the step size fits equation (28) quite well.

- *Mixed type chromosome* (section 4)

Again, we use PGAPack in last section to solve the mixed integer nonlinear programming problem posed by the ELAP. Since mixed type chromosome is not a native type chromosome used in PGAPack, we have to use a user-defined type chromosome consisting of 10 real coded genes and 55 integer coded genes to represent a solution point in the search space. A population of 4 times the length (65) of a chromosome is maintained in each generation, and a maximum of 20000 generations of genetic operations is implemented in a single run of the procedure.

- *ALA* (section 4)

To start with, we generate the initial facility locations randomly from the square that encloses all the customers' locations. Then, the UW IPMIXD *B&B* solver is used to find the allocation variables from this set of facility locations. When the new allocation variables are found, we use William Goffe's Simulated Annealing (*SA*) in last section to determine the new location variables. Alternating steps of *B&B* and *SA* for deciding allocation and location variables are performed 100 times to get the final answer from the *ALA* heuristic method. A 0.5 temperature reduction factor and 1000 function evaluations at each temperature level are used in the *SA* procedure. The *SA* procedure terminates when the final objective values of the last four temperature levels have not changed more than 10^{-6}.

A Fermat problem is a location problem where one wants to find a point on the plane such that the sum of its distances to the three given points is minimum. This problem was solved by Torricelli by geometric argument, and the solution point is called a Fermat or Torricelli point. A generalized Fermat problem is to find a point that minimizes the sum of its distances to more than 3 given points on the plane.

Courant et al. [6] refers to these types of problems as the Steiner's problem. Looking back at the equations (15)–(18), when we fix the allocation variables, deciding the best facility locations becomes several independent generalized Fermat problems because of the single sourcing constraint. The single sourcing constraint assigns a group of customers to a facility, and the facility location is determined by minimizing the sum of distances between the facility and the assigned customers. (The actual objective function in equation (15) is $\alpha = 4$ times the sum of the distances.) However, we are not using the closed form solution representation from Fermat problem to find the facility location, since SA is quite capable for solving the location problem numerically and flexible enough for us to extend the objective function to other non-Euclidean based distance.

- *NEOS server* (section 5)

In order to compare the results, we use the $MINLP$ (Mixed Integer Non-Linearly constrained optimization Package) from NEOS and submit the same data in GAMS format to the server. A listing of the GAMS code is illustrated in Table 9.

Having discussed the various settings for the proposed methods, we list the implementation result in Table 10. All of the above methods except the NEOS server are stochastic in nature, therefore a couple of runs should be implemented for each solution method. Multiple restarts are generally needed for local search heuristic such as the ALA method, however a global optimization method such as GA or SA may still get stuck at a local optimum in practice, given finite computing resources. Table 10 is the statistical result from 10 runs of each heuristic method and one run of the NEOS service. The Time row indicates average time for a single run of the method, Mean, Std Dev, Range, Min and Max represent the average objective values, the standard deviation, the range of objective values, and the minimum and maximum values of the 10 runs of the method.

Nested GA and $GA + B\&B$ consume much more time than the other methods. All of these implementations are performed in an Intel Celeron 2.0G machine with 512 MB of memory. The operating system is Redhat Linux 9 and we use GNU's C (gcc) and Fortran (g77) compilers to compile the programs. Though a parallel version of GA (PGAPack) is available, we do not turn the feature on. Thus, the execution time is for a single CPU machine. $GA + Lagrange$, ALA, and $Mixed\ typed$ GA consume about the same order of CPU time. Regarding the accuracy, Nested GA has the worst result compared to the NEOS server. This could be attributed to the weak precision level of solutions obtained from the bottom layer GA for solving the allocation variables. Assuming a maximum of 500 generations in the bottom layer GA might not be able to produce high quality allocation solutions in this case. On the other hand, assuming a higher value of generation numbers will cause the program to consume more computer time and may produce higher quality solutions. The other 4 methods have better average objective values than the NEOS server. In particular, the $GA + B\&B$ method has the best average and smallest deviation values. This could be attributed to the high solution quality provided by the $B\&B$ solver, which is the UW IPMIXD routine. Unfortunately, high solution quality does come with a high

Table 9 GAMS input program to NEOS server

```
Sets
      i /1*5/
      j /1*50/;
Parameters
   d(j) /
   1   12.
   ...omitted to save space
   50   25. /
   a(j) /
   1   439.
   ...omitted to save space
   50   733. /
   b(j) /
   1   360.
   ...omitted to save space
   50   474. /
   q(i) /
   1   500.
   ...omitted to save space
   5   400. /
   f(i) /
   1   500.
   ...omitted to save space
   5   700. /
   Binary Variables
      y(i)
      x(i,j);
   Positive Variables
      u(i)
      v(i);
   Variables
      dist;
   Equations
      demand(j)
      capacity(i)
      obj;
   demand(j) ... sum(i, x(i,j)) = e = 1 ;
   capacity(i) ... sum(j, x(i,j)*d(j)) = l = y(i)*q(i) ;
   obj .. dist = e = 4*sum((i,j), x(i,j)*sqrt(sqr(u(i)−a(j))+sqr(v(i)−b(j)))) + sum(i, y(i)*f(i));
   Model process /all/;
```

Table 10 Statistics of 10 runs of each method

	Nested GA	GA + B&B	GA + Lag	ALA	Mix GA	NEOS
Time	570 sec	>4000 sec	150 sec	84 sec	65 sec	
Mean	46572.92	30111.37	30397.80	30739.38	31309.70	31595.90
Std Dev	3591.50	450.35	766.64	1154.43	1431.93	0.00
Range	9982.86	1699.93	2755.26	3776.20	4327.47	0.00
Min	41519.27	29401.99	29186.55	29159.82	29891.73	31595.90
Max	51502.13	31101.92	31941.81	32936.02	34219.20	31595.90

tag of computing time. The $GA + Lagrange$ method offers the next best solution at a reasonable price. The average and the minimum values all compare favorably to the NEOS server. The local search ALA heuristic method provides the best minimum value (29159.82), but with a larger mean (30793.38) and deviation (1154.43) values than the $GA + Lagrange$ hybrid method. Mixed type chromosome GA is the speed winner with less quality for solution. Though a higher generation number (20000) is implemented in a mixed type GA, it is still fast since unlike the other 3 hybrid methods, there is no tedious computation in the bottom layer of the hybrids to solve a $SSCFLP$. The computation of the fitness value of a mixed type chromosome is straight forward by plugging in the objective function formula in equation (15). On the other hand, the result is not as good as others and this might be attributed to the fact that since real coded genes (the location variables) and integer coded genes (the allocation variables) appear differently in the structure of the objective function, different designs of crossover and mutation operators should be used for different types of genes to improve the accuracy of the algorithm.

Over all, all studied methods except the Nested GA provide better average and minimum objective values than the NEOS service. When computation efforts and solution quality are considered together, it seems that the $GA + Lagrange$ hybrid offers the best value, and the tradition ALA method comes next in this particular experiment.

7. CONCLUSIONS

In this chapter we first introduce facility location problems, which are becoming more important than ever for planning facility or service locations to serve customer demands well. Most studies in this area actually deals with the service allocation problems that are special cases of mixed integer linear programming problems in operations research (OR). We consider an extended facility location problem that involves the decision of facility locations and service allocations simultaneously. This $ELAP$ (Euclidean Location Allocation Problem) is a nonlinear mixed-integer programming problem that many optimization software packages cannot solve directly. Some of these optimization packages will do continuous problems, and some of them can solve mixed integer programming problem with linear or quadratic objective function, but not many of them can solve a mixed-integer nonlinear programming problem of the type in equation (15).

Because of equation (29), we can translate a joint minimization problem into a repeated minimization problem that allows us to treat the decision variables separately. By using this separation of variables we introduce three hybrid methods in section 3 to tackle the $ELAP$. Continuous location variables and discrete allocation variables are taken care of by different optimization techniques respectively. For example, we treat the continuous variables by a genetic algorithm (GA), and the discrete variables by a second layer GA, a branch-and-bound ($B\&B$), and a Lagrange relaxation and sub-gradient method. We also couple a Simulated Annealing (SA) procedure with $B\&B$ to implement the traditional Alternate Location Allocation (ALA) heuristic method for solving the $ELAP$. Some of these optimization techniques are deterministic algorithms from OR, e.g. $B\&B$, Lagrange relaxation and sub-gradient methods. Some other techniques such as *GA* and *SA* are computationally intelligent search methods from Artificial Intelligence (*AI*). In section 6 we show that it is possible to combine freely downloadable software packages from the Internet to implement a customized solution package for solving the *ELAP*, which is a computationally hard problem. We compare the results with the one from a state-of-the-art optimization system (the NEOS) and find that the custom made solutions are quite competitive.

From this experience of dealing with the *ELAP*, we feel that some of the work that we have done can be easily extended. We summarize it as follows:

- The facility location problem that we dealt with does not involve any obstacles in the plane region. Gong et al. [10] consider a special planar location allocation problem with obstacles in the region. The hybrid methods proposed in section 3 can be extended to this type of *ELAP*.
- Since the fixed cost f_i for setting up a facility is most likely location dependent in many businesses, it is more realistic to assume that f_i is position specific, e.g. we may assume that $f_i = f_i(u, v)$ is a constant when the facility is opened in a specific region, and another constant in a different region. The hybrid methods can also handle this kind of problem extension.
- The *ELAP* we treated before is a special type of mixed integer non-linear programming (*MINLP*) problem with the continuous variables appearing inside a square root function in equation (15). The hybrid methods in section 3 can be easily extended to other *MINLP* as long as the objective function has good separation property of the variables.
- From the experiment, we see that it is easy to combine different optimization techniques from *OR* and *AI* using readily available Internet resources. Some meta-heuristic methods such as Tabu search and scatter search are becoming more important search methods in *AI*. Thus, in the future it will be interesting to experiment hybrid methods to solve hard optimization problems by incorporating advanced techniques from *OR* and *AI*.
- In order to make the proposed methods more efficient, it is important to fine tune the parameters in the respective methods, for examples the various system parameters required for the *GA* and *SA* procedures.

REFERENCES

[1] Bradley, S. P., Hax, A. C., and Magnanti, T. L., Applied Mathematical Programming, *Addison-Wesley Publishing Company*, 1977.
[2] Bespamyatnikh, S., Kedem, K., and Segal, M., Optimal Facility Location under Various Distance Functions, *International Journal of Computational Geometry and Applications*, Vol. 10, No. 5, pp. 523–534, 2000.
[3] Cooper, L., Heuristic Methods for Location-Allocation Problems, *SIAM Review*, Vol. 6, No. 1, pp. 1–18, 1964.
[4] Czyzyk, J., Mesnier, M. P., and More, J. J., The NEOS Server, *IEEE Computational Science & Engineering*, 5, pp. 68–75, 1988.
[5] Carter, M. W., and Price, C. C., Operations research: a practical introduction, *CRC Press, Boca Raton*, 2001.
[6] Courant, R., and Robbins, H., What is Mathematics? *Oxford University Press, London*, 1978.

[7] Doong, S.-H., Lai, C.-C., and Wu, C.-H., A Hybrid Model for Solving Single Source Capacitated Facility Location Problem, *14th IASTED International Conference on Modeling and Simulation*, pp. 395–400, Palm Springs, USA, 2003.

[8] Fisher, M. L., The Lagrangian Relaxation Method for Solving Integer Programming Problem, *Management Science*, 27, pp. 1–18, 1981.

[9] Goldberg, D. E., Genetic Algorithms in Search, Optimization, and Machine Learning, *Addision-Wesley, Reading, PA*, 1989.

[10] Gong, D., Gen, M., Yamazaki, G., and Xu W., Planar location-allocation with obstacles problem, *IEEE International Conference on Systems, Man, and Cybernetics*, Vol. 4, pp. 2671–2676, 1996.

[11] Glover, F., and Laguna, M., Tabu Search, *Kluwer Academic Publishers, Norwell, Massachusetts*, 1997.

[12] Gong, D., Yamazaki, G., and Gen, M., Evolutionary Program for Optimal Design of Material Distribution System, *Proceedings of IEEE International Conference on Evolutionary Computation*, pp. 139–143, 1996.

[13] Holland, J. H., Adaptation in Natural and Artificial systems, *The University of Michigan Press, Ann Arbor*, 1975.

[14] Hakimi, S. L., and Kuo, C. C., On a General Network Location-Production-Allocation Problem, *European Journal of Operational Research*, 55, pp. 31–45, 1991.

[15] Holmberg, K., Ronnqvist, M., and Yuan, D., An exact algorithm for the capacitated facility location problems with single sourcing, *European Journal of Operational Research*, 113, pp. 544–559, 1999.

[16] Kirkpatrick, S., Gelatt, C. D., and Vecchi, M. P., Optimization by Simulated Annealing, *Science*, 220, 4598, pp. 671–680, 1983.

[17] Klose, A., and Wittmann, S., Facility Location Based on Clustering Methods, *Proceedings of the Second International Workshop on Distribution Logistics*, pp. 93–96, Oegstgeest, The Netherlands, 1995.

[18] Love, R. F., Morris, J. G., and Wesolowsky, G. O., Facilities Locations: Models and Methods, *North-Holland, New York*, 1988.

[19] Mitchell, J. E., Branch-and-Cut Algorithms for Combinatorial Optimization Problems, *Handbook of Applied Optimization*, Oxford University Press, 2000.

[20] Michalewicz, M., Genetic Algorithms + Data Structure = Evolution Program, *Springer-Verlag*, Berlin, 1996.

[21] Polyak, B. T., Minimization of un-smooth functions, *USSR Computational Mathematics and Mathematical Physics*, 9, pp. 14–29, 1969.

[22] Pierrot, H. J., and Hinterding, R., Using Multi-chromosomes to Solve a Simple Mixed Integer Problem, *10th Australian Joint Conference on Artificial Intelligence, Lecture Notes in Computer Science*, 1342, pp. 137–146, 1997.

[23] Ronnqvist, M., Tragantalerngsak, S., and Holt, J., A repeated matching heuristic for the single-source capacitated facility location problem, *European Journal of Operational Research*, 116, pp. 51–68, 1999.

INDEX